To: Steve Cowgill

Love you and
glad to know we
are related   .

Helen Ogden Widener

James Mackay
a man to cherish 1761-1822

PINE MOUNTAIN BOOKS

ISBN: 0-9761466-2-2

Library of Congress Number: 2004094583

Published By:
Pine Mountain Books
307 Steeplechase Drive
Irving, Texas 75062-3822
pinemountainbooks@verizon.net

Book Cover: Designed by Tad Browning

Printed in The United States of America

JAMES MACKAY

a man to cherish 1761-1822

HISTORICAL NARRATIVE

HELEN OGDEN WIDENER

Dedicated to the Memory of

James Mackay 1761-1822

and all the men, women and children who left Scotland

looking for a home

ACKNOWLEDGEMENTS

Special thanks to my editor, Bobbie Thomas her skills and suggestions for this book, my labor of love. To my husband James Widener, my love and thanks for his encouragement and support. To my traveling companion, Ruth Lowery, Scotland couldn't have been covered with such enthusiasm without you.

To my son, Tad Browning, thanks for your special talent with photography, digital imaging and the creations of the book's cover. Thanks to Billie Campbell of Color Advantage for the wonderful portrait in oil of James Mackay. Thanks to my artist friend, Pete Fernandez, for her help and support.

To those wonderful people in Scotland, I thank you. Thank you, Andrew Innes for playing the bagpipes at the ruined croft site of James Mackay May 1, 2003. To James Innes, thanks for a wonderful time and for warming our toes with a nip of Single Malt Scotch Whiskey. To Elizabeth Frazer, my thanks, for her help in finding just the right bagpipe player for us. A big thank you to Angus Ross for the wild ride across the moors in an Argocat, unforgettable! To Don and Nancy, owners of La Mirage Restaurant, my thanks for the "taste of Scotland" and making sure we got connected to the people we needed to see. Thanks to Christine Mackay and The Clearances Center of Helmsdale for the efforts they are making to identify the people of Scotland who left to find homes in other countries. I hope you will be as proud to call James Mackay your own, as we are to have him for an ancestor.

Most of all, I give thanks, for the historical and biographical help of Mackay researchers and Missouri Historians, Thomas Danisi and W. Raymond Wood who were responsible for documenting the Library of Congress "Indian Map" as being the one drawn by James Mackay. Thanks to the Missouri Historical Society and Missouri Historians Marj Miller and John Jackson for their help. Thanks to W. Brecht for background information on Spanish Officers' uniforms.

Historical Fact:

James Mackay's life, during the time he lived in the Spanish held territory, known as the Louisiana Purchase, is a well documented account. In Mackay's letter to his son Zeno, he tells about members of his family in Scotland.

A few remaining references to Mackay in the Canadian Fur Trade lead us to believe he arrived in Canada about 1775 or 1776. Family documents place his birth at May 1, 1761. He and his brother John arrived in Canada to work as Clerks when he was 15 or 16 years of age and John two years older.

Surviving segments of his Journals and Indian Notes, used by the Lewis and Clark expedition, relate some of the places he explored in the wilderness. Mackay is credited with being the first white man to record the river Rochejaune or Yellowstone. It is apparent he spent a great amount of time trading with the Indians and visiting in their villages. He spoke several Indian dialects.

The meeting with the Spanish Ambassador, Gardoqui, in New York in 1789 is documented through the Ambassador's correspondence with other Spanish officials. The map he copied from Mackay at that time has not been found.

His employment with the Spanish in St. Louis, Missouri is well documented as well as the meeting he had with William Clark. Documents he wrote in French and Spanish, as well as English have survived. His native tongue was Gaelic. He was a skilled surveyor as well as Map Maker. James used the French *Fleur-de-lis* as the North Point on his maps.

Mackay's expedition up the Missouri in 1795-97, which led to the drawing of the Library of Congress "Indian Map" used by the Lewis and Clark Expedition, has recently been documented as being the map Mackay drew.

There are gaps in Mackay's life where speculation is our only resource. Documentation and family lore help to fill in some of those time periods. Names and dates of birth of family members and Missouri friends are factual.

About the Book Cover:

The cover was created by Tad Browning, Photographer, Journalist and Graphic Artist.

The signature of James Mackay was digitally lifted from a copy of his Original Will and laid over four edges of an old book to create the ancient look.

The portrait is a digital overlay of James Mackay's grandson, John Barker and the image was compared to a photo of an unknown daughter. The shape of eyes, jaw and lips were the same in both photos, discounting the softness of the daughter's jaw line. The hair, jacket and cravat are from the early 1800 French time period. The frame is a part of an antique miniature Ivory Painting.

The rose jar is known to have been in the John Barker family since the early 1850's.

The Books: The bottom book is a copy of the 1833 Fifth Edition of *The Cook and Housewife's Manual: A Practical System of Modern Domestic Cookery and Family Management* by Mistress Margaret Dods. The top book is an 1882 Twelfth Edition of the works of Elizabeth Barrett Browning. The Cover is Gold Leather, painted in red and elaborately stitched with silk thread. The book belonged to John Barker.

The antique document at the bottom of the book cover is a sheep skin of a land indenture, hand printed in brown ink, and dated during the time of King Charles II of England.

The Clan Plaid used for the background is the modern Mackay Plaid.

CONTENTS

CHAPTER ONE

A Letter from Gram

St. Louis, Missouri
May, 1859

To: John M. Barker
Flint Hill, Missouri

My Dearest Johnny:

    I AM SO PROUD to hear of the success you have achieved in your studies, and it is with the greatest delight that I learn you have decided to study for the law.

    It would please me more than I can express if you were to call upon me, your old granny, at your earliest convenience. Should you be able to spare a few days, we could remember some of those years gone by, too many now for me.

    I long now for the great joy of joining your grandfather, my James, and reuniting with him in a less troublesome place of peace and freedom from this shell of earthly flesh I am now subjected to. I long to see again my youngest daughter, your Mother Louise, who was so cruelly taken from me at such a young and tender age, that I fear you will have forgotten her.

    Come to me Johnny, so I can put my arms around you again.

Your loving Grandmother
Elizabeth Mackay

Flint Hill, Missouri
One week later

Sweat dripped from the face of John Barker, as he chopped wood from the trees that had been felled only yesterday by his father, Simeon Barker, with his, and his brothers help. The work was hard, and he could feel the muscles of his arms and shoulders respond to the hard chop each time the ax came down upon the limbs he split. The wood would be seasoned by winter and used in the hearth for cooking food and heating the house. The summer months were used to store up wood enough to last through the cold Missouri winters. Great piles of the split limbs would have to be made to assure they had a good winter's supply.

John pulled a rag from the back pocket of his overalls, wiped the sweat from his face and squinted at the sun to see how much longer he would have to continue with this job before he could go to the house. An hour left; he thought the sun was unusually warm for June. He guessed they were in for a hot summer which would be most unpleasant for the work that had to be done on the farm.

Last week they had planted the last of the garden for a time when the early plantings were exhausted. The garden, which the younger boys, along with his older brother Stephen, were hoeing today, was already providing the family with a variety of vegetables. John was looking forward to the first green peas he knew they would be picking. The yellow squash, two days ago, had looked about ready to begin harvesting. There were peaches and plums in the orchard and blackberries and strawberries in the garden. John's stepmother, Camelia usually had something for dessert. Some blackberry cobbler would really taste good to him tonight. Keeping wood for the fires for cooking and the weeds from the garden took almost all of the families' time to provide for the many children.

This December, John would be eighteen and off to study for the Law. It had been only two weeks before that he had written to his grandmother, Elizabeth Mackay, that he had decided his

future would best be served if he became an attorney. He had not received a letter in reply, but hoped that she would help with the finances, if there were enough money for her to do so.

John had day-dreamed the hour away thinking of his grandmother and planning what he would do when he got his law degree. The sun had finally reached the point in the sky when he could stop his work and return to the house for supper. His sweat soaked shirt was sticking to his back and large stains showed on the shirt and sleeves under his arms. The shirt was bleached across the back from the salt stains of his sweat and repeated washings. It would take some cleaning up at the well before he could go into the house.

Camelia had washed earlier in the day and the clothes were dry upon the lines his father had stretched between a couple of trees. Taking his dirty shirt off, John washed in the basin that was kept by the well. He pulled a clean shirt from the line and, turning towards the cabin, paused while he looked at the home where he lived.

The cabin was a rambling old house of squared off logs with a long porch running across the entire front. Two large cut logs formed the steps to the porch. These types of cabins were called *dog trot* cabins which had the cooking room on one side of the house and the living quarters on the other side with an opening in between. All were connected by the same roof. Lofts over the whole house provided sleeping areas for the children. The house was in poor shape as they couldn't afford to keep it maintained with the little income they had.

Entering the house he found that his younger brother, Zeno, and his father had returned from town. It was Saturday, and the afternoon was the time that his father went into town to buy the weeks supplies as well as pick up any mail that might have arrived during the week. Today had been Zeno's turn to go with their father.

Zeno met him at the door with an envelope in his hand. Getting a letter was about the most exciting thing that happened in their lives. It meant news from loved ones, and he immediately noticed that it had come from St. Louis.

With a whoop, John grabbed the letter and raced for the loft as fast as decorum would allow. He loved letters from his grandmother, Elizabeth Mackay, who always had a good story to tell, and good things to eat. He seemed to bring a special pleasure to her with his visits, which he thought were much too few, and he decided it was probably due to his resemblance to his grandfather, or so his aunts had told him. He was the son of Gram's youngest daughter, Isabella Louisa, named for her own self. His mother had died when he was only ten years old, and Gram had been heart broken over it. The name Isabella of course was in the old French and Spanish manner, as the territory was owned by France or as the Spanish claimed, owned by them. Either way, Missouri was now part of the United States and someone else would have to settle their disagreements. If he were the lawyer for the Spanish, he thought he would side with them. It seemed the French had not done well by their allies.

After giving his father seven children, his twin brothers had died shortly after birth, his mother died at the age of 30 during a cholera outbreak. He thought now, as he had so many times during his young life, of the words his mother had spoken with the last breath she took on this earth, "be good children." Thoughts of momma never failed to bring a sting to his eyes and a knot to his throat. He was almost grown now, and eight years older. Maybe it's a good thing that a person never forgets a good form of memory for those you love and hope to meet again in the afterlife, as he was sure he would. His mother hadn't one enemy in the whole world and was sure to be waiting for her children in Heaven.

Entering the loft room he shared with his brothers, Stephen, Zeno, Mackay and LeGrand, he quietly pulled the curtain so he could read the letter alone. Later he would share it with the family, but for the moment he needed the intimate contact between him and his grandmother.

Letters were few and precious but more often than not contained bad news. John, sitting down in the old rocking chair which had belonged to his mother, carefully opened the envelope so as not to make any tears, took out the single sheet of paper and began to read.

That dratted lump of emotion was back in his throat again, for he knew at his dearest gram's age, life was all too short to be smiled upon. He leaned back and slowly began to rock, as was his habit, and let his sentimental feelings roll over him in waves of pain and loving memory. He wondered just how he could make it through his life without the help and support of his grandmother. Heaven only knew there was little demonstration of affection from his father and near none from his stepmother. His little sister needed the most affection. It wasn't her fault their stepmother was not interested in raising another's women's children. He and Stephen gave his younger brothers all the attention they could to make up for the lack of affection from their father and stepmother. He had always tried to keep his promise to his dying mother and looked after the younger boys and his young sister Gertrude. He would never let the memory of his mother down, and he would watch over the children just as she would have done. When he got his law degree, he would take them all to live with him, and he would build a new house in a larger town, where he could be successful.

He hadn't realized he had stayed in his room so long, but suddenly the noises from downstairs told him it would be almost time for supper.

John picked up the letter to take downstairs as he knew all were waiting to hear what Gram had written. They would share the letter around the table after supper was finished. He made a visit to the back porch where a wash basin and bucket of water was kept so the children could wash their hands and comb their hair before each meal. The dirty water was then poured into a trough that ran the water into a holding barrel to be used on the garden. It had been only an hour since he had washed at the well, but his father expected them all to wash just before sitting down to the table.

His father Simeon, at the head of the table, gave the blessing and began to pass the food around so all could share the farm's bounty. He said, "I am told you received a letter today, John, from your Grandmother Mackay."

"Yes, father, would you like me to read it now?"

"No, it can wait until after supper; I hope there is no bad news."

"No Sir, but she has asked me to come for a visit."

"Well then, we will hear the rest after supper."

It was a slow dinnertime, with the kids fidgeting in their chairs as ready to hear the letter as John was to share. The family was a large one with his father and stepmother, Camelia, their four children Edward, Louise, William and two month old baby Maud Mary, in her cradle in the curtained off area that his father shared with Camelia. The children of his mother added to the family; Stephen was the oldest of the children named for their grandfather Stephen Barker. John was the second named for their grandfather, John Long. His brother, Zeno was named for his Uncle John Zeno Mackay, and there was James LeGrand Barker and eight year old Gertrude Darling Barker, whom we all called "Darlin." We were ten at the table.

The table had a wide variety of dishes containing a ragout of beef with a nice gravy, mashed potatoes, young carrots, beans and yellow *crookneck* squash, cornbread and a variety of onions, radishes, tomatoes and a few other small condiments which, when passed around the table, made for a lengthy meal. John noticed there were no fresh green peas, but the *Kentucky wonder* beans were very good. Then there was dessert, tonight was Sally Lund Cake with fresh strawberries and cream. All would have to be finished in their own time before the supper was over and he could share his letter.

While the family waited, three year old Will finally finished off his dessert so the family could leave the table and set by the hearthside where the letter was read.

After reading the letter, there was a small silence. It was a painful memory for his father to recall the bounty he had shared as a member of the Mackay Family. It was his mother's land that supplied the family its home. Added to that, it was Gram who was paying for the Law School as well. He hated that he could not see Gram more often. It seemed that there was never time enough to leave the work of the farm.

His father did the best he could, and in most ways was a good, if not a little over stern father, but he hadn't been able to provide for the family in the manner his mother had lived, and his father never quite overcome the guilt he felt for not being able to care for her the way she was raised. His little mother, Louise had never complained, and was dearly loved by anyone who had met her.

"Father, might I take one of the horses and ride across country; could I leave on the morrow?"

"Yes, you can leave tomorrow; however, it means there will be extra work for Stephen and Zeno. John knew his not being there would cause extra work for the whole family. He would not think about this, as Stephen had visited Gram last year. He was already getting his education going off to school, and only home for the summer. And Zeno would get his turn for a visit with Gram in due time, he hoped.

CHAPTER TWO

House on the Gravois

IT WAS LATE IN THE AFTERNOON the next day by the time John arrived at his grandmother Mackay's house near St. Louis. He had attended Church and then left on one of the families old horses, used both for work and pleasure.

John took the horse to the barn where Uncle Zeno's family kept their horses. He took off the saddle and rubbed the horse down before giving him a few oats and a bucket of water. He would not need more attention until the next day, when he would be turned out into the pasture with the other horses.

Walking to Gram's house, which stood behind the house of Uncle Zeno's family, John stood at the gate leading into his Gram's lovely yard. He could just see her off to the side of her little cottage, sitting under the arbor. She sat in her white wicker swing reading the old family Bible, with some occasional petals of the wild roses, falling around her. Gram was dressed in black, relieved only by the white lace on her bonnet and around the neck of her gown. She had refused in the thirty-seven years since his Grandfather's death to wear any other color. The swing was newly painted as it was each year, when the weather allowed, and attached to a lattice work arch, now covered with the flowering *Eglantine*, her favored flower. Gram refused to call them wild roses or sweet briar as they were more commonly called. Gram said, "They were much too elegant to carry such common names".

Gram used the rose hips for many things, powdered and mixed with white wine they strengthen the kidneys, or mixed with wood ash and honey and applied to the head they cured problems of the scalp. The roots could be boiled and used for a poultice on any poisonous bite. When the hips were at the peak of their growth, she carefully gathered what she needed and made a wonderful conserve, which she said, was not only delicious but very good for the body's overall health and Gram was nearing eighty years of age. Then, there was the delicious and very delicate rosehip wine she made. He must remember to ask for the recipe before he left. Someday he would have a wife and family of his own. It would be important to learn all he could and he believed this trip would be a learning experience that would take him through his entire life; an experience he thought he would want to pass on to his children. He had always found that stories of Grandfather intrigued him. He remembered the tales his mother had told him and his brothers that she had heard from her mother and brothers and sisters. His mother had been a little over a year old when grandfather had died. She did not remember him except through the memories of others and the small painted ivory miniature that belonged to Gram.

He walked toward Gram, she was not yet aware of his presence. With a lurch of his heart, he noticed that she appeared frailer than the last time he had visited. Framed by the Eglantine, she made a far more breathtaking scene, in this natural setting than could be captured on the new picture cameras. He just wanted a moment to stamp it upon his heart where it could be called up at will, and be a comfort that all was well. The moment was far too short as she raised her head and saw him there, just as if his presence had made itself known without benefit of sight or sound. Her smile was like that of an angel, welcoming him to her side. She waited for him to come to her, which he did feeling all warm and happy inside.

Without speaking, both of them with smiles splitting their faces and messages of love flowing from one eye to the other, John went to his grandmother, who stood and hugged him to her even though she only reached to the top of his chest. When she let him go and returned to her seat, he sat upon the stool at her feet, and took her tiny little hands into his own larger ones. Gram wouldn't let them stay, but removed them to frame his face with her palms as she said "Johnny."

"Johnny, you are well I can see, and how happy you have made me this day."

"Yes, Gram, I am well and strong as any full grown man could be, I am now in every way my own man and so looking forward to the next years of my education."

"Johnny you were always the little man of the house, the care you have given your little brothers and sister has been commendable and I thank you for it. Your stepmomma, has she not softened, even a little over the years?"

"Ah, Gram, I think she does as well as she can; we are a constant reminder that we live on my mother's land. We have another new sister, now three months old. I am sure there will be more. We have become quite a large family. As much as I hate leaving my little brothers and sister behind, I do so look forward to receiving my Law Degree."

"Now, tell me of the other children and then we will go in for a glass of iced tea, with a little sprig of mint, just as you like it."

"Tell me, how is my dear little Stephen, has he even grown a little?"

"Stephen, is forever the quiet one, but eager enough to beat me when we are all trying to outrun each other along the road. We make a game of racing each other from one tree to another. He is fast even though he is still too small for his age, and I fear he spends too much time reading and not enough with the joys of life, of which there is not nearly enough. I do wish he were bigger and stronger like Zeno and me."

"And, Zeno is he as full of mischief as ever?"

"Oh Gram, Zeno still has a prank or two, but is such a wonderful young man, I wish he could have come with me, but two of us gone from the farm would not get the work done. He has

the look of our dear mother and her kindness, which makes it all the more difficult for him with our stepmomma. We, of course, don't call her Mother, but Camelia, which we are only too happy to do, for she could never take the place of dear momma."

"LeGrand, if I must call him that instead of James, does he follow you around as he did as a child?"

"LeGrand is forever following in my footsteps, just as he used to stretch out his little legs trying to take steps as big as I, and has declared he will be a Lawyer, just as I intend to be. He is such a dear, and at fourteen can already do the work of a man."

"Tell me, Johnny, what of my little Gertrude Darlin, I feel I must laugh each time I say her name, your momma was insistent that she be called Darlin' for she was her only 'little darling', and you and your brothers were rowdy, noisy little boys."

"Little Darlin' is a beauty and next week she will be nine. She thinks herself to be quite grown and too old for her dolls. She has so many 'real life' dolls, that I can't think but that she is right and her old dolls must be put away. Already she fetches and carries for Camelia all day. Darlin' changes the nappies on little Mary and constantly watches over Edward, Louis and William. Four children for a nine year old to care for, is far too many for such a little girl. Father says nothing, and my brothers and I are far too busy in the fields to interfere. Darlin' never complains, but she has already told me she doesn't intend to marry and have a bunch of whiney children. There seemed to be far more cares in this world than a little child should have to carry."

"Now, I bet you have been outside long enough, what about that tea you promised, I will pick some mint to freshen it with."

Gram busied herself making the tea, and set out her favorite teacups which were a beautiful deep pink patterned around the edges with a lattice work of gold, and in the center was a porcelain cameo of a perfect full rose ringed with wild flowers. They were far too delicate for a man, but she loved them dearly and it was a special occasion. The china she had inherited from her mother, Elizabeth Long.

John washed the mint, ridding it of any excess stems to make it ready for their tea. He lightly crushed the leaves against the bottom of the tea cup before adding the tea.

Gram set the tea on the table, excused herself and said she would be right back. John glanced over at the old Bible which had belonged to his grandfather and was now Gram's constant companion. Just the act of holding it seemed to be an unbroken connection with him. It touched John as nothing else that he could recall. He promised himself to copy all the family information it contained before he left from his visit.

Gram returned with quite a number of items in her hands. She sat down and placed on the table her Silver Plate Rose Jar that grandfather had given her for a wedding present, a sheath of papers which had been carefully copied from some ancient documents, and an old cookbook. She then picked up her beloved Bible and laid it upon the papers. She held in her hand a small miniature of grandfather, so often held that the velvet was completely worn away from the edges of the frame. This of course, was never far from her side.

Gram said, "Johnny these are the things I wish to give you, for your very own, for I know you will cherish them even as I do. The Rose Jar, the Bible and the cookbook, you are to keep, the papers must be copied for each of your brothers, so that they may also know of our family. My china I would like to go to Gertrude Darlin' for her own. Since my dear son Zeno has died, I wish to give you these things now, so that there will be no question about who is to receive them when I am no longer here."

"Gram, I never want to think that you will not be here, but I know all to well that life comes as it will, but I will miss you more than I can comprehend."

"Johnny, in my life, I have lost my beloved husband, my dear parents and three of my very own children, which is more pain than the human heart can tolerate, but you must always, leave to God those things that we are without power to control. It is the only way one can live on this earth. First it was William, before he was even grown, then your dear momma who had been my constant companion and lifeline after James' death and then just three year ago, my dear Zeno. I do not want to feel the pain of loss of another loved one's death. I pray that God will take me, and that death will be no more a part of my life."

"Gram, the rose jar, I will save and give to my daughter. I will cherish the Bible and hold it dear to my heart, but you must keep it until such a time as there is no further need for it to be next to you. The papers I will study and copy for my brothers, but do you really wish to give me a Cookbook?"

"Johnny, the cookbook is now twenty-five years old. Your great Aunt Kitty sent it to me from Scotland before her death. It is *Meg Dods' Recipe Book* of Scottish Recipes, the first recipe book written for the Scots. She wanted me to have it so that I might learn the foods that were so dear to the Scots and pass them on to our family who know so little of Scotland. I am putting the book in your hands. You must care for these things and teach your descendants of them. It is very important to remember your family history, for how can we prepare for the future without knowing the past?"

"Gram, I am most anxious to begin my learning at your capable hands and what a pleasure it will be, for I can stay with you for two whole weeks, if I don't tire you out."

"On the morrow we will begin to talk of my dear James and the wonders of the things he did. Tonight, I have a little surprise, for I knew you would come right away, just as you have done. We begin by trying some of those same Scottish dishes that your grandfather loved. There is Haggis, and as bad as it sounds it is really quite good and very spicy to the taste and not unlike the Boudin, the people of New Orleans consume in great amounts. However, Haggis is made with toasted oats instead of the rice used by the Cajuns. The rest of the ingredients are whatever you might have on hand, as everyone has their own special recipe. I have prepared the recipe from Meg Dods' Recipe Book. We will have *Neeps and Tatties* or as we think of them, turnips and potatoes and oatcakes and apple cider to wash it all down. What a delight it is to have the company of my best loved grandson."

"Thank you Gram, I can think of nothing better than spending time with you. Your wisdom inspires me to be a better person and I thank God everyday that he chose me for your grandson."

Gram left John to read his grandfather's papers and the family history from the Bible. It was time for Gram to retire for a night's sleep.

"Good morning Johnny, I have made for you James' favorite breakfast of *Oatie Cakes*, Sausage, Bacon, *Blood Pudding*, eggs with the eye up, just as you like, and some of my own special *Rose Hip Conserve*. As soon as we have eaten, we can go to the arbor and I will tell you wonderful things of Scotland and your grandfather James. I am as anxious to begin our adventure as I know you are, but I must have my breakfast, just as you."

Elizabeth and Johnny moved to the Arbor, just as he had found her the day before, looking lovely with her tiny delicate face and lively blue eyes twinkling with the secrets she was about to tell him.

"Johnny, first I need to tell you, you are so very much like your grandfather with your red and gold hair, and the same silver blue eyes that could cut a person in twain, if he were displeased. Your grandfather was a man of wonderful humor. His eyes shone like silver stars when he played his fiddle, usually the old Scottish and Cajun songs. He was not a tall man, only five foot and seven inches, but he could dance a jig, and our guests could not help but to dance with him. He was amazing with his fiddle music; people would come from many miles around to hear him play. Sometimes I would join in and play the harp. James was so well loved, that never would the French and Spanish have shown him the disrespect that came when the Americans moved in, but that part is

for later. I do hope you will not need to do the physical labor that gave James his tremendous strength. The carrying of fur bales caused him to have muscles that were the envy of all who met him. He never lost his physique, even when he was near to his death."

Elizabeth settled into her swing and brought her cushions around her and then she began her story.

CHAPTER THREE

The Old Scotland

"MY DARLING GRANDSON, I am telling you the story of your grandfather, James Mackay. However, to truly understand his life you must know the times and the circumstances in which he lived. With these few words about your grandfather's ancestors you will understand something of why they were as they were and comprehend the things which had the most effect on James' own life."

"Johnny, we as individuals are never only the sum of our selves, but of the influences surrounding and happening during the lives of our parents and grandparents as well. Your grandfather, James was very much the result of the happenings of his day. Just as you have decided to study law, in part I think, due to the injustices done your grandfather long before the time of your own birth."

"Of James' grandfather, James Mackay, I know nothing of his personal life, only those things happening through the study of history during the time he lived. Of James' father, George, I can pass along those stories of his life and character as were told to me."

Gram began her story:

James was born May 1, 1761 at Arichlinie, near the Achentoul Forest, Parish of Kildonan, in the County of Sutherland in the North part of Scotland. Family was of great importance to James, and he corresponded with his family on a

regular basis, as we still correspond with your relatives in Scotland.

From James back to his father George Mackay, a Judge or minor Clan Chief, who held land leases called "Wadsets" that allowed him to have crofters under his care and direction. His mother was Elizabeth MacDonald. They lived in the same croft where James' grandfather, James Mackay, had lived and where his father George was raised. From this James was his father John, and John's father was William, and William was the son of Murdoch Mackay, who was known as the Great Murdoch due to his prodigious personal strength. James' branches of the Mackay family were descendants of Lord Raey who received his Peerage and became the first Lord Raey in the year of 1628 or during the life of the Great Murdoch.

The Great Murdoch Mackay, as told to me by your grandfather, lived during the time of the dark ages. He was born sometime around the year 1600 or during the reign of the last King of Scotland, James VI. Murdoch was a mighty warrior and making war was all that men of that time did, leaving the women and children to bring in the crops and take care of the animals. Murdoch must have been much in his element, for it was said he loved to fight and had a tremendously strong arm. The clans were constantly at war with each other or being mercenary soldiers for the wars of other countries. From each other, they stole cattle, chickens and pigs or whatever could be carried away. It was a terrible lawless time and only the very strong survived.

James Mackay, the father of George and the grandfather of your grandfather, James, moved to Arichlinie when George was a small boy and before the time of the battle of Culloden in 1746. George came to look upon the place as his own, increasing the herds of cattle and sheep and taking on the responsibilities of other crofters, collecting their rents, settling their arguments and helping in what way he could to create a better life for them all. He educated his children at school and home and inspired an interest in happenings in other lands and especially the Canada fur trade and exploration of the unknown.

James remembered his father, George for the shrewdness he acquired with his constant dealings with his laird as well as the crofters living under his care. He had a wonderful sense of humor, which must have found its way to James as your grandfather was a lively entertainer with more wit and humor than the most of ten men. George loved playing the fiddle and dancing, even though it was sometimes frowned upon by the church, and George was a pious man in his beliefs.

George was a big bear of a man, not in height, but with the same kind of strength which James inherited along with his silver blue eyes and hair of fine gold, some people mistakenly call this color hair ginger. It was told in the old days, men made their blond locks even more so with the use of lime water.

George cared about the welfare of his friends and those who looked to him for guidance. James' dear sister, Kitty, wrote to us often, telling us amusing and interesting things about the family and what they were doing.

There were many men of the inland parts of the Highlands like George Mackay who lived in their stone and turf houses, spoke their native Gaelic language, had sub-tenants and controlled large tracts of moorland owned by the Sutherlands. These men were educated, very hospitable, enlightened by divine truth and well versed in their Bibles. They were men who were often referred to as "the Country's Pride."

In the Highlands of Scotland during the 1600's John Calvin's book of Catechisms was published in Gaelic. Calvinism spread throughout the country. With a little bending, it blended along quite well with the old and ancient Celtic beliefs. Most of the people of Scotland took to the new religion, forsaking the dictates of the Churches of Rome, which many had ignored anyway. The Calvinists were strict and disciplined in the teaching of their religion. It allowed men to talk directly to God. The Mackays with their Celtic heritage had been talking directly with their gods for centuries, so what did it matter, if there was now only one. The one God became a well known acquaintance with some of the Gods the Celts still held in high esteem.

In many ways the new One God acted in the same way as the old Celtic ones. When crops failed and people became sick, it was seen as a direct punishment for some unknown wrong doing. The Reformed religion began to penetrate into every corner of Scottish life, through their schools, clothing, food, education and even how their crops were grown. The Mackays, already religious, took to the Calvin's Reformed Religion with fervor. They found the religions of England far more compatible to their Celtic teaching than were the teachings of the Church of Rome.

The Reformed People of Scotland did not realize that the embracing of a new religion would bring such devastating results to their country.

The Catholic people of Scotland were referred to as Jacobites. The Jacobites were against the new religion as well as being against any King of England or Scotland who did not profess the religion of the Church of Rome. They made many attempts to put the descendants of the Catholic Stewart Kings back upon the throne of Scotland and England. The Stewarts, under the influence of the French adopted the spelling of their name as "Stuart" due to the lack of a "w" in the French Language. The change from the English spelling of their name, might in itself caused the English to reject them as the rightful monarchs.

The English, tired of the constant threats of Catholic pretenders to the throne, ravished the country sides of Scotland in their attempt to free themselves of the troublesome Jacobites.

Most of the Mackays as well as most of the lowland Scots stayed loyal to the King of England. England with its superior numbers and seasoned warriors executed the final blow to the Jacobite cause in Scotland at a battle called "Culloden" in 1746. The ending battle was the birthplace of the English war cry of "No Quarter."

Whole families of the Jacobites, men, women and children, loyal to the Stewart cause, were rounded up and either killed or deported to the colonies. During one such roundup there were three thousand men shipped to Boston, Massachusetts and sold to the colonist as slaves, some of which were Mackay kin.

For their loyalty, the Mackays, were allowed to keep their lands and were saved the terrible fate of the Jacobites.

The English passed many laws and rules to govern the unruly Scots. The people were forbidden to bear arms and soldiers came around searching for, and taking away, all the guns they could find. The Scots were forbidden to speak Gaelic, the native tongue of the Highlanders. They were forbidden to wear the Clan Tartan, the dress that distinguished one family from another. Forbidden too was the beloved music of the bagpipes. The English made every effort possible to break the traditions and close family ties of the clan. However, the only one of these conditions which the English could completely enforce was the bearing of arms. Anyone found with guns in their possession were severely punished. The Mackays, being a very arrogant people, mostly ignored all the new laws and rules. All, that is, but the bearing of arms. If they had any guns, they were well hidden. Many of the people turned all the old pistols and firearms in, but hid away the better ones for a future time. As long as there were no troubles, the soldiers generally ignored the people of the countryside. The Scots dyed their tartans with vegetable dyes to make them all one color. It didn't change the fact that they still wore their tartans and knew their own colors by heart. Clan systems had been banned; the Lairds had no more power, and some betrayed their people by selling them as slaves or selling the lands on which they had lived for generations. Men of Scotland were forbidden marriage and forbidden ownership of land. Sometimes it seemed that even the air they breathed was forbidden.

And yet! It was the beginning of a time when the people of Scotland produced its greatest architects, poets, artists, and world

explorers. This last, the explorer, the call of adventure, lured James Mackay from his homeland along to the shores of North America. The Mackays and other clans, all across the Scottish Highlands, began to emigrate to countries around the world in search of freedom and new homes.

Many immigrants, who found a homeland in North America, fought in the Revolution for America's Independence and many fought to remain part of England. There were Mackays on both sides of the battles.

James Mackay often spoke of the time he had been caught with some Canadian Fur Traders, during a wilderness battle, and lent his gun and dirk to secure the freedom the Mackay descendants have enjoyed since the last battle of the American Revolution. The Scots had lost the Battle of Culloden in 1746, but with their help, their fierceness, their loyalty, the freedom they sought was theirs even if their homes were on far away shores.

CHAPTER FOUR

The Long-house Croft at Loch Arichlinie

IN THE ARBOR Elizabeth sat upon her little white wicker swing, well padded with the colorful cushions she had embroidered. John was at her feet sitting on a small three legged stool formerly used for milking. John was as ready and eager to hear the tales as Elizabeth was to tell the story, for in telling the story she brought back to life the joy she had experienced with her long dead husband.

"Johnny, sometimes it is hard to describe a person who excels in all things without any seeming effort; more than what is believable."

"Sometimes, it seems God has made a huge joke of creating a man, such as your grandfather. James was a man's kind of man, but women loved him, children adored him and old ladies wished he were their son."

Gram continued with her story:

As a young boy James both delighted and worried his parents. They were still so close to Celtic Mystics, they often feared he had some special mystical power pushing him along to achieve excellence in all he did. He always wanted to do everything better than anyone else, which often led him into difficult situations.

James' mother Elizabeth told me, "At the age of four he could read, write his name and had command of a good vocabulary both in Gaelic and English. He was sturdy in his build and was

always climbing and trying to do the things the older children could do."

It was a surprise to the family that he began to educate himself. His memory was such that anything that he saw or read was forever stamped upon his mind for recall at his moment of need.

Old people loved it when James came around and began asking his many questions. They delighted in telling him all he wanted to know, they made him feel important, and he gave them the love and respect that should be given to the elders. He learned all manner of agriculture, the breeding of cattle and other animals. He was forever penning up the chickens, one type to another, according to his mother, in an attempt, he said, "to create a chicken with more meat." On one occasion one of "his chickens" ate too much corn, which he had fed them and was in such a terrible way that he feared the chicken was about to die from an overstuffed craw. He took his little knife, cut open the craw of the chicken and cleaned out the excessive amounts of corn. James borrowed one of his mother's new sewing needles, some hand spun wool and sewed the chicken back together, just as if he were a physician. The chicken lived and he said he had read about sewing people up and thought if a physician could do it with people, he could do it with animals.

By the age of fifteen, James knew, in addition to his native Gaelic, Scottish which was half English and half French, and English which had to be written and spoken in school. He was studying Latin and working on perfecting his French. His writing was excellent and easy to read. Already, less educated neighbors brought papers and documents for him to see and read. George, as well as some of his more educated cousins took great delight in James' desire to learn. All the family in their own way added to James' education because he could not seem to learn enough to satisfy himself. There were great libraries in Scotland and it was a very enlightened time. Even the daughters of George Mackay were taught to read and write.

James was fascinated by the stars and could easily find his way with their guidance. He knew latitudes and longitudes of every known country of that time. Any travelers in the area would bring him the newspapers, and he horded them like treasures. He loved to read about anything that was happening in the "New World" as the colonies of England were called. He made himself a promise that as soon as he was old enough he would go there and see these things for himself. There were so many stories coming back from those early explorers about rivers and mountains that were too big to imagine; a land so vast it was beyond the imagination, and animals the like of which could be seen nowhere else. Then there were stories of savages who painted themselves, wore almost no clothing and scalped the white man every chance they got. He had doubted this part, but it hadn't been so many decades since the Scottish people had painted themselves, so that part he could believe. Taking scalps didn't make much sense to him, but one never knew.

The violin was James' musical instrument of choice and he loved to fiddle the Highland Reels as well as play classical music. He had a fine baritone voice and loved to sing and dance as he played. Just to see and hear his entertainment brought many visitors to our home. James told me that his father was great with the bagpipes and his brother John played the flute and William also played the bagpipes, but they had to learn in private. James often wished he could have his family come to see the country where he grew up and they could gather around and play and sing together like when they were young.

"What I guess, I am trying to tell you Johnny, is that it is rare that God pours upon one person so many gifts, so that all who meet him know that he is special." James was such a person. It was both a blessing and a curse. There were people who loved him, for he was ever a kind and helpful man. There were people who hated him because the jealousy in their own heart ate away their goodness causing them to act in malicious ways.

The home where James was born was called a longhouse croft and was fashioned like other houses of the time period. It was situated on a hill overlooking Loch Arichlinie with a lovely fine sandy beach at the Loch's end. The house was about 100 feet in length. The walls, 14 inches in thickness, were made of granite rock and stood about three feet in height. The rock was stacked together around couples, which were made of "bog fir" and birch in such a manner, that mortar was not needed to hold them together. The couples were tied to form an arch roof over the house which was then covered with turf and heather. A netting of woven flax or other straw was laid over the roof and weighted down with stones to keep it in place. The floors were covered with sand. Slate was then laid closely together on the layer of sand, and then more sand was swept between the cracks making a very nice hard floor.

There were several sections or compartments to the Longhouse. It had living quarters, sleeping and kitchen areas and a servant hall. The cooking stone was an open hearth cooking area, backed against a wall which separated the kitchen from the servant hall. There was a hole through the roof above the fire pit to allow the smoke from the peat, which was used for cooking and heating, out of the house. The chimney was made of wicker and covered only the hole in the roof. The cooking and living areas along with a bed were in the same compartment.

The food they ate was common to the area, and their main food was oatmeal which was stored in a protective chest called a *girnel*. Elizabeth made oatcakes called *bannocks* and *brose* which was oatmeal mixed with water and milk. They also had *gruel* which was a type of thin porridge and sometimes had sour oatmeal which was called *sowans*. The family ate a lot of *kail,* a cabbage-like vegetable, that could be put into a soup which was very healthy. There was also a plentiful supply of herring and sometimes George bought a full barrel, which was roasted or boiled and eaten. Any that was left was mixed in a barrel with vinegar and spices or salted and smoked and saved for the winter months.

James grew potatoes which were a fairly new vegetable to Scotland and also turnips, which were boiled and mashed together and called *neeps* and *tatties* or *clapshot*. They were eaten with a mixture of mutton or pork, spices and toasted oatmeal, which was called *haggis*. Only on a rare occasion did they eat the beef which they raised. Most of the beef went to the market to sell for the income that provided for their needs. When the occasion warranted and one of the animals had to be slaughtered, then part of it was eaten, but most of it was salted and stored for winter use.

Most of the milk the family used came from the ewes and goats and not milk from the cows. The milk that the children did not drink or was not used for cooking went into the making of cheese. Tea had become a favorite drink for the more affluent families and the Mackays drank tea on special occasions. The favorite drink of the family was ale which all but the smallest children drank. Most of the families like the Mackays had their own special recipes and were very proud of the ale they made.

The furnishings consisted of cupboards made of stone set into the walls. The sideboards where the dishes were stored were also made of inset stone. There were many shipments of lumber coming into Scotland before James left for Canada. The family had begun to replace their furniture with the nice woods being brought from Canada and the Americas. Elizabeth had her spinning wheel and rocker along with a loom to weave the wool she carded and spun. There were even new little stools for the children which were called *creepies*. The family had a sofa which was covered with cushions made by Elizabeth. Life was good during the years before James left, even with all the restrictions that were placed on the families.

There was a section attached to the house for animals. It was particularly convenient in the winter when the cow had to be milked and fed and the eggs gathered from a few laying hens, without going through the snow which could get very deep in

Scotland. There were beds in at least two sections of the house. One was in the living area for the parents or if guests were staying overnight, the bed was turned over to them. The younger members of the family shared another section of the house. Some beds in the crofts were called tent beds, others were platforms built against the walls in two or three bed layers. The bedding consisted of cloth bags filled with corn husks to make a mattress. If there were servants in the household, they would use another section called a *cearn* or Servants Hall. There were five sections to James' Family's Longhouse.

The walls were mudded and white washed, and James' mother, Elizabeth, planted vines of Clematis which grew over the door and spread up and over the thatched roof. Beginning in May, when the Clematis began to put out its pale pink blossoms, it must have been a beautiful and charming croft. I can just imagine an evening with the sun sinking in the West and casting a golden glow upon Loch Arichlinie with the family sitting upon the stoop of the house doing their mending and patching in the last fading moments of light before the darkness forced them indoors for the night. In addition to the Longhouse, the Mackays had a barn of about the same size as the house and it was made in the same way, not white washed but left in its natural state of mixed colored rock. It was used for animals, harvesting tools, thrashing the wheat and oats and for storing the winters' stock of food. There was a stone walk connecting the barn to the house. The barn or *byne* was directly behind the house and was separated by only 20 feet. The barn was paved with closely set stone with a trough running down the middle so manure and old straw could be raked into the trough and pushed out the door. It was then stored upon piles and used for the crops. The barn contained two doors, so that during thrashing time the wind could blow through and separate the grain from the chaff. Most of the time the barn set downhill from the house, but was reversed with the Mackay house due to the old house that was there before James' Grandfather took the lease. The old house was turned into the barn and a new house was built closer down to the loch, which was a much prettier view than looking down upon the barn.

There was also a large open, mixed stone walled round pen where the cattle and sheep could be gathered for protection or to be made ready for the drovers to take to market.

The Mackay family was more fortunate than most and cultivated a good portion of land in corn, oats and vegetables. James was an avid gardener and curious about the many different kinds of seeds and vegetables. He was well known to plant any type of seed that came into his possession. The family raised the shaggy black, brown and red highland cattle, sheep, goats, chickens, ducks, geese, a few hogs and a loft of pigeons and hutches of rabbits.

There was brown trout and fresh water mussels in the burns or little streams in the area, as well as in the Loch, and salmon in some of the rivers. Much of the fish was dried and stored for the winter. There were stags and red deer for venison, rabbits, grouse and a large variety of birds that flew inland from the sea.

The fishing and hunting was fun and provided the family with most of its food. The cattle, goats and sheep were more often sold as a source of income to purchase provisions they couldn't provide for themselves. Elizabeth kept a plentiful supply of eggs, milk, churned butter and her own special home made cheese. There was a great supply of food and some left to share with neighbors or give as offering to the Parish Minister, which was more often than not the way he was paid for his services. Hives of bees made particularly wonderful tasting honey from the heather around the Mackay Croft, which was sold in town for extra income. Elizabeth sold to others a goodly amount of items she raised and made. She and her daughters carded the wool, spun the thread and wove the thread into the cloth of the family tartan. George preferred the soft colors of the ancient Strathnaver Mackay Plaid. Now that the laws had forbidden the wearing of plaids, so that is the plaid Elizabeth made, before she placed it into the dyes

to cover the colors until the laws were changed and the dyes could be washed out of the material.

After a little pause, Gram said, "If it seems I speak over long about domestic matters, let me explain."

It was always a struggle to make sure the family was fed. Most of the time was spent working to provide the family food. It was never known from one day to another what disaster would befall the families.

The grains must always be gathered and stored in such a manner to keep out mold and insects as well as protection from the invading rodents. A barrel or pouch of spoiled oats could well be the difference of plenty and need. When eggs and milk were plentiful, they had to be properly preserved. Eggs could be kept for long periods of time simply by rubbing with well salted butter, or preserving them in barrels of salt brine and spices. Butter had to be well salted and packed in barrels to keep it from spoiling even in the cold climate of Scotland. Milk was made into cheeses which were carefully buttered and wrapped in waxed cloth.

The families' clothing came from wool sheared from their sheep. The wool was washed and dried, then carded and spun into thread. The thread was then woven into lengths of plaid or plain cloth which could be used as the family needed.

Part of each day was spent preparing for the following days.

CHAPTER FIVE

Auld Handsel Monday

JOHN HAD PERSUADED Gram to leave the arbor and to come into the house for awhile. Gram consented to lie down for a nap. While she napped, John went out to the garden his grandmother shared with Aunt Maria, the widow of Uncle Zeno Mackay. He picked up the old garden hoe, kept carefully hung on the wooden garden fence, and with a few well practiced strokes he began to rid the garden of the weeds which had sprung up almost overnight.

John picked the remaining curly leaf lettuce, as it was getting too hot and late in the year for lettuce, a few tomatoes, some little green onions and some big ripe strawberries. Carefully returning the hoe to its proper place on the fence he took the vegetables to the water pump standing near the garden. A pump or two of the pump's handle, brought water gushing forth to wash the vegetables. A small bucket was kept under the spout of the pump for just such uses as washing fruit and vegetables.

In the house Elizabeth was still napping, so very quietly John began to prepare the evening meal. He laid the table with Elizabeth's lovely china and set out the silverware and napkins. He mixed the fresh vegetables in a bowl. He sliced the tomatoes and placed them upon a plate. He then went outside to the well house for milk, butter, cream and cheese, then to the smoke house where he found a slab of bacon. He sliced off enough for their dinner salad. John cooked the bacon nice and crisp and poured up two glasses of milk. He found some of Elizabeth's delicious salt rising bread, sliced it and laid it on a toasting screen placed over the open hearth fire to toast. He placed a few chunks of Elizabeth's fresh vinegar cheeses spiced with chives upon the table.

The table was all set and the supper ready and just as if Elizabeth knew all was ready, she came into the room. The supper was really good and consisted of a wilted salad made with lettuce, onions, bits of bacon and a little bacon drippings and vinegar drizzled over the salad for a dressing. Served with cold milk, buttered toast and cheese, the supper was perfect. For dessert they shared fresh strawberries sprinkled with sugar and topped with cream from the well house.

After John and Elizabeth had finished their meal they retired to the small living room to continue the story of Grandfather James.

 Christmas and the days before and after was a very important time of the year for the Mackay family. Bannocks of fresh ground oats mixed with caraway seeds and shaped into rounds with a hole in the middle were made for the Christmas morning meal and great care was taken not to break the cakes during the baking. Broken cakes were thought to bring bad luck into the house for the coming year.

There was a special cake called Twelfth Night Cake or *Black Cake* and was made with dried fruits, nuts, spices and brandy and baked in a pastry crust. The Twelfth Night Cake was a very popular cake for the *first footers* to take when they called on the first day after the New Year.

On the last day of the year a silver coin was placed upon the doorstep and if the coin were still there in the morning it meant that good fortune would visit the house during the coming year and if it was gone the house was in danger of poverty. It was also considered lucky to carry a silver coin around in your pocket on the first day of the year.

The *Auld Handsel Monday* or first Monday after the first day of the year was a wonderfully special day and if the family had servants they were given a special day of gifts, a breakfast of roasted meats, cakes, puddings and other special things. Since the Mackay Family usually didn't have servants, relatives and friends who helped out with some of the chores were treated in some special way; with families getting together in a reunion and visiting back and forth having a great time. There was a special drink called *Het Pint* made of whiskey or ale mixed with spices, well beaten eggs and sugar. It was served to visitors as well as being brought by the first footers.

On the last day of the year or *Candle Night* a candle was lit in the window to welcome the first footers or the first visitor of the New Year. The first footer would bring gifts of cakes and drink and would be welcomed into the house with cakes and drink, so there was plenty of food and drink to make a merry good time. It was always hoped that the first person would be handsome or beautiful, good and kind which would bring good fortune to the family.

James said he would always remember the last day of the year of 1767. He had already had his sixth birthday and the Christmas celebrations were particularly exciting that year. He woke in the morning to hear some tiny noises coming from the area of the hearthstone. He sat up in his bed and looked over to where his Da was setting near the hearth fire and saw that he was holding something wrapped in a fine old tartan made by his mother, Elizabeth. He rubbed the sleep from his eyes and went over to his father George and wanted to know where the new baby had come from, he had thought baby William now four, was enough and there was his older brother John, whom he adored and his eight year old sister, Jean.

George turned back the edge of the tartan and showed James the new baby and told him the baby was a girl and her name was Catherine. James immediately said, "She is not a bit pretty and

looks just like a kitten" and from then on James always called his little sister "Kitty."

"She doesn't have very much hair, why is that Da? Kitten's have hair."

"Babies sometimes don't have much hair when they are born. They are born in the house where it is nice and warm, so they don't have to have hair like kittens who are born in the barn."

Kitty had had enough of this talk and let out a screech and was now ready to be fed. George quickly took the new baby over to Elizabeth who was still in the bed on the other side of the room, where she would remain for a few days to recover her strength. James watched in fascination as his mother guided the baby's mouth to her teat for nursing. There were a lot of noises coming from the baby who was happy to be getting fed and James was learning a lesson he would remember.

James liked to sit upon his father's knee but now there was Kitty and there was William who sat upon his knee the most and Da was always laughing and tickling them and giving them rides on his foot. James would miss Da's knee but he guessed that he was getting to old anyway, he was six and that was pretty big to be sitting on Da's knee. He would just sit beside John and listen to all Da's stories and there were lots of stories, because that is how the family passed down their history, sitting around the hearth fires.

James loved his brother, John who had whittled him a small wagon and horse, but his older sister, Jean was forever putting her doll into his wagon, and he couldn't get her to leave his wagon and horse alone, she was so bossy always telling him what to do. John had made her a little dolls buggy for Christmas, so now his wagon could be his own. This year for Christmas John had carved some little baskets to go in his wagon, so he could play the basket peddler. He was always careful with his toys, because there were so few of them and he hid them away when his cousins came so they wouldn't get broken. Sometimes they found small pieces of drift wood that washed upon the beach of the loch in front of the house. Sometimes Uncle William brought pieces of wood from the foreign countries he visited. Uncle William was a Sea Captain and had the most wonderful stories to tell. John was such a good brother and he didn't even mind that James followed him around all the time. Now that he was six he could help feed and milk the goats, ewes and cows. John was not at home as he had gone to visit cousins during the Yule Season, but he would be home tomorrow and wouldn't he be surprised when he saw Kitty.

It was time for his breakfast which was usually fixed by his mother, but today Da fixed some oatie cakes left over from Christmas and some cold sweet milk to go with them. James couldn't be happier, it had been a very good Christmas and tomorrow the first day of the year would be another great day.

Even though it was a special day, there were still many chores to do and because John was not there Da had to do the milking and feeding that John usually did. James, always eager to help and learn, went with his Da, to milk and feed and check the farmstead to make sure all the animals were safe and in their shelters. James felt very grown up.

In the barn, there were all manner of animals for the use of the farm, because much of their food came from them. In one corner there was a hutch where John kept his rabbits. Beside the rabbits was several boxes, lined up for the hens to lay their eggs, and some perch logs for the rest to sleep on at night. During the day the chickens were allowed to roam around the farmstead as they liked eating all they could find. James took turns with William to care for the chickens, picking up the eggs every morning and night unless a hen was setting on them. Taking eggs from a sitting hen brought a painful peck to the hand, so these he left alone, and soon there would be more chickens to add to the flock.

James asked his father, "Da, when am I going to get a rabbit like John?'

"Soon, he said, you have done very well with the chickens and I think it is almost time for you to start with a young doe."

When the chores were done, eggs gathered, ewes, goats and cows were milked, all was taken into the house. The eggs were buttered and placed in a large wooden bowl to be used or sold as the family needed. The milk was set out in it's container to let the cream rise. Some of it was drunk, more was used to made cheese.

Milk from the day before was taken up to make the cheese. James watched as his Da poured a good container of milk, about a gallon into the great pot used to cook the meals, hanging over the firestone. Da heated the milk until it was quite warm but not boiling. James watched as Da poured into the milk a little vinegar and stirred the milk. He then set the milk aside for a few minutes until the curds began to form. Da then spread a cloth across a large bowl and poured the milk and curds over the cloth, the whey from the milk ran through leaving the milk curds in the cloth. Da pulled the ends of the cloth together and tied it with a leather thong and hung the curds up to let the whey drip, leaving a nice soft cheese. Later in the evening, when all the dripping was finished, the cheese was taken out and put in small wooden molds. The cheese was ready to eat when it was needed. The longer the cheese sat, the firmer it became. A mold was needed for only one day; it was then emptied so it could be used again to repeat the cheese making process. James' Mother, Elizabeth, made her cheese the same way it had been made by the Norsemen, centuries before, in the county of Caithness where she was born.

With Mamma still in bed with baby Kitty and John gone to visit cousins, it had been a full day of chores and activities and the night saw all ready for bed and the coming of the first footer in the morning. Da put the silver coin on the doorstep, closed the door, and Da, James, Jean, and William gathered around the bed of Mamma so they could all join hands and say the evening blessing before they went to bed.

The blessing was a short one, but very thankful for the new baby, Mamma's health and all the blessings of the farm's bounty and the coming of the New Year.

An early morning banging on the door brought the "first footer" which turned out to be Uncle William, his family and brother John. Uncle William was loaded down with packages for the family. In his hand was the silver coin, Da had left on the doorstep the night before, all would be well the coming year.

Packages were all put aside and silver coins were given to all the family members to carry for the day. Baby Kitty even had a special pocket for her own silver coin. It was hoped all would have good fortune with health being the most important good fortune that a person could have during the year.

Da had been up for a time readying the day for all the activities to come. The oatie cakes were hot on the hearth stone. There was spiced ale, brought by Uncle William and milk for the children. Aunt Isabella was at the bedside of Momma making over little Kitty. The croft was full to over flowing with all the Mackays gathered there.

James had observed there was much movement coming from one of the packages. "Da, he said, there is something living in that pouch, what do you think it is?"

With the eating finished, George declared, "It is time too open these packages and find out what good fortunes the 'first footer' has brought. James, see that package that is moving around, think you maybe we should see what needs to be turned loose?"

James rushed to the package and in a blink had it opened, and with a squeal of delight, he pulled out a beautiful white angora rabbit. "Is this for me Da?" James asked with hope and excitement filling his voice.

"Yes James, this is the first of your rabbits, a doe to go with the rabbits which are Johns. You will need to work out an agreement with John to have the doe serviced by one of his bucks."

Immediately James sought out John who was busy opening his own packages of precious wood Uncle William had brought from a recent trip to the American Colonies. "John, look I have a doe," and he proceeded to push the doe right into John's face.

"How much will you charge me to let your buck 'Maney' mate with my doe?"

With a thoughtful look on his face John said, "Well, let me think on this, but I think "King Charles" would be the better match for your doe, he is a white angora and will give better little ones than 'Maney' and a much finer fur, what do you think, James?"

"Oh yes, could it really be 'King Charles', I didn't think it possible, he already has his quota of does."

"I had been thinking to put my doe 'Lizzie' to 'Maney,' I think 'King Charles' could take on your doe. What will you name her?"

James looked at his sister, Jean and gave her a mischievous smirk.

Jean instantly hollered, "You can't name that rabbit Jean, I just can't stand it."

This brought a laugh from all the family and James had accomplished his goal by getting Jean riled up as he loved to do.

James declared he would name the little doe 'Princess Kitty' because after all a name was an honor to be bestowed only on someone that was really special like the new baby Kitty.

Upon hearing the name James would name his little doe, William laughed and laughed and said *"Katie na h''aridh"* meaning Katie is special. All the children chimed in with a chorus of "Katie na H''aridh, Katie na h''aridh" and the name stuck and from there after the new baby, Catherine, was called by everyone "Katie na h''aridh or as James would always say "Kitty."

The price of the mating had not been established. James, knowing that 'King Charles' was much the better buck and he would pass on his luxurious fur to his young, was very worried at the price John might extract from him. But he would have to pay it because Da always said the boys must learn the art of business dealing and the time to start was when they were very young. So they, like most of the boys in the area, had their own animals and were allowed to keep much of the earnings of the animals after they reimbursed their father for the food the animals ate. All was carefully calculated as to cost, it was one of their lessons in math.

John thought a minute and said, "half, I think James, of the litter would be the right payment, unless there is only one and then you must keep it and I will give you a return breeding and take half of the next litter, I must get at least two rabbits from you for the breeding. Since this will be her first match, she may not have more than one or two young."

With a quick agreement from James and a firm handshake between brothers the deal was made. The handshake deal was considered one of honor, and it would be a very bad smear on a person's character to break the bond of a handshake.

With all that conversation being exhausted, the boys John, James, William, their cousins James and Will all took off for the barn which was only a few feet from the house across a small rock walkway.

In the barn were the two small Shetland ponies to pull the small carts that were used to go into the nearest village and also for riding when the walking distance was a little too far. There was Da's old gelding which could sometimes be ridden by the children. Isobel and Maude, the family milk goats were happily chewing on their ropes which meant more would have to be made before long. The chickens were in their corner, hens setting on their nest and some setting on the cross poles of the barn. In another corner were the rabbit hutches. All was quite and peaceful in the barn, that is until the boy's arrival.

It was William's turn to gather the eggs, and he had brought along his basket to do the chore while bringing the new rabbit to the hutch. William, being four years old, wasn't old enough for a rabbit but he was old enough not to be afraid of any pecks from old hens. With a whack of his little fist he sent the hens flying and screeching from their nest and picked out all the eggs that were not marked which indicated they were to be left to hatch. There were plenty of eggs and some left over to sell in town. That

done, he went over to watch the rabbit fun. He knew in a year or two he would have some rabbits too.

To James' surprise the Hutch next to 'King Charles' was empty. The latch was opened and 'Princess Kitty' was placed in her new home. There was a small divider between the two hutches. The boys hung around, talked, scuffled and had a good time while the new doe got used to her new home. John then went over and pulled out the divider between 'King Charles' and 'Princess Kitty'.

They all held their breaths to see if the two rabbits would find an interest in each other. 'King Charles' first put his nose through to 'Princess Kitty's' side. She returned the curiosity and hopped back into her side and 'King Charles' followed. In ten seconds of time, 'King Charles' made his move on 'Princess Kitty' and the boys all knew in 31 days the kindling would produce a new batch of young.

The barn was filled with the exuberance of the boys, who were laughing, joking and making a big fuss over the natural processes that went on in the barn. James' chest was swelled with pride and he calculated he was going to be a big success at this business. Being six years old was very good.

CHAPTER SIX

Rosslyn Chapel

JOHN WAS SOMEWHAT in shock to hear his little Grandmother speak of the copulation of the farm animals.

Elizabeth seeing his startled expression explained, "John people are much too prudish about the natural functions of the body. These are things that are taught by religions and have nothing to do with the natural way of things. All animals including humans must copulate to procreate."

Of course, John already knew this but it made him red in the face anyway.

Elizabeth continued, "In the old country, there was little room for privacy and people gave little thought to the things of nature, and sharing their beds with their children didn't stop the natural urgings we were fashioned to enjoy. What is not natural is that the marriage bed is for procreation only. I, in truth much enjoyed the marriage bed that I shared with your grandfather. I would not have you believe that this is not so. We will talk more on this subject later in my story for a young man must proceed into manhood with caution else he will never have healthy children."

"Now," Gram said, "I shall continue my story."

In the extreme north of Scotland where the Mackay Clan families lived, cattle were the most important export of the counties of Sutherland and Caithness. The cattle provided the means of securing the monies needed to pay the yearly lease rents. Some money was made from the wool sheared from the

sheep, but most came from the cattle that were yearly driven to market.

There was a tremendous demand for cattle which were collected from neighboring crofts into herds. They were then driven to area markets, such as nearby Wick, where some of the beef were slaughtered, packed into barrels of salt, and shipped to any country that had ships in port and were in need of beef.

A great many more of the cattle of Sutherland County, where George Mackay lived on the Halladale Strath with his family, were gathered into herds that were driven along the Strath of Kildonan and the Helmsdale River to the coast and along the coast to the annual markets in Crief, a distance of about 100 miles.

Cattle were rounded up from their grazing locations and contained near the home croft. George had a large stone round pen for the containment of his cattle. Each calf had been marked at birth with a special mark used by George to tell his calves from neighboring calves which all used a common grazing meadow. Just before the drove trips, the cattle had to be shod. The drove roads were covered with rock along the way and very treacherous going for the cattle. A broken hoof could mean the death of the animal.

During the fall of 1773, when James was twelve, he joined his father George and fifteen year old brother John on one of these annual droves. The cattle raised by George and his sons were the black cattle which were superior in quality, were studier and could make the trip better than the smaller less hardy cattle that were raised in nearby Caithness County. Near the Loch Arichlinie there was more grass for the cattle to graze which helped them withstand the rigors of the four-week trip. They would arrive in better condition for the sale and bring more money. For four years now James had had his own cattle to care for and money from the sale would pay his school expenses for the following year and maybe longer. The cattle were short and small with long shaggy hair hanging from their backs and down their faces completely covering their eyes. It was a wonder they could even see, but

James believed the hair kept their eyes from freezing in the wintertime. Their horns were long and sharp and care had to be taken to avoid them. The cattle were placid in nature but with a toss of their head, if you were standing too close, a serious injury might be the result.

Drove trips required a lot of planning and packing to get ready for the journey. Most important was that each of the drovers had a long staff to carry for prodding the cattle as well as an occasional help up a steep hill. There were extra long cloths taken for when the weather turned bitter cold. To be unprepared for these terrible weather changes was to risk taking a chill and possible death. There must be enough food for the men and skins for ale and nettle beer and some for home brewed single malt whiskey.

Elizabeth made plenty of oat cakes to take along as well as dried fish, dried and powdered beef for soup, cheese and bags of oats and barley. Wild greens and nettle grew along the route and could be mixed with the beef, oats and barley for the making of *brose*. Occasionally a rabbit was killed or snared along the way to supplement the meals. The men took along their woolen long cloths to wrap around themselves at night when they slept on the ground. Elizabeth didn't worry that there wouldn't be food and ale on the trip if they ran short there were places along the way to purchase more but most of the men preferred their own recipes for ale. The preferred drink was ale whether at home or on the journeys, which Scots took without thought of the distance.

The first camp was halfway to the coast at Helmsdale where they joined local tacksmen and other drovers. It was a great and exciting time for all involved for the trip had truly begun. The first camp provided a time to learn the set up of a camp and the duties they would need to know throughout the drive. A small two wheel wagon carried several bags of wool shorn from their sheep. The wagon carried small bags of angora sheared from James and John's angora rabbits and all manner of pots, pans and other supplies needed on the trip. They carried peat to be used for the camp fires. The wagon was being pulled along the route by one of the two Shetland ponies owned by the Mackay family. When George had decided to bring the pony both boys had been surprised, since it was usual for packs of goods to be carried by the men and boys. There was a decided gleam in George's eyes, and the boys knew he was up to some surprise, probably something for their mother. It wouldn't have done one whit of good to ask, they would have to wait and learn when their father decided to tell.

George, John and James drove their cattle and some belonging to other crofters in the area. During the fall, the herds were like long dark undulating strings wending their way down the mountain passes, over the moors and bogs and across the rivers and streams. The more cattle and men with the herds, the safer they would all be. Thieving, without respect for life and property, was practiced by many of the different clans.

Disaster struck less than half way to their destination when one of James' little steers stepped onto a stone which rolled causing him to fall and break one of his legs. George quickly dispatched the animal, taking him out of his pain. In the wagon was a barrel holding some of their supplies. The barrel was emptied and the animal was skinned, cut up and packed in the barrel with salt and water. This would keep the meat fresh and could be eaten on the way to the market. Being an enterprising young man, James thought to sell the beef to the other drovers who liked a fresh joint now and then. Any that might be left could be traded for goods. The outcome was not as severe as had been thought when James recouped his expenses and made a small profit. James had learned another lesson in survival and commerce.

Around the camp at night was a time of singing, dancing and the telling of ribald jokes, as all that were present were men used to such crude behavior. There was a lot of merriment with the men drinking their ale and the younger boys getting a little also, for by the age of twelve, boys in Scotland were used to the rigors and work of any man and weren't denied drink a little stronger than milk and water. The cold and rain no more bothered them than their fathers. It was all considered part of life and went without complaint. Cussin' wasn't complaining, just cussin' and that was frowned upon by George, so John and James learned all their words when their Da was not within hearing.

The cattle were driven along the coast to cross the Kyle River at Creich, and then driven up the river from the coast, where the crossing was wide, to a shorter more shallow part of the river where the cattle could swim in greater safety. The pony and wagon were ferried over to protect all the goods which were being carried. Usually the cattle jumped right in and swam across without any problems. The road made by numerous cattle drives created the only roads available for travel in the Scottish Highlands. In many places rocks lined each side of the road to provide the path that was to be taken and to keep the cattle from straying.

The drovers were careful with the cattle not allowing any to stray from the herds as the land owners along the way were very adept at confiscating any strays they could claim as their own. The landowners also had large fees to cross their lands; that is if they caught you crossing of course. The Mackays didn't care to lose even one of their cows or pay the fees if it could be avoided. Along the routes there were toll roads where the payment of crossing fees could not be avoided.

Crief was reached in due time, without many delays, and the crossing had gone well. No further cattle had been lost and the Mackays would have a good year. A large fair was being held to provide necessary items and items of luxury were offered to separate the drovers from as much of their money as possible. The first order of business was to take their money to the accounting house for drafts with which they would pay the annual lease rents on their return trip.

The boys were allowed spending money for the fair where they could buy meat pies or haggis with neeps and tatties, a wide variety of cakes, tarts and *clootie dumplings*. There were gifts to buy for their mother Elizabeth, William now ten, Jean who was seventeen and Kitty who was now six years old. There were jesters doing their acts, men and women walking on stilts and all manner of interesting activities. James decided to use part of his money to buy a couple more rabbits. He also picked out a particularly nice little doe for William. He felt around her abdomen and found that she was already very early pregnant and would have young not too long after William received her. James was elated because he was quite sure the Seller hadn't known or the price would have been higher. William would have to learn not to whack the rabbits like he did the chickens to get them off their nest; rabbits didn't like such things and would eat their young when they became too excited.

John found a new pot for Elizabeth to hang over the cooking fire. For Jean he found a beautiful piece of cotton material from some place called Georgia in the Colonies, to make a new dress. He thought, now that she was being courted by all the boys in the area, it would be a welcome gift. They bought stockings, which were hard to find in the north, for the women and for Kitty a new doll which had just come from Germany. It was made of porcelain with a beautiful painted face and a dress made of silk. Kitty was sure to love this gift. For the three year old Robert, a block of white oak wood from the colonies was purchased so John could make him some soldiers. He had already decided, at three, he was going to grow up and protect Scotland, and he would raise his little wooden stick gun and shout "bang" to anyone that would listen. James bought himself a compass which he had wanted for a long time. Someday he intended to go to one of the colonies and make his fortune. John purchased a new carving tool as well as a book on advanced math; he was quite good with numbers and would also seek his fortune in the colonies for there was little future in Scotland for enterprising young men.

Loaded down with all their purchases and stomachs stuffed with the foods they had consumed, they went to find their Da and settle in for the night. When John and James reached their camp site they found that Da had a very strange looking package in the wagon. It looked something like a coffin but was much too thin and long. Da wasn't sharing his secret but he was whistling a lively little ditty and dancing a little jig. Once in a while he broke into song. Da loved a good time and the keeping of secrets.

A side trip had been planned by Da for his lads to visit the Chapel of Rosslyn. James was now twelve, it was time for him to make his holy pilgrimage to the chapel of divine secrets.

The Chapel of Rosslyn was said to be the repository of the secrets of the Knights Templar and was built on a centuries old Celtic site. Built during the fifteenth century, the Chapel contained many carvings that represented the secrets of Knowledge and Wisdom and of Spiritual Enlightenment. It was there in The Chapel that anyone who wished to study and learn those secret lessons could do so, for their own salvation and without fear of persecution.

In the nature of young men James and John determined they would, without benefit of teachers, go to the chapel and take oaths they had written up themselves just as the Knights of old took their sacred oaths. It was daring and romantic and they each had seen the secret hand sign.

They both remembered the day they had come upon an old man dressed in rags carrying a pack upon his back. He stumbled and fell just as they were passing. They had run to his side and he had gasped out that he was finished and could go no further.

"Take my pack to the good man George Mackay and have him inter my body in a secret place."

"We are his sons," they said.

They had watched in fascination when he raised his hands in prayer and intoned, "Lord, by the sacred oaths I have taken to the keepers of the secrets of Christ, and by my sign, I beg you now to take my soul into your keeping." He then made a sign and breathed his last breath.

George had made arrangements with one of the other Tacksmen to take the pony and wagon with their gifts and

purchases on to Golspie, where they would all meet up, pay their rents and return home.

George and his sons set upon the journey, which was not a great distance, with only their packs upon their backs, their hats and long cloths. It was not more than a two day's journey. Rosslyn lay at the edge of the Esk Valley south of Edinburgh.

With the utmost reverence for the elaborately carved chapel they were about to enter the boys removed their caps, washed their face and hands, removed their shoes and walked into the chapel. In front of the Alter were three great carved pillars. The Apprentice Pillar was immediately recognized as it was by far the most intricate and beautiful.

Da had already told them the legend of the Apprentice Pillar. The Master had asked the apprentice to carve one of the pillars, but having other tasks to perform left the apprentice to his own devices for a very long time. While the Master was gone, the apprentice received a divine revelation as to the manner in which the pillar should be carved. He proceeded, without the instructions of the master, to carve the pillar. On his return the Master found the pillar had been completed. When he viewed the work of his apprentice, he became so enraged and jealous that he slew the apprentice with his own carving tool.

The divine pillar was itself a statement that each individual can have direct communication with God. The boys knelt before the Alter.

James and John together made the hand sign they had witnessed the dying old man make. They said their own secret oaths to the keepers of the secrets of Christ, even though they didn't know what the real oaths were. They again made the sacred hand sign they had seen before the Madonna, carved and clothed in black that represented Wisdom, and each in silence repeated their oaths to commit them to memory. James felt a cooling wind that came from he knew not where. As it washed over him it left contradicting warmth in its place, and in that moment, James knew he had been changed in a way that would comfort him throughout his life.

After the oaths were taken, the boys explored the chapel and its small chambers marveling at the carvings that covered every surface and at the stained glass windows which held the secrets and knowledge that could only be known through imagination or revelations from God.

To the right of the chapel were stairs leading from the chapel down below, it was an undeniable impulse that led James and John down the stairs and into the small rooms. It was apparent that stones had been removed exposing one of the chambers, and the boys wondered if the room was the gateway to the treasures that were rumored to still be hidden in the chapel somewhere and whose secrets would not be revealed until the year of 2012, a very long time after they would both be in their graves.

Leaving the chapel with George, who had joined them after they had finished with their oaths and prayers, they began the trip to Golspie to meet the other drovers and Tacksmen and pick up the pony and wagon, with all their supplies, to go to near by Rhiaes to pay the next year's rents to the Sutherland factor.

From Rosslyn, they took the shortest route to the River Forth where they caught the ferry across and traveled on to Perth and Pitlochry. The route took them along the River Garry and around the Grampian Mountains and up to Inverness. In Inverness they ran into one of their many cousins, James MacInnes, who was on his way to Golspie, so they saved themselves a considerable walk by boarding their cousin's small fishing boat and taking the trip to Cromarty and then around the Tarbat Ness and then to Golspie where they met up with the other drovers and collected the pony and wagon with all the gifts and supplies intact.

The rents were all paid, the market had been good. There was great good humor all around for they were within two days of their journey's end after a grueling four week trip.

Da with James and John were spied long before they reached their home at Loch Arichlinie. William, Jean, Catherine

and Elizabeth were all outside waiting for the arrival of the returning drovers.

As soon as the pony came to a stop, eager hands began to pull packages from the wagon.

"Stop," Da said, "first we must remove the box."

With Da at one end and John the other, the "coffin box" was removed and carefully carried into the house. Taking great care, Da lifted off the lid.

Accompanied by the oohs and aahs of the family members, Da and John removed the families' new "tall case clock" from all its protective covering. The clock crafted by Samuel Bailie of Dundalk was a gift fit for a Laird.

Placing the clock in a well sheltered area, George hung the pendulum in place. With a tiny flick of his finger the clock began to tick.

The gifts brought by James and John were no less well received, but the clock was now a family treasure.

The following morning hearing the sixth hammer strike upon the clock's little brass bell, all the family began to stir.

Kitty was up immediately on the sixth strike heading for the clock. Before anyone realized what she was about, she had opened the clock's door and stopped the pendulum.

"Kitty, why have you stopped the clock," Da asked.

"Because, today is the Sabbath, and 'tis a sin to be workin' on the Lord's Day" she said in a voice that showed she had learned her lessons from the Bible.

Much to Kitty's embarrassment, all the family had a very good laugh.

"Kitty, 'tis a fine instrument, made by man, meant to work every day. It is the creatures who have life that need a day of rest." Da explained.

CHAPTER SEVEN

Hill O'Stanes

JOHN ASKED ELIZABETH, "Gram, what kind of schools did grandfather attend when he was growing up? How did he learn about all those things?"

With a faraway look in her eyes, as she was remembering some things told to her a long time ago, Elizabeth said, "In Scotland there were many kinds of schools and the Chiefs of the Clans as well as the Tacksmen all thought education was very important to their lives. James' father George was a well educated man for the times and head Tacksman in the area where they lived. When it came to learning, no expense that the family could afford, was spared in the education, of the children. Even the girls were educated which I am sorry to say is almost ignored in this country as well as it was in England. Promise me this, John, that you will see to the education of your daughters as well as your sons."

John said, "Gram I promise, I will make no difference between my daughters and sons as to their education."

It was not a hard promise and very heart felt; after all he would have promised his grandmother anything.

After a few moments, Gram continued her story:

The cattle sales had been good, and it was time for James to leave for school. John had finished The Parish School the year before. The Country of Scotland had become the most educated country of all the countries in Europe.

James was going to a school that specialized in the teaching of Mathematics, History and Geography and now he would travel to the far north of Scotland on the coast where the Mackay Clan Chief dwelled at Tongue.

Until James' twelfth year he had taken his education from the local ministers and the Parish School as well as from his father and mother. He had learned English and Latin, and he knew some French as well. He had studied math and the Sciences. He would learn to Survey as well as Navigation and Cartography, Longitudes and Latitudes and their relationships to the stars as well as the directional lines of North, East, South and West. He would learn accounting and clerking at the new school.

For the past one hundred years, groups of Scots had been leaving the lochs, rivers and moors of Scotland to settle in the more productive lands of the world. There was a constant demand for men who could survey and map these foreign lands. It took a man of intelligence and education as well as strength and stamina to fill these positions. Scotland had an ample supply of both.

The schooling for James required little money. His needs were few for school, a good jacket, a couple pair of pants, shirts, stockings a pair of shoes and his long cloth to keep him warm was all he would need plus a room or garret in which to sleep and enough porridge and herring with oat cakes to keep away the hunger. There was a saying in England of Scotland Schools, "they cultivated literature upon a little oatmeal."

The most important part of school life was how much a student could learn in his short few years of Academy Education.

When James was 16 he planned to leave Scotland with John and seek their fortunes in Novia Scotia or Canada. He would go where the best opportunity presented itself.

The three years James spent away at school passed very quickly, with only a few short trips home to break the fast pace of learning. School was not difficult for James. He was used to long hours of study. There was no time for roughhousing with the other students; he had left that behind with his Parish School. Every waking hour was spent in his studies to prepare him for his future. He rarely paid attention to what he ate and wore but focused all his energy into learning.

The last year of James' school, the school Master gave each of the students the assignment of constructing a mode of transportation with materials which could be easily found around the village or in the home.

James chose to make a replica of an ancient Welsh Coracle, used on the rivers for fishing in centuries past.

The circular boat was approximately 50 inches in diameter and about 15 inches deep. The students were given the full school year to gather their materials and complete their project. On James' first trip home he secured a large bull hide to use for the project. He gathered small logs of bog fir and cut lots of heather. With the bog fir, he stuck the logs into the ground in a circle, to make the ribs of the boat. He notched the wood to make braces between the ribs. He then laid a flat piece of wood, notching and wedging it between the logs that formed the ribs. Leather thongs were woven back and forth across the top to make a solid top to the framework. James then smoked the hide and boiled it in tallow. While the hide was still warm he stretched it over the frame work. The edges of the hide were tied around each rib stuck into the ground. Wax from the bee hives was melted with more tallow and rubbed into the hide to waterproof it and then it was left to dry and harden.

When the drying was complete, the boat was picked up and turned over. The boat was round with a seat, braced between the ribbings where one person could sit. He made a paddle of a long flat piece of wood and fitted it to the end of a small log of bog fir.

James could sit in the boat and by leaning forward from the seat and dipping the paddle in the water in front of the boat and paddling a figure eight in the water, the boat moved along quite nicely. The boat weighted only about 25 pounds and could easily be picked up and carried on his back. He already thought it would

be a great boat for William, who could help in catching brown trout in Loch Arichlinie behind their croft.

The students were preparing to leave when the Head Master called James into his library. He had a visitor, who he introduced as Angus Ross, a representative of some Fur Traders in Canada. Mr. Ross had come to the school looking for students who would be interested in hiring on with the company as clerks and surveyors in Canada. They would need to chart the rivers and carry supplies to the fur trappers and pick up their bales of fur at fur post or, as they were called, 'factories'. Mr. Ross was very impressed with James' Coracle.

James told Mr. Ross, yes, he would be interested that he and his brother John had already planned to go to Canada. He would need to talk to his brother and his parents. He took the name of the inn where Mr. Ross would be staying for the next two weeks.

Upon arriving home, James told John and his parents of Mr. Ross and his offer and assured them that the Head Master said he was a man who could be trusted to see to their safety and welfare. John was also offered a job. They would receive a good salary of a Thousand Liveres a year to work as clerks. Mr. Ross' arrival at the school was stroke of good fortune, and arrangements were made to meet Mr. Ross and the Fur Company's schooner The Andrew at the end of August for their long anticipated trip to North America.

During that summer of 1776, James spent his time helping on the farm until their departure in late August.

James had his fifteenth birthday in May, John was eighteen, and Jean had married and left home with her husband. William was now thirteen and nearly a man. There was Kitty age nine and Robert age six and his little brother George age two.

George and Elizabeth were in good health and the management of the farm would not be a great hardship without their two older sons.

James would certainly miss his mother and especially his little sister Kitty but such was the way of life. He knew few of the people, leaving by the shiploads, ever returned.

Many things had been changing in the Highlands. Some of the area families' leases had not been renewed and they were being forced to move to the coast to work in the kelp fields, which was very hard work. There was talk that the Sutherlands were going to import sheep to take the place of the shaggy cattle the Mackays had always owned. The Arichliney *Wadset* the Mackays' leased was a prosperous property, and George had lived on the land for 36 years and made many improvements. They had been reassured by the Sutherland factor that next year when their lease was up, that it would be renewed for the next Thirty Seven years which was the term of a *Wadset Lease*. The lives of the Achentoul Mackays would not change drastically with the leaving of their two older sons even though they would be missed.

The summer was spent in visitations to friends and the places they loved. The pony and cart to carry Elizabeth with Robert and George was readied along with enough food and drink to supply the family on a trip to Lybster and Clyth to see the MacDonald's, relatives of Elizabeth who lived near the *Hill O'Stanes*.

James was most interested to see the stones again, with his great knowledge, or so he thought, of the stars he would be able to read the ancient stones. He took his compass with him.

The trip was an easy two day journey. The family arrived at the MacDonald's in time for a good supper and the talk and good humor of catching up on everyone's lives. Visits between relatives were not made overly often and were much enjoyed when the occasions arose. This trip was a celebration of the boy's good fortune in their coming trip to Canada.

The morning offered a hearty meal of kippered fish, porridge and oat cakes. The youths of the families were going on a trip to the stones a two mile distance from the MacDonald home. The group consisted of the Mackay boys, John, James, William, sister Kitty and little Robert. The MacDonald cousins were Donald and Angus with their sisters Jean, Margaret, Mary and Isobel. Isobel and Robert were really too young for the trip and would probably have to be carried part of the way but none had the heart to refuse their request to go.

Covering the hillside were over 200 stones of heavy granite in shades of the colors of white grey, black and pink and in various heights up to three feet. They were in rows which curved into the shape of a fan. There was much speculation between the young scholars as to what position each stone must represent or what relationship to the position of the sun and moon each would have, as the youths played and toad jumped over the stones.

The stones had been there longer than history had been recorded. They were objects of curiosity and strangely enough few of the stones had been carried off for the building of crofts and fences. The stones were sacred and mysterious and connected the people to their Celtic Heritage.

There was certain mysticism in Scotland and many sacred sites of the old Celtic religion. Many people had "the sight," one of whom was Kitty. James would not forget the time he and John had gone to see one of the Brochs, scattered around the highlands. They had been homes of an ancient and now extinct people. The boys had gone into the houses climbing up the stairs, lying upon the shelves and imagining how the people had lived. They were strange structures about 30 feet in height, round and conical shaped. The stones were placed together without the use of mortar. There was no top but at some time they probably had roofs made of skins or turf like their own croft.

Kitty had refused to go into the Broch, she said there had been a terrible tragedy there. She said there were strange men who came and captured the people and took them away. She simply refused to go near the Brochs. One never questioned "the sight" but listened to the visions. They never went to one of them again, even to play or imagine what or who had been there.

After the trip there was little time left before John and James would depart. On the week before their departure all the neighbors dropped by for a celebration with the music of bagpipes, violin and flute as well as dancing. Much of the earlier restraints on the bagpipes as well as the wearing of kilts had been ignored and the people were not too concerned they would get into trouble as in the years past when almost everything in their lives had been forbidden.

On the night before their departure, the table was set with a great platter of haggis with side dishes of potatoes and turnips. There was oat flour scones filled with currents to be served with clotted cream and grape conserve. For their departure meal, their mother had prepared a feast!

While Da hitched the pony to the wagon, so Elizabeth could ride with the new baby George, the boys began saying their goodbyes to the family, even though they would all accompany them to Helmsdale to watch their departure. Two year old Robert rode most of the way "piggy-back" on William's shoulders. Their mother, Elizabeth and sister, Kitty cried and James and John had constricting lumps in their throats. Their father George was overly hearty they thought, to keep from showing his emotion. After all the children were hugged and carried around and mother and Kitty were hugged again and again the family set off toward the coast at Helmsdale, where they would meet with their cousin, James MacInnes, and sail to the far north tip of Scotland called John O'Groats.

CHAPTER EIGHT

Beannachd lebh M'athair and Scotland
(goodbye Mother and Scotland)

THE NIGHT BEFORE, Gram had continued her story until the evening had grown quite advanced.

The sun was well over the horizon when Gram came into the kitchen to find John had already prepared a simple breakfast of oatmeal with strawberries and milk.

When their breakfast was finished and the kitchen tidied, John and Gram took a little walk around the house and garden. They walked to the river bank where a small seat overlooked the river Gravois. After the arbor, this was Gram's favorite spot. The few acres of land had been part of grandfather's Original land grant.

After tossing a few pebbles in the river and watching the widening ripples fade away into the sluggish running water, Gram began again with her story.

Coast of Scotland, August 29, 1776

With great excitement, John and James endured and embraced the hugs and tears from all the neighbors and relatives who had walked along the river of Helmsdale with them to the coast. The little fishing boat of their cousin James MacInnes waited to take them to John O'Groats. They would take a ferry to Stromness on the Isle of Orkney.

Jokes and caring remarks, laughter and tears accompanied the boys along the river. Little Bessie Fraser with her lovely ginger colored hair, had picked heather along the way to present to John before he left on his trip. He had given her a great kiss upon her cheek. She blushed prettily and hung onto his hand as long as she could, she was of the same age as their little sister Kitty. It seemed the whole countryside had attended their leave taking. On foot and by cart, they had come to the sea to bid their two lads farewell.

Elizabeth their *M'athair* cried copious amounts of tears and only quieted after James promised, should he never return, her name would be on his lips even until the moment he passed into the keeping of the almighty father and that she would ever be the most dear person to his heart.

From George, their *Da'*, they received a stout hug and a mighty handshake along with the spoken words of the motto of the Clan Mackay, which were *Bidh Treun* or be valiant.

The boys hopped aboard the boat in the agile way that young boys can do. The bags were dropped without thought of contents, and they turned to face the dear friends and family still on shore. The lines were cast off by willing hands, and the little boat slowly pulled away from the dock. The boys drank in the sight of all those they loved, stamping their faces forever into their memories. The crowd in unison raised their right arms, hand open in the sign of The Mackay, and there was a thunderous yell of "Bidh Treun." Again and again the yell was sounded until the boat passed around the point of Helmsdale and out of sight of the well wishers.

The little fishing boat plowed along the coast of Scotland, passing by all the places they knew so well, Dunbeath, Lybster and then Clyth.

It had been such a short time ago that they had visited their McDonald cousins in Clyth and visited the Hill O' Many Stanes. Much to the boy's surprise as they passed by they saw upon the shore their cousins, Donald and Angus MacDonald, with their arms up and hands open and heard the distant shouts of "Bidh

Treun." Seeing their cousins provoked such emotion that only the excitement of the voyage kept the tears in check.

The town of Wick went past their view and they could see the spire of the Old Wick Parish Church of Scotland which had always been so dear to their hearts, for it was the burial place of their Mackay grandparents. On along the coast, skimming lightly over the waters of the North Sea, they sailed until they reached the very last point of the mainland at John O'Groats. James MacInnes wished them good success in the fur industry and hugged them both and asked them to be sure to write. They departed from their cousin to catch the last ferry of the day over to Stomness on the Isle of Orkney.

The wait was not long, and they would be on the last boat of the day. The ferry, crowded with people, plowed through the North Sea which was always a little rough. The ferry headed around the island of Stroma into the port of Stromness and from the ferry deck, they could see The Andrew taking on the last of the supplies for the voyage to North America. The ship would sail with the morning tide.

The Andrew was a sleek little three mast schooner which weighed only 100 tons. In addition to Captain Macneil and his first mate, there was Mr. Ross and six crew men. The ship was a real beauty and a new acquisition of Mr. Ross' employer. The lads were shown to a small cabin which they would share with William Gunn and Roy Sutherland, two other young men who were also on their way to work for the Company. The baggage was stored with haste, so all could return to the deck to watch the casting off of the ship.

Within a very short time, the ship was dipping and swaying to the roll of the ocean. The wind had picked up and snapped the sails to their fullest, and the ship was truly on its way. Salt spray splattered their faces while the wind blew their hair in wild disarray, and the sun shown down warm and wonderful. It was a perfect beginning for an exciting adventure. An adventure was the way the young men looked upon this voyage into a world unknown, except for the wonderful and fearful tales that found their way to every corner of Scotland.

With the exception of a small sea squall, which was more exhilarating than frightening, The Andrew reached the coast of North America without incident in only 59 days.

John, James, Will and Roy became fast friends long before the end of the journey. They had spent time with Captain Macneil, much to his delight, learning about navigation and the use of the instruments and charts. He pointed out Guide Stars and how their placement should be and on which side of the ship to show they were headed in the correct direction.

The ships crew was just as interested and eager to teach the young men about the ship, making knots in ropes and climbing the rigging, as well as cleaning and polishing the ship to keep all in good working order.

The Andrew put into shore on Newfoundland at St. John for fresh water and supplies. James and John got their first look at forests like they had never thought possible; trees so thick a man couldn't pass between them. The mountains were covered with snow and so tall the tops were lost in the clouds or poked through above to appear suspended in the sky. It was a glorious site. They saw dogs pulling sleds and little carts piled high with goods. They saw their first "red" man all clothed in animal skins with black hair hanging down his back and eyes black as night. He carried a weapon in his hand and a long skinny sack upon his back. Mr. Ross explained that the sacks were for the arrows. He said, "An Indian can notch and loosen a number of their arrows faster than a man can load and fire his gun."

James made his decision right then to become proficient with the bow and arrows as well as the use of his gun and knife and the small dirk he kept hidden beneath his stocking.

The stay in Newfoundland was brief, just long enough to take on the fresh supplies which were most welcome. The boys knew of the importance of lemons on board ships. They learned of a little shrub that grew in Canada which had a fruit called

"cranberries" that could take the place of lemons and keep away the ship sickness that caused peoples teeth to fall out. There would be many many new things to learn in this new land.

The ship headed its nose around the coast of Newfoundland and through Cape Ray and into the opening of the St. Lawrence River which was ninety miles at its mouth. A ship could travel 500 miles into the interior of Canada without going aground.

They saw numerous prosperous looking settlements along the river banks as they passed along. The gardens were lush and the houses looked sturdy and well built. There were endless miles of forest and animals too numerous to count. This land was indeed a rich land.

They continued along the river and passed Quebec, the Capitol of Canada, and then sailed on by the Trois Rivier'es so called for the three waters that emptied into the St. Lawrence. Their destination of Montreal, the fur capitol of the world, was finally reached.

Upon their arrival in Montreal, Captain Macneil turned the lads over to the care of Robert Grant, their fur company employer. It was the last day of October 1776 and James would not reach his sixteenth birthday until May next.

The winter was spent in the company of Mr. Grant learning the accounting system they would use in the fur industry. They were taught about weight and quality of furs and the prices different furs should bring and how much to pay the seller.

They were taken by canoes up the rivers to learn rowing, packing and unloading of supplies like they would be carrying to the fur factories.

James began to grow in height, weight and put on muscles from the lifting of supplies and bundles of furs as well as the carrying of canoes. Mr. Grant taught the lads the sign language of the Chippewa Indians and the Algonquin language which most tribes of the Northwest understood. They learned simple Indian words, for the trade goods in the languages of the different tribes.

Mr. Grant left them in an Indian village near Montreal to learn the manners and customs of the Indians and practice their language.

The first thing they learned was how to make the caribou skin leather shirts that were worn by both the braves and the squaws. They were like ponchos which slipped over the head. A slit was cut in the middle of the skin so the neck of the front came to a "V" shape, leaving a point that came up behind the head. It was a strange shirt, and apparently the point in back was to help keep the insects away from the back of the neck.

While James and John were in the village, there was an incident when one of the children became ill with chills and fever. It appeared the sickness was the same sickness Mr. Grant had told the lads about. They had in their supplies some powders of the Wild Sage and Peruvian bark which Mr. Grant had told them to carry at all times to use should they have this sickness. John offered to give the Shaman some of the powders for making a tea. The Shaman believing the child was dying took the powder and forced it down the child's throat by holding his nose closed. The Shaman always ready to lay any blame at another's hands was only too happy to have someone to blame if the child died. The child recovered and the Shaman's esteem to his tribe became greater than ever. He didn't bother to tell them he had gotten the powder from John.

As apprentices, the lads were not allowed to keep company with the Indian women as Mr. Grant wanted their attention focused on the things they would need to learn to survive in the wilderness. Some of the Indian girls were very comely and most were married by the age of twelve. Many of their husbands felt honored if white clerks and trappers wanted to bed with his wives. However, James and John had their orders as well as their strict religious upbringing to protect them.

Mr. Grant allowed the boys very little time in the town. Montreal was a rough and dirty place and he didn't want anything happening to his lads. The Indians came and went through the town in constant streams. Some bartered their furs for the outlandish silk and satin clothing worn by some of the French. It was a sight to remember seeing an Indian with his long hair, decorated with feathers wearing a satin jacket over his fringed leggings of buckskins. The native women were no less attracted to the finery and glitter of beads, which some wore in multiples of long strings hanging around their necks, as well as large wooden crosses that the Priests were handing out. The Priests were vigorous in their attempts to make all the Indians believe in Christianity.

James loved all he saw and wondered at the differences and at the similarities. Gaelic was spoken frequently as was French. The English and Indian dialects joined in to make an interesting mixture of languages, customs and clothing that greeted their arrival in the New World.

Spring finally arrived in Montreal after a winter of learning. The lads would accompany Mr. Grant to England to learn more of the accounting system and deliver the furs that had accumulated in the warehouse. They would also pick up supplies to take to the traders who spent their winters in the wilderness trapping and trading with the Indians for more furs. The ship voyage was greatly enjoyed, although there were many chores aboard ship, and they were expected to lend a hand just as any other sailor aboard the ship. It was another learning experience. Every day brought knowledge into their lives which they met with the enthusiasm of the young.

The trip went without incident except for the sighting of an American Privateer. Because it was wartime, at the sighting of any ship they were obliged to turn the other direction. Their cargo would have been prime goods to the privateers, but there were plenty of British Warships plying the seas to protect their precious cargo.

When they arrived at the dock in Liverpool and the ship was being unloaded, Mr. Grant went into town to check in with the offices, where he sold his furs. The officials of the fur company warned him against letting his lads come ashore. The incidents of kidnapping the young men for the British Army were high, and it was not safe for a young man to venture into the town or along the wharfs.

The Andrew had been at sea for two months, and it was a bitter disappointment to James, John and the crewmen when Mr. Grant commanded them not to leave the ship. He explained the risk they would take of becoming unwilling soldiers for the British. Mr. Grant had far too much invested in his lads to have common dirt soaking up their blood. He was privately in agreement with the Americans and their bid to govern themselves. However, he didn't want the American's in Canada.

Their ship was in port little more than a week when they were headed back out to sea and to Montreal. The trip was uneventful. Their return would bring them back just in time to load up the canoes and head for the Grand Portage. There they would take their supplies and pick up furs for Mr. Grant.

CHAPTER NINE

Coureurs du bois

FROM JOHN'S SEAT overlooking the Gravois, he leaned forwards towards Gram in anticipation of the continuation of her story.

"What happened next, Gram, were grandfather and great uncle John excited to be going into the wilderness?"

"Excited? Oh yes, they could hardly contain themselves. James had been excited when it was his sharp eyes that had first spotted the "Privateer" even before the "lookout" on their trip to London. The return trip was mild, as there wasn't even a little storm to break their routine.

Gram noting John's enthrallment with the story continued:

James and John had hired on as clerks and *voyageurs* to Mr. Grant, their proprietor, who provided them with their *Conge's* or license for the fur trade. Before the spring thaws began, they started out for the Grand Portage. However, because of the Rebellion in the Colonies, changes had been made in their original plans, and instead of returning with the canoes and furs, the lads would head into the wilderness and become *Coureurs du bois*. These were men who roamed the forest, rivers and mountains bringing in news and letters from the far reaches of the wilderness. They would seek out areas where beaver and other animals were in abundance, make council with the Indians and secure trade agreements with them. They learned how to map the rivers, make notes on the Indians and what dangerous areas were to be avoided.

James and John, while not experienced enough to really be *Coureurs,* would have to learn on the job.

In preparation for the trip, the canoes were laden with trade goods and supplies for the trappers, which included knives, beads, blankets and vermilion powder, which the Indians used as a red paint to paint the parts in their hair. It was time to begin a new life and a great adventure. In their packs, James and John each had a blue capote, a red shirt, a red wool cap, leggings and moccasins, which they had to learn to make, tobacco with a pipe, a really gaudy sash and a bag to hang from it, which contained their personal items, like James' compass. The total of Mr. Grant's employees was three squadrons which contained thirty men plus three canoes. James and John had their places in the middle canoe. Will Gunn and Roy Sutherland, their friends, were in the third canoe. The precautions of traveling together were taken, as much of the country was inhabited by hostile Indians. The canoes were made of birch bark, very light in weight and could be carried across the portages by two men. The weight each boat carried was about twenty-five hundred pounds. The canoes were called *Canot du Nord* or Canoes of the North.

The groups were divided into two or three divisions, each containing a guide, whose duty it was to be in command and to direct the course of rivers to be taken and see that the goods and canoes were kept in good repair. The canoes were so fragile and easily broken it was a constant necessity to tie into shore. There they would melt a little pine resin to make liquid rosin that would seal tears and small holes. It would even stick together squares of birch when the holes were a little too large. Resin powder, made from the pine tree, which grew in abundance in Canada, was one of the most precious items the boats carried, not only for repairs and waterproofing, but it could be melted with a little bear fat and packed onto any cuts to draw out putrid matter when the cuts became inflamed. Each boat carried a *"hogshead"* or barrel of this resin powder so in case any of the boats were lost, they would still have a ready supply. Keeping their equipment dry and in good

repair would mean the difference between life and death in their hostile environment.

A custom of the voyagers was to stop at the settlements or small homesteads along the way for drink and entertainment. People living in the wilderness mostly welcomed these men as they brought news from the outside; it also relieved the men of the weariness of travel. The voyageurs expected the forest settlers to furnish drink in exchange for goods which they might need. It was a smart guide, who kept his eye upon the good of the voyage and let the men have enough drink to make them happy, but not enough for drunkenness.

The Grand Portage was situated on the North side of Lake Superior and the trip from Montreal along the River Ottawa to the Grand River took about twelve days. There would be over one hundred fifty miles of hard rowing, pulling the canoes along, hunting for food and sleeping in a tent or the open air every night. The insects were like black clouds that descended upon the men when they set up camp at night. A smoke fire was kept going to help keep them away; the mosquitoes were by far the worse. The men rubbed themselves with bear fat, melted with the leaves of chaparral, which was purchased from the Indians. The fat and chaparral smelled terrible. But, it really did repel the mosquitoes which would have rivaled the size of small birds.

From the Grand River, the squadron of voyageurs came to Lake Nipissin, then entered the French River and boated down to the Georgian Bay which they crossed to come onto Lake Huron.

Having come from the far north of the cold rough country of Scotland, the trip was of little hardship to James, John and the other Scots on the trip. Hunting was a pleasure for the lads. The woods were full to overflowing with animals of every description and learning the names and habits of each was a mind bending chore. There were deer, bear, otters, beavers, squirrels and many more animals they saw on the trip but were too busy with their duties, to ask their names. It was not difficult to keep themselves supplied with food by shooting pigeons, ducks and other wild birds, catching fish and hunting deer. The deer meat made a hearty meal roasted over the open fire. All these things James and John had learned at a very young age in Scotland. Growing in the wild were grapes and lots of cranberries as well as numerous other plants and roots that could be eaten when a man was hungry. The banks of the rivers were dense with birch trees, which were used to make the canoes and pine trees for the resin which may be needed if their supply should run low. There were trees of poplar, aspen, cedar, hemlock and so many more that the lads didn't know the names. The poplar was particularly interesting as the bark was completely green in color. In the spring the tree bore large clusters of white flowers and then a large cup shaped flower dropped down from the clusters center. It was a most curious tree and had the largest leaves of any other tree around.

It was frequently necessary for the canoes to put into shore for repairs. It offered a small respite from the constant work and also allowed for a quick snack, usually pemmican and water and sometimes, when the weather conditions were very bad, a dram of whiskey or rum. On those evenings when it was too late to hunt, it was necessary to eat from the provisions carried in the canoe. Salted pork was easy to carry, as it did not often spoil. In Scotland James and John had not eaten a lot of pork so it was a novelty to them and they didn't mind the servings nearly so much as some of the more seasoned men. It was a staple in their diet when the hunted provisions were not to be had. New recruits or green horns were called *Mangeur de lard* as they were the ones who had to eat the pork first, leaving the other food stuff for the more experienced men. Another food which was relished by the men was *boudin* or buffalo gut, which was often eaten just as it came from the freshly killed buffalo. Others cleaned the gut and stuffed it with any chopped meat available along with rice or oats and wild onions which grew along the rivers. Boudin was a sausage that was considered a great delicacy, favored by the Frenchmen and easily prepared on a stick over an open fire or in a pan.

The evenings were short and the work day was long, but when all was done it was time for a little merriment. The fellowship amongst the men was friendly, with music and dancing around the fire. James, whom the Frenchmen called *Jacque,* was always ready to join in the fun with the more experienced men. The songs sung usually were in French, as most of the voyageurs were Frenchmen. It didn't take James long to improve his French so he could speak and sing along with the best of them. Will Gunn had a particularly fine voice. John, or *Jean,* as he was called, brought out his flute and Roy Sutherland was learning the harmonica. Even the few Indians, along with the voyageurs, joined in and added to the merriment. Dancing around the camp fires was not only fun but helped to keep the legs of the men in good shape after they sat in the same position, except for portages, for fifteen to eighteen hours a day. Roy was most often cast in the role of the woman dancer, as he was the smallest of the group. It was hardly ever that anyone complained of their long hours. "Voyageurs" felt they were specially chosen for their jobs and were quite conceited over their abilities to remain months or years at a time rowing back and forth along the rivers or carrying heavy burdens from portage to portage. Their strength and stamina was legendary.

The Indians were always eager to take the lads into the woods for hunting and teaching them to track and recognize animal signs.

A Paducah Indian named *Warbishca'r Moos-toosh* which meant "White Buffalo" decided to attach himself to John and James. They learned he was from a part of the country past the Great Missouri River. White Buffalo had blue eyes. The lads assumed he was of mixed blood. However, when talking to him one day, he said, "There are many of our people who have blue eyes and skin like the white man." They did a closer examination of him and realized they had not noticed that he had skin not as dark as the other Indians they had seen, nor were his features much different than their own. White Buffalo taught them signs to look for, such as leaves stripped from a tree, which meant a deer had recently passed along the way. They learned to recognize the different paw tracks of each animal and the leavings of spoor, its look and smell to know which animal had been that way and how long it had been by the condition of the spoor. James took to these surroundings and loved every minute of it, along with the challenges and dangers they faced every day.

The small portages from one river to the other were numerous. It was a custom of the Frenchmen to remove their hats and say a short prayer when leaving one river to cross to the other. Deaths were common in the wilderness and the Frenchmen showed the same respect when passing a cross where someone had been interred. There were many deaths from accidents, illness and drowning. On one day James counted thirty crosses.

From Lake Huron, they went past Sault St. Marie and around the banks of Lake Superior until they reached their destination.

It took six weeks and some fifteen hundred miles from Montreal before the men came to the Grand Portage. The boats were loaded with trade goods to exchange with the trappers for the furs brought in. One of the clerk's jobs was to account for the goods brought in and tally the supplies they took. They also had to count the furs they brought in and determine how much money was owed them. Sometimes, if the trappers indulged in too much drink and gambling, they went back up the rivers for the next winters trapping in debt to their employers. The process of living would start all over again in the same way as the year before. Many of the men took Indian wives and never left the wilderness.

The Grand Portage was a welcome relief from weeks of constant work, drenches in the river, crossing portages, freezing cold, snow and rain. The Grand Portage Fort had a variety of dwelling houses and shops where items of clothing, tools and Indian items could be purchased. Houses of commerce were set up by the Hudson Bay Company as well as the group of men who were Mr. Grant's partners. The entire fort was surrounded by logs which were about a foot and a half in diameter, driven about three feet into the ground and rising about fifteen feet into the air. The fort sat at the foot of a large hill next to the Hudson Bay. To reach the fort from the bay, which was very shallow, a boat had to be lowered from the ship, loaded up and rowed to shore. It was time consuming and hard work, but supplies from all over the world came into the little port. The fort measured three hundred ninety-six feet in width and four hundred and ninety-five feet in length.

In anticipation of the fort's dance, James and John along with Will and Roy, washed and cleaned their leather pants and moccasins, washed their shirts, gave each other hair cuts and shaved off their shaggy beards, or what little beards their young faces could grow.

Great dances were held at the Grand Portage Fort during the time trappers were returning with their furs. Indians were allowed to come in for the dancing. The trappers and voyageurs came neatly dressed in their best clothes and the ladies wore their best dresses. In the commons house was music from the bagpipes and young James joined in with the fiddle and John the flute, and when they were not providing music, joined in with the dancing. James was surprised to find the women to be good dancers and to comport themselves with propriety. The young lads were very popular with the women, and there were any number and variety of women who came to the forts, French, Indian, English and many mixed bloods.

One lovely young mixed blood Indian girl attached herself to James. She told him her grandfather was one of the Chiefs of the Mandan Indian Village. She hoped that James would want to visit her tribe. She told him her grandfather sometimes brought the tribes furs into the fort. James told her he and his brother John, had heard of the village and wanted to visit. The young girl's name was O-*saw-wow Pe-a-sis* which translated as Yellow Bird, so called because of her light hair and lyrical speech. She was the wife of Pierre Fontenot who was a trader that spent his time in the forest. Pierre was also very possessive of Yellow Bird, whom he had bought from a Piegan Blackfoot Indian for a few furs. The Blackfoot had told him he was her husband.

Yellow Bird was very young, James guessed about twelve or thirteen at the most and it was obvious that she was not happy to be the purchased squaw of Pierre, who had been watching her all evening, giving her mean and hateful looks whenever she talked to any of the young men.

Fortunately for James, one of the more seasoned voyageurs who knew of Pierre's readiness to lay a knife upon a person he didn't like, took James outside and offered him a dram of whiskey and told him about the dangers of being friendly with the old trapper's wife.

The common factor that brought all these diverse men, women and their children together, in addition to the exchange of furs for goods, was the relief of loneliness and companionship after spending the long winter months in inaccessible places.

CHAPTER TEN

White Buffalo and Black Crow

GRAM EXPLAINED TO JOHN, "The Dance at the Grand Portage could have ended quite differently for James, had the older man not taken James outside away from the attention of Yellow Bird. He explained Pierre Fountnot was very possessive of Yellow Bird and being forty-years older than his wife, didn't like her dancing with any young and handsome lads, like James and his friends."

Gram continued with her story while they relaxed in the afternoon shade on the front porch of her little house.

July 1, 1778

The morning finally dawned when the furs were packed and loaded into the canoes that would make the return trip to Montreal. James and John had done the accounting and it had been a reasonably good year for Robert Grant. Now, they faced the biggest challenge of any man in the wilderness.

Mr. Grant assigned another Indian to accompany them. He was of the Assiniboine Tribe. His name was *Kuske-ta-wow Ka-Ka-Ku* which translated to be Black Crow. The lads and White Buffalo welcomed him to their little group. All their lives would depend upon each other. James and John would be completely alone, except for their two Indians for help and companionship. They would see animals they had never seen before. They would experience the fickleness of nature in the extremes of climate in this new world.

Robert Grant had done his best to teach his lads all that he knew about survival in the wilderness. But for the war between England and the Colonies, their jobs would be much different and safer. James and John had been taught what to do in many different situations, but no one could know all that might come their way. Their safety would be entirely in the hands of the Indians and themselves. Should misfortune fall upon them, then they would fail to exist with no one to tell their relatives and friends of their fate.

The young James and John shook with excitement over the prospect of places to discover. Already they had studied the Journals of Pierre de la Verendrye who had logged his trip across the country in the 1730s and 40s. They were fascinated by his trip to a tribe of Indians who were rumored to be the descendants of the Welsh Prince Medoc. The prospect of visiting the "White Indians" and setting up trade with them overcame any thoughts of danger. After all, a man died when he died and nothing could be done about it.

From the Grand Portage the lads paddled their canoe up the Winnipeg River passing through Lake *"LaPluie"* or Rainy Lake and then *"Lac de Bois"* or Lake of the Woods.

At the night's camp the lads brought their journals up to date, making careful notations about their days travel and drawing their maps. In the wilderness, life depended upon knowing your way. They would have to return by their same route until they knew the rivers better.

James and John had devised a method of record keeping by stating the month and date every Sabbath day. They made a mark next to the date every day whether or not they made an entry. It was in this way that they counted the days to always remember the Sabbath.

The following morning, with the canoes loaded, they continued on their way for the Great Lake *Ouipigue,* or Lake Winnipeg, following the course of the river around the south end of the lake and descending the Red River, they paddled past the open mouth of the great Assiniboine River to the little Pembina River which flowed into the Red River. It was here they planned to set up their winter camp.

The brothers made themselves a crude cabin of raw logs and stuffed the clinks with mud and moss and prepared themselves for what they had been told would be an unpleasant winter. They made a hole in the top much like the one in their home in Scotland. The floor was covered with river mud, packed hard and dried. The roof was covered with a thick layer of river grasses, mud and moss atop this to hold it all in place. The cabin would serve the purpose of keeping out the worst of the cold as well as wild animals and a place to stretch and store the furs from their trapping. They laid out their Journals and traced the route they had come all the way from Montreal to the place where they were now on the Red River across from the mouth of the Pembina River.

Black Crow and White Buffalo didn't care for the cabin and set up their skin lodge nearby. The Indians were quite pleased with their names when the lads explained the animals and colors their names represented. Especially pleased about his name was Black Crow, when he understood the meaning of Black. There was fierceness about Black that White didn't bring to the mind. He held himself to be superior to White Buffalo whom he thought was too pale. He looked to be as ill as James and John even though he conceded they were strong men.

The lad's Indian companions and teachers gave them instructions on making snow shoes of woven willow and fasteners of leather strips and animal sinew.

They had been in their wintering place for a month. It was time to hunt for that special animal that would make their first fur hat. The first trapped animal was traditionally used for the men in the wilderness to make their first hat. After their time at the Grand

Portage both lads knew the furs and what could be bought with their value. If they were lucky they would catch fox or mink which made good hats. The small heads of the animals would sit upon their hats like little animals sitting upon their heads. The furs would surround their heads with pieces which could be pulled down around their necks. Both lads set the size of the traps needed to trap a fox.

The fox was the most cunning and difficult of the animals to trap. They began to search the river banks for imprints of the fox paw and then follow the small animal paths for signs of fur caught in the limbs and river plants.

Each of the lads was to be in the company of one of the Indians, both wanted White Buffalo who was the more cheerful of the two and the most eager to be around them. The decision was decided by making a circle upon a tree and the one who could throw his dirk closest to the center, which was well marked, would be the winner. Both boys were excellent throwing the dirk. This contest went to James who took White Buffalo.

James took one side of the river with White Buffalo and John the other with Black Crow. They kept themselves within a safe distance of each other. White Buffalo showed James some hair of the red fox which had caught on some briars. He followed along the trail and found a few more. It was probably a regular trail the fox followed from the river back to his den. All animals had to come to the river to drink and for sure the fox would find his way along this path again. James set out three traps, hiding the traps and marking the areas so he could locate them again. He would come back and check every day for at least a week. If he didn't trap the fox during that time he would move on to another area. They had seen the evidence of numerous beaver in the area and set out their traps for those also for that was the purpose of the trip.

Once the lads set up their traps and got accustomed to checking them out, their Indian companions went out into the forest to make "a hunt" as they said.

John had the best luck of the two by trapping a blue fox on the second day. He immediately began making his hat. James continued to check his traps every morning and evening. He finally got lucky on the morning of the sixth day. He gathered up his traps and his red fox and returned to the cabin. John had finished his hat and was working on drying the deer and elk meat and stretching out their skins. The lads and their Indian companions had made a good supply of willow frames to stretch the skins.

James made his hat of the red fox, which caused a great deal of fun for his brother and their Indian companions, because when James put the fur hat on his head, it was very difficult to determine where the hat stopped and the head and hair began. All were nearly the same color. The lads had become very good with their bows and also the catapult or slingshot. Both were always on their person as were their compasses, an axe, a large knife, their highland dirks and their guns.

On their trip to England, Mr. Grant had purchased James and John the *elegant fusil* a scattergun made by Mr. P. Bond of London. They were the best guns of that time. The guns, light in weight, were favorites of the Canadian boatmen. The lads called their guns *fuzees*.

Walking along one of the forest paths to the lake for water James came upon a very fat black bear catching his evening dinner of fish. He had his gun with him however, if he failed in his shot he would be in big trouble. Bears were very hard to kill. He back tracked until he came within distance of the cabin and got John's attention. The brothers had perfected the call of the loon so they could call to each other when in need, without rising suspicions of hostile Indians who might be about. James let out the call of the loon and John picked up his gun and returned to the river with James, the bear was still busily catching fish. Both lads, with their guns at the ready took aim on the bear. A perfect shot from John severed the neck bone of the bear, instantly killing him. John delighted in "crowing" over that perfect shot he made. While James had not even fired his gun at the bear he had found.

Black Crow and White Buffalo returned soon after the bear was killed. They quickly and easily skinned and dressed the bear and divided him in pieces so all could carry him back to the cabin. The bear would yield them four or five gallons of rendered fat. Bear Fat was a necessity for the winter months; it was mixed with the pemmican and berries and would not turn rancid.

Their Indian companions were glad of the bear kill, but cautioned the lads against ever trying to kill one of the big brown bears that might also be in the area. They were very difficult to kill and it might take a dozen shots in vital places to bring one down. A wounded bear was vicious.

On November 10, 1778 the little group celebrated the day of John's 20th birthday with a breakfast of *Flatjacks* made with oat flour, duck eggs and rum water. Dripping with wild honey, the flatjacks were wonderfully delicious.

Each of the group had twelve traps, called a "String" which was the number that a trapper was supposed to be able to check and care for. By the first day of December most of their trapping had been completed and the furs stretched. Their group had trapped one hundred thirty beavers, a lynx, five foxes, one bear, eight minks and ten otters. Their canoe would not hold much more than this as well as the four trappers.

James and John loaded their furs into their canoe and with their Indian companions, returned to the fort at the mouth of the Lake Winnipeg where they turned the furs over to Mr. Grant's agent.

CHAPTER ELEVEN

The Mandans

AS THE SUN CONTINUED its descent toward the horizon, John and Gram thought a nice cup of tea would quench their thirst.

John left Gram in the shade of the porch while he fixed them a cup of tea with sprigs of fresh mint. He prepared the tea and returned to the porch. Gram then took a small sip of her tea, pronounced it just right, and continued with her story.

James and John told Mr. Grant they were going to the Mandan Village, which Yellow Bird had told them about, and map the route. It was their hope to begin a trade with the Mandans. They told Mr. Grant that Black Crow told them, his people, the Assiniboine, had their camps near the Souris River and would welcome them and loan them horses to go across the plain. White Buffalo was familiar with the route across the plain to the Missouri River and the Mandan Village. It was the hope of Mr. Grant to make arrangements for the Indians to bring their furs to the Qu'Apelle River where they could be picked up and returned to the fort at Lake Winnipeg.

They loaded their canoe with their packs, weighing about ninety pounds each, containing their food and supplies. Each lad could easily carry a pack upon his back for long distances without tiring. This weight was considerably less then the hundred and sixty pounds each carried between the portages. The Indians would carry their supplies as well as help carry the canoe over the portages. Leaving the fort at the mouth of Lake Winnipeg they followed the course of the Red River to its junction with the Assiniboine. They followed the Assiniboine which flowed from the Rocky Mountains running east through immense plains that were very fertile and would make good farm land for future settlers. During their frequent stops for repairs, they made notes in their journals about what they saw and the curves of the river. They traveled the river until it branched into the River *Catapoi* now known as the River Qu'Apelle. They paddled the Qu'Apelle to the *Souris River* which was the French word for Mouse.

Late in the evening they reached the Souris River and came upon the cabin of the Frenchman, Pierre Fontenot. It was the last cabin on the river before they would come to the Great Plain crossing to the Missouri River.

Pierre was known to use excessive amounts of rum and the lads and their Indian companions would have rather not stopped. However, it would have been considered extremely unfriendly as the trappers and traders depended upon each other. Just that morning they had killed a deer and the extra meat would be welcome to Pierre and his wife Yellow Bird. The lad's supplies contained several small kegs of rum. A gift of a keg would make them welcome by Pierre.

There was some smoke coming for the chimney signifying that someone was there. They "helloed" the cabin and Yellow Bird came to the door. She was really glad to see the travelers and explained that Pierre had gone out to check his traps several days ago and had not returned. They told her they would all go out and have a look and see if he could be found, but would have to wait until the following morning. They set up their camp by the river and Yellow Bird prepared some of the fresh killed deer, which was a welcome relief from their own cooking.

The next morning with a few words and a quick breakfast of pemmican, the men set out on their search. There were many small streams flowing into the Souris where Pierre might have set his traps and it could prove a difficult job to find him.

They paddled along the river for about an hour when they came to the first small stream, where John was discharged to search for signs of Pierre. The next stream was taken by White Buffalo.

James and Black Crow were to stay together and they had gone some distance up the river when they knew they would have to return before the nightfall. The plan with John and White Buffalo was to pick them up where they had been put ashore. It was White Buffalo who found Pierre. He was dead. It was impossible to tell the cause of death as the animals had found him, and there was little left. They gathered the remains and wrapped them in his blanket and buried him where he was found, as was the custom, and put up a cross marking his grave. John said a few verses of the Bible for Pierre's passing. They gathered what supplies and traps were still useable to take back to the cabin.

James, with Black Crow and White Buffalo, returned to their canoe and stopped at the side creek to pick up John who was waiting for them. The evening, by that time was well advanced. With some quick rowing they would make it back to Pierre's cabin before it became too dark to see their way.

When they reached the cabin they told Yellow Bird that her husband was dead. She asked them if she could go with them to the Mandan Village, back to her family.

Black Crow told James and John that when they reached the Assiniboine, he wished to stay with his people instead of traveling on to the Mandan Village. When they returned the horses to his tribe, he would again join them in their travels. All agreed it would not be a great inconvenience to take Yellow Bird along with them. Having an introduction to the tribes would not be a bad thing either.

The canoe was prepared with Black Crow being the canoe guide as he knew the river. When the Souris River began its curve back north they came upon the camp of the Assiniboine that Black Crow rejoined. Arrangements were made for horses to carry Yellowbird, James, John and White Buffalo to the Mandan

Village. Upon the return of the group, the horses would be returned to the tribe. They would also serve to bring back any furs they took in trade with the Mandans. The furs would then be placed in their canoes to be taken to the fort at Lake Winnipeg.

The last night of their stay with the Assiniboine was the eve of Auld Handsel Monday in Scotland. The new year of 1779 had come upon them. John, being the oldest, placed a silver coin in front of their lodge of skins. The lads both couldn't wait to see who the unsuspecting First Footer would be.

In the morning a scratching sound on the skin flap, told James and John they were about to receive a First Footer. It was Yellow Bird, and she held the silver coin in her hand. She held it out to the lads as she was sure they had lost it. John tried to explain the tradition of the First Footers, but the meaning was lost in the translation. Yellow Bird had come to invite them to a breakfast of corncakes and venison stew before they left for the Mandan Village. John took the coin and with his knife made a small hole which he threaded with a thin strip of leather. He put it around Yellow Bird's neck and told her it was the good spirit of the night. She was very pleased with the gesture, she knew about good and bad spirits; that she understood.

They loaded their supplies on horses loaned to them by the Assiniboine, who were great friends of the Hidatsa Tribe. The Hidatsa camps were situated near the camps of the Mandans. The party set out on their journey to the Mandan Village which would take, they thought, about two weeks of travel by horseback and sleeping on the open plain.

The terrain of the journey consisted of open plains and marshes and some poplar trees of very poor quality. There were hills and valleys to cross, but the going was not difficult, just tedious. They hunted along the way to provide themselves with fresh meat.

Yellow Bird was constantly asking to stop to gather some wild plants or dig for some kinds of roots. Just coming out of a marsh area one day she became excited to see the dried remains of a certain plant she said was called *Snake Lilly*. They stopped and with their large knives helped her dig up almost all of the Snake Lilly growing in the area. She told them they must not take it all so the plant would multiply and grow the next year. Yellow Bird told them Snake Lilly when dried and powdered was used for illness in the tribe, especially during the winter months when the old people took the choking sickness and had problems getting their breath. She explained the people were given the Snake Lilly Root mixed with choke cherries and put in a purification lodge so they could get well.

The travelers were met by the Mandans many miles before they reached the Village. Yellow Bird's friends were happy to see her, and the rest of the group was welcomed. Yellow Bird was taken to the lodge of her family.

White Buffalo was made welcome by one of the young women who had lost her husband, in hopes he would find the lodge to his liking and decide to stay. It was not to the liking of Yellow Bird who insisted that White Buffalo had saved her life. If you saved a person then they became yours and she now belonged to White Buffalo. White Buffalo made no objection, so neither did James and John but they were quite amused to see White Buffalo in the position of owning Yellow Bird. Yellow Bird's family was pleased to be taking White Buffalo away to their earthen lodge. White Buffalo was indeed a very handsome brave. He had seen seventeen summers he told them. He was tall and well made and he was a good hunter. Yellow Bird was lucky that he had come into her life.

The family had no sons and the prospect of securing White Buffalo into the family was looked upon with great favor by Yellow Bird's parents and her five sisters. If the sisters were fortunate White Buffalo would take Yellow Bird as his wife and maybe some of them as well. It was a common custom for the Indian men to have several wives. They often took their wives' sisters or other female relatives into their lodge as additional wives. The Mandan Chief had twelve wives.

With gleeful grins upon their faces, James and John thought about the good life White Buffalo was going to live.

CHAPTER TWELVE

White Wolves and Big Horns

IT WAS ONLY after the sun had set, before John and Gram left the porch to come into the house. After they had a light supper of left over spoon bread with buttermilk, John and Gram moved the chairs by the side of the hearth. John built a small fire to chase away the chill of the night air.

John asked, "Gram, when did grandfather go to the great Yellow Stone River that you told me he named?"

"Johnny, I was just going to tell you the story of James' trip that took him to the River he named 'Yellow Stone', actually he called the river 'Roche Jaune,' which is French for Yellow Rock or Yellow Stone."

Settling into her rocking chair, Gram began to rock, and continued her story:

January 25, 1779

It had been a very long time since the Wanutarice or Mandan tribe had white visitors. James and John were taken into the lodge of the main Chief as his guest. They were directed to ledges covered with furs to sleep upon. A feast was prepared by the women from all the lodges, bringing food which had been cooked in earthen pots they made themselves and which withstood the fire as if they were made of iron. The Indians placed great value on friendship and welcomed the opportunity to share with the visitors. The guests were served stews made with buffalo, rabbit and deer. James and John enjoyed a large variety of vegetables, of which they had eaten little on their trip. They were served squashes, beans, pumpkins and corn which had been dried and preserved for winter use. The women of the village had cultivated many acres of garden and grew a large variety of vegetables, which were stored for winter. It was a village of plenty.

After each evening meal, a large circle was formed. The Chief passed around a Calumet or pipe. The bowl of the pipe was intricately carved out of red stone, and was an elaborate smoking instrument. The stem was made of young ash wood, beautifully carved and adorned with porcupine's quills, tails of the ermine or mink, horse's hair and feathers. It was beautiful to look upon and represented many hours of loving labor. The pipe was filled with a mixture of mild tobacco and *Kinnikinnick* leaves. It was smoked for pleasure as well as medical purposes. Once this ritual was preformed, other activities of celebration and dancing began.

Every day a group of the Mandans took James, John and White Buffalo on hunting trips or visits to the villages near by. Sometimes they stayed with the Hidatsa and sometimes with the Arikara. The tribes were very similar in their languages and habits. They had special societies which were in charge of different activities. The women had a society called the *Goose Society* who were in charge of the gardens. It was a privilege to belong to the Goose Society, and the membership was passed from the mother to the oldest daughter. It was these women who sang the *Corn Song* to make the corn grow. Every night the different societies held one of their dances to entertain the visitors. Yellow Bird's mother was a member of the Goose Society. Her membership would be passed on to one of her daughters.

The area along the Missouri River held a dozen villages and was situated on a high bluff overlooking the River. The Villages spread out over an elevated plain which was even and fertile and extended a considerable distance in all directions. James thought at the time there might be as many as 15,000 people living in the combined villages.

The lodges of the Mandan were scattered around without any formal design and were made in conical form, the frame fastened together with Hickory, Willow and other strong and tender plant shoots and branches. This was covered with a layer of coarse grass which was overlaid bottom to top with a coat of earth from ten to twenty inches thick. The fire pit was dug in the middle of the floor, a hole left in the top to emit the smoke and give light. The door of deer skin was low; the shutters made of buffalo and bearskin. A ledge about four feet wide and near the same height was raised along the wall for beds. Around the fire were mats of Sandbar Willow, buffalo and bearskins for seats. The Chief's lodges could accommodate forty to fifty people. Each evening the ritual of the pipe of tobacco would be passed around the fire between the chief and his visitors, and the lodge was usually filled until bedtime. The old men and women told stories of things which happened in their lives and the lives of people who had been long dead. A drink the Indians called Kinnikinnick was passed around. It had the pleasing aroma of tea but was extremely bitter. It was the same plant used to put in the ceremonial tobacco. The Chief explained the drink was for making good water and clearing out the congestions in the chest. The Indians also put pinches of it in their cheeks when they had congestions. It was a great privilege to be asked to stay in the lodge of the Chief and be a part of the customs of the people.

White Buffalo made arrangements with the family of Yellow Bird to take her as his squaw. He had to pay a bride price, but since she had been married before it was acceptable for her to stay with him. White Buffalo told James and John about his tribe, who lived further down the Missouri. When the tribe hunted they went across a large plain where they killed buffalo and the animal with *Big Horns*. The horns of the Mountain Sheep were highly prized by all the tribes. They were used to make drinking vessels, spoons and platters. The horns were so highly prized that a couple of horns would pay the bride price for Yellow Bird. White Buffalo wanted James and John to come with him on a hunt, where he could kill enough animals to pay Yellow Bird's bride price.

Having the opportunity of mapping a new area, and the use of guides who knew the way was exciting news for James and John. That night in camp there was a great celebration for the departing visitors.

Outside the Chief's lodge a circle was formed of many braves. James and John were invited to join in the fun. A warrior came out wearing the head and skins of a red fox. He began a dance of intricate foot steps and wild gyrations. There was the music of drums and reed flutes. After some time of dancing he grabbed up another brave who joined in the dance with the Fox Warrior. The dance was called the *Fox Dance.* One by one all the braves and their guests were pulled into the dance. James wasted no time in learning the yelps, barks and yowls, the intricate steps and body gyrations of the dance. The fox hats on the heads of James and John blended very well with all the headdresses of the other dancers. The dancing continued long into the night. James and John determined they would need to make a good showing to earn their host's respect. Much to the delight of the other braves, they held out until near the end of the dance before falling upon the ground with other fallen braves.

While the men were doing their dances, the women formed groups to watch, drink their leaf and root teas and to gossip. When attending the ceremonies, the women wore dresses of deer and antelope skins made into elaborate costumes that were beaded and fringed and looked as wonderful and intricate as any finely made silk dress. The men wore their buckskin shirts and trousers fringed down the sleeves as well as the outside of the trouser pants. The yolks were beaded with glass beads, porcupine quills, pieces of human hair and any other thing they might think good medicine.

Men and women wore their hair hanging long down their backs and some of the old men had hair that swept the ground. They combed and dressed it every day and worked in bear grease.

The women braided their hair at night and wore it loose during the day. The braiding caused the hair to flow down their backs in undulating waves. Many of the women and men had completely grey hair, at very young ages, which made them look more European that other tribes. The men were handsome and the women very beautiful.

The following morning a dozen of the braves, with half as many women, including Yellow Bird, loaded the horses with food, weapons and some dismantled Bull Boats. The skins of the bull boats had been smoked and boiled in animal fat to make them waterproof. They would be used at night for shelter and assembled when needed to cross rivers. They were equipped to travel over the plains by horse and to cross the rivers using the bull boats.

The party started West and Southwest across the plains. It was a cheerful group of youths. They were headed along the Cheyenne River where the Paducahs, White Buffalo's tribe, lived.

The camps at night were fun with James and John providing the music on the violin and flute. The Indians made their own dances to go with the new music. They laughed and joked with each other and played pranks just like their white friends. With the skins of the bull boats for shelter, everyone had a place of protection against the weather which was sometimes very cold at night. The women found roots to supplement the hunting skills of the braves. Food was plentiful even in this month of February 1779.

It took the group about a week to reach the Paducah Tribe. They were met with enthusiastic friendliness. White Buffalo was awarded the honor of a great feast to welcome him home. White Buffalo was one of the sons of the tribe's *Medicin' Man* or Shaman who was called Red Feather and his mother was White Buffalo Woman. She was one of the *Wise Women* of the tribe and helped the other women when it was their time to birth a child. His parents were very happy to meet Yellow Bird.

James was more fascinated by this tribe because they appeared to be a different race of people than any he had met before. He learned that many of the Mandans and Paducahs had married each other. Their manner was more civilized, their skin more fair, their countenance more open and agreeable. Most of the tribe had features resembling the white man. James wondered if these people were not the descendants of the Welsh Prince Madoc. It was impossible to know, as they spoke not one word that might have sounded Welsh. He talked with White Buffalo's father about their history and where they came from. Red Feather told him many seasons before they had come from the river near a big water falls called O-Hi-O, by the hostile Indians that lived there. He told James they had been gone so many moons from that place, there was no longer memory of it in the minds of their people.

The party stayed a week with the Paducahs before they left accompanied by another dozen young men and women from the tribe. This made twenty eight people in their group. Leaving the Paducah Tribe, the large group rode in a Northwestern direction toward the mountains where they would find the big horn animals. James had heard some of the fur traders call the mountains, The Rockies.

James and John were treated with the affection and respect of honored guests. Every camp site was a time of celebration with food, dance and music. More often than not James' violin and John's flute were part of the evening's entertainment. Sometimes the women joined in the dancing or performed one of their own dances. During the time of the full moon the women all moved away from the braves and didn't share sleeping skins with them. They had a ritual of drinking root teas which were sacred and kept from the men. It was a great curiosity to James, but they would only tell him they drank the *medicin' women's root* which was for purification.

At night, around the camp fire, James and John found time to write in their journals and make their maps, using the North Star as their guide to calculate where they were.

Late one afternoon, when the group had put up their sleeping shelters, they heard the howl of wolves. The howls were close to the camp. The moon was up and very bright. Several of the braves were going on foot to the top of a small hill to take a look. James and John were invited to go along. The hill was close, about a half mile away. The moccasin clad feet of the group made no noise. Upon reaching the top of the hill, they all lay down on their stomachs and crawled and wiggled their way over the top to see what was down below.

They looked down upon a freshly killed buffalo bull surrounded by not less than a dozen white wolves. The Indians were very excited, as the pelts of white wolves were considered "great medicin."

A plan was devised to split the group, fan out and kill as many of the wolves as possible. With their bows ready, the group of six spread out and with the hoot of an owl each arrow shot found its mark in six of the wolves. Four more were quickly brought down with only two escaping the fate of the deadly arrows.

White Buffalo's specially marked arrows claimed three of the wolves. James and John had each brought down a wolf. Two of the other braves had gotten two wolves each. They checked out the buffalo and salvaged his tongue, the hump and part of a front and back leg. The Indians, who wasted nothing, also took the hoofs and horns. They took the part of the skin that had not been destroyed by the wolves.

They shouldered the wolves and took them back to camp. The women helped with the skinning and parts of the wolf were saved for food. The meat tasted something like the dog meat they had been served at the Mandan Village. Dog meat was considered a great delicacy by the Indians. James didn't much like eating dog meat, but it would have been considered an insult to refuse, as dog meat was served only to esteemed guests.

A pit was dug to cook part of the meat. A large pot made by the Mandans was filled with water, buffalo meat and prairie turnips and was left over the fire's embers to cook all night. Some of the meat was put on sticks to dry near the fire to make jerky.

They would have enough meat to last for several days. When cooking on an open fire on the plains, dried buffalo dung was gathered to make the fire. Not an hour had passed that the group didn't see buffalo. The large herds left behind plenty of dung. By the time the group sought their sleeping skins it was very late, and the moon had lost its brightness.

There was no embarrassment at all that the women on the trip shared the sleeping skins of one young brave or another. All the women on the trip had been married before or were one of the several wives of some of the men. Yellow Bird and White Buffalo shared their skin only with each other as they had since the beginning of the trip. The white wolf pelts were already enough to satisfy the bride price for Yellow Bird even if they did not find the big horn animals.

Although some of the women offered to share their skins with James and John they declined. They told the women their God didn't allow sharing of skins unless it was with their wife. They couldn't take a wife without the permission of their employer, Mr. Grant, who was not there. The real reason was to avoid fights and jealousy that a sharing of skins would cause between the braves on the trip. Mr. Grant had cautioned them never to share a skin with one of the women unless offered by the husband. In that case it would be a breach of etiquette to refuse, but avoid sharing if at all possible. The Indian's respect for their Spirits as well as the Spirits worshiped by others gave credibility to the God story James and John depended upon to keep them out of trouble.

The young hunters and gatherers moved across the plains on their horses in gentle camaraderie, without any cross words with each other. Sometimes they rode and raced; sometimes they hunted along during the day slowing down their travel. The group had been gone from the Mandan Village a month and traveled near nine hundred miles when they spotted the mountains and their destination.

The last river the group crossed before reaching the mountains was, they said, called Big Horn River. It was passed this river that the Big Horn could be hunted. James made a notation in his journal about the river. The Indians told him the river flowed into a bigger river that would take the group back to the river that ran passed the Mandan Village.

They crossed the river but it took three more days of travel to reach the mountains. The Big Horns were down from the mountains eating the dried grasses. It was still a month until spring and the lack of food further up the mountain had driven them to grasslands below.

One of the Paducah braves finally killed the first Big Horn. It was a great occasion for James and John to see this strange animal up close. It had fur that was brown across the back and very similar to a deer. Its face looked similar to the Mackay families' sheep back home in Scotland. It tasted like mutton. James and John both concluded the animal belonged to the sheep family and started referring to them as Big Horn Sheep. They had short tails and a large white patch on their rumps. They were agile enough to jump from rock to ledge without any difficulty. Sometimes they seemed to go straight up the mountain side. They were not as easy to kill as James had thought. It was difficult to get a shot with bow and arrow. For the first time on their trip they took out their Fuzees and shot at the Big Horns Sheep. Working with the Indians and their deadly bow and arrows the group killed fifteen Big Horns the week they spent camped at the foot of the Rockies.

When the work was finished, the meat dried and the skins stretched and cured, and after a long night of music and dancing, the group parted from each other. The Paducahs' loaded their share of the Big Horns, White Wolf skins and Buffalo robes and left to return to their village.

The Mandans with James, John, White Buffalo and Yellow Bird rode their horses, by now heavily packed with meat and furs, to return across the plains to the Mandan Village.

The group met some friendly Blackfoot Indians and James and John traded their two white wolf skins and a set of the Big Horns for two of their horses. One of the horses, James really fell in love with. It was a big mare, strong and deep in the chest. She was a beautiful red color with white spots sprinkled across her big rump. The Indians said she had come from a tribe that lived across the mountains called Nez Perce.

The Indians told James and John they were near a big lake and the river that would take them back to the river, which James called the Missouri.

The group, coming to a large lake, was witness to one of nature's most beautiful creations. Before them, the sun glistening from its waters was a fall of breathtaking height and majesty. The sun slanted across rocks which were a brilliant yellow in color. In stupendous awe James murmured the words Yellow Stone.

James drew his maps and wrote in his Journal about the Yellowstone and the lake, the falls and the river. They followed the mountains for several days before they came to the river that flowed through the mountain across the plains to join the Missouri River. They saw bear, antelope, elk, deer and many other animals along the river banks. There were numerous beaver that were bigger than any they had seen before.

They called their river the Yellowstone for the beautiful yellow rocks they had seen. After two weeks of travel along the river they turned from the river to cross the plains. They were only a few days from the Mandan Village. From that point, they continued their journey across the plain and along the banks of the Knife River. It was near the end of April 1779 and the group had been gone over three months. James and John had to leave soon, so they could reach Lake Winnipeg by the first of June.

White Buffalo made his "bride price" for Yellow Bird and after three days of celebration the group took their leave of the Mandans. They promised to be back to trade the following year.

Taking the horses belonging to the tribe and James' new horse "Spotted Blanket," the group started their trip back to the

Assiniboine River where they would pick up Black Crow and return his tribe's horses.

They made good time on horse back and reached the Assiniboine in the late evening of the fifth day. James left Spotted Blanket with the family of Black Crow for he could take her no further. James and John had been treated with friendship, honesty and kindness by all the Indians they had met. They had not once been in a position of fearing for their lives like the stories they had been told.

From the Souris River they retraced their earlier route back to Lake Winnipeg for the annual fur trade exchange.

Mr. Grant was pleased with the maps and journals James and John had made on their travels. They had located many sites for future trapping, especially along the Yellow Stone River.

After the big dance, Mr. Grant told James and John that, when they returned to the Mandan Village for trading, he had further plans for them.

Black Crow was returning to his village with the supplies he had traded for his tribe. Yellow Bird was now expecting the baby of White Buffalo. She told James and John she had eaten the "medicin' for women roots" when she was married to the Blackfoot Brave and to Pierre Fontenot, because she didn't want babies by either of them. White Buffalo was a great hunter and would be good to his children. She was going to keep him.

James enjoyed telling the French Boatmen about their trip and the "River Rochejaune" they had found where the beaver were the biggest he had ever seen. He told them the beaver were so abundant that their dams were not more than a half mile apart. John would show the two big horns he had taken from a Big Horn Sheep that lived in the mountains and tasted like mutton. The Frenchmen believed the horns because they could see them, but they didn't believe James' story about the beaver.

CHAPTER THIRTEEN

Hello William: Visit to Petersburg, Virginia

GRAM SAT COMFORTABLY in her rocker, in serene contentment, before the hearth, with the fire just barely casting up a little flame now and then.

John said, "Gram, do you think Grandfather was happy being away from his mother and family? I miss my mother even though she has been gone for many years."

"Oh yes, Johnny, he missed his family, but he loved living in the wilderness and on the rivers. Game was so plentiful they were never without food very long. The most tedious times were their stays in the Indian villages with their over-abundant hospitality. James' red-blond locks were a constant subject of amusement with the women. More than once they were faced with an old woman trying to cut locks of hair, which they considered good medicine. Yellow Bird wore locks of hair from the heads of White Buffalo as well as James and John. John was the shy one of the two brothers and much more serious. He was much less comfortable among the Indians than was James. For James it was a time of fun as well as business."

Slowly rocking, Gram continued with her story:

November 1780

Leaving Yellow Bird and White Buffalo at the cabin near the mouth of the Pembina River, James, John and Black Crow made a trip to the fort at Lake Winnipeg. They turned in the furs they had trapped since July. They picked up supplies and trading goods, including twenty pounds of blue glass beads, a dozen knives and axes and three iron pots to trade with the Assiniboine, Mandan and Paducah tribes.

Departing from Winnipeg, the canoe loaded with supplies, they allowed the Red River's current to carry them along, without much effort on their part, towards their camp at the Pembina River. The green of the pine and fir trees stood out in stark contrast to the leafless branches of other trees lining the banks of the river. Seeing strangers in their midst, animals either plopped into the water or darted into the cover of the woods. Soundless mist hovered over the river creating a sense of mystical wonder.

At the cabin, Yellow Bird and White Buffalo added their possessions to the canoe. Yellow Bird had not mentioned her condition before, but it was now quite obvious that she was expecting a child.

The group was taking a different route on this trip to the Mandan Village. Black Crow had told them his main tribe lived near the Turtle Mountain, and the Pembina River would take them closer to their village. There they could secure some horses to take them to the camp at the foot of the Souris River and from there they could go to the Mandans' Village.

The Pembina flowed through gorges dug deep by the flow of the river's water, creating banks that shadowed the group as they paddled their canoe. The river, this time of the year was laced with ice. Paddling upstream they came out where the land flattened into a fertile plain. In his journal, James would note this was another area that would be good farm land for settlers.

Reaching the Assiniboine tribe, James and John stayed just as long as politeness demanded. The customs of the Assiniboine were much different than the Mandans and not nearly as much fun.

James and John were treated to a session in the village "Sweat Lodge." The lodge resembled a turned over Bull Boat or coracle, but large enough for four to six people. Rocks were heated and placed in a pit. When the participants were seated upon a floor covered with sage, water was poured in a small stream over the rocks. The water produced clouds of steam causing the participants to sweat profusely. The men then ran from the lodges, completely nude, and dived into the cold waters of the river.

James met the old grandparents of Black Crow. He presented the old grandmother with a small doeskin bag full of the blue glass beads. Before his departure the old grandmother gave James a pair of new moccasins, beaded with nearly all the blue glass beads James had given her. One present always demanded another so upon their departure James gifted old grandmother with one of the iron cooking pots and showed her how to place it over the fire. The Assiniboine used a method of cooking by heating rocks and dropping them into a skin lined hole. They filled the skin with water, meats, vegetables and herbs, until the water boiled. The rocks, when cooled, had to be removed and replaced with hot ones over and over again until the stew was cooked. It was a slow and tedious way to cook. The cooking pots brought by the traders were especially prized by the women as you can see.

After leaving the Assiniboine Indians, James and John started their return to the Mandan Village, on horseback, with their Indian companions. Their arrival started a long evening of pipe smoking and entertainment. When the evening was finished the Old Chief brought two of his young wives and presented them to James and John to share the comfort of their sleeping skins. The lads were dismayed at the gesture of the chief. Mr. Grant's warnings of sexual contact with the native women and the diseases that white men had given them rang loud in their ears. To refuse the Chief's prized wives would have been a terrible insult. The smirk on the Old Chief's face and the gleam in his eye told them they had been maneuvered into doing his bidding. They would have to watch their dealings with him; he was a sly old fox. James and John had not shared sleeping skins with any of the women on their last trip. Courtesy demanded they spend two nights in the Chief's lodge before they could continue to the Paducah Village.

Sometimes it was prudent to put aside one's teachings and values for the sake of good will and harmony. In this wilderness, a man did not insult the beliefs and customs of his host.

After honoring the chief with two nights visit, the group departed. White Buffalo and Yellow Bird took two of the Bull Boats, tied together by the buffalo tails left on the boats. The currents of the Missouri River allowed them to drift along with little effort on their part. James, John and Black Crow rode their horses following the paths along the river's banks. There were many half buried limbs, submerged trees, roots and logs floating in the river as well as many sand bars. Great care had to be taken to keep the boats from being destroyed. The Bull Boats were easier to steer and more durable than canoes in this kind of water.

Yellow Bird now advanced in her pregnancy, rode in one of the Bull Boats. The pace was slow traveling by both methods. When the group arrived at the mouth of the Cheyenne River, which flowed down from the Paducah Village into the Missouri River, they changed their direction to paddle up the river to White Buffalo's village. Paddling upstream was much harder. The men frequently changed places to row the boats which were tied together making only one rower, in the front boat, necessary. Yellow Bird rode in the boat behind with some of their supplies. Yellow Bird, always busy, used her time to weave baskets or plait together strings of fibers into rope. The rower made a figure eight paddling motion from the front of the boat, which gently moved the attached boats through the water.

Every night at camp, James and John wrote in their Journals and worked on their maps. Snow laden clouds often obscured the stars making it difficult to get the proper settings for their maps. Sometimes they played soft music and Yellow Bird hummed or sang one of her songs.

They reached the Paducah Village during the middle of December with the year's first snow fall. The smells of cooking meats, burning wood and buffalo dung were familiar and welcome scents. James and John felt more at home with these Indians than with any other. White Buffalo had become a trusted and true friend.

White Buffalo Woman, White Buffalo's mother, gave them a good scolding because they had kept Yellow Bird from her so long. She was past due to start drinking the birthing teas that would make for an easy delivery. She took Yellow Bird into her lodge and immediately started the preparation of her teas, all the while mumbling and scolding White Buffalo for his carelessness. Yellow Bird would have to drink the tea twice a day instead of the usual once a day to prepare her for the birthing. White Buffalo Women told the men to go hunting and bring back many rabbit skins for the baby or maybe two babies.

Next morning, in a group of six, they started from the village heading south onto the plains. In a couple of days they had ridden a hundred miles and realized they were in the middle of large amounts of rabbits; because on the light powdering of snow the rabbit's prints stood out like pebbles in a clear brook.

These rabbits were quite different from the rabbits in Scotland. They had very long ears which were tipped with black, and they had big powerful hind legs. They were brown in color with short fur. Their numbers were so great that in two days the group had killed all the rabbits they could find willows branches on which to stretch the hides. The group had eaten roasted rabbit until the smell of their cooking flesh had become nauseating.

Between the six men they had killed three hundred rabbits without going more than five miles from their camp. The rabbits kept the grass so nibbled-down; there was not enough for larger game. They had not seen a deer, antelope or buffalo since the night of their first camp.

At the time, James thought he would have traded half of the rabbit furs for some of his mother's chicken and suet-dumplings. When James and John were most sick of something they wished for the smell of a baking current filled scone or the taste of haggis with neeps and tatties.

December 17, 1779, Yellow Bird delivered twin boys. A few days after the birth of the boys the tribe held a naming ceremony, which was a very important custom. James and John were named their alternate fathers. The babies' names were "John First" and "James Footer." Yellow Bird had named the babies for the First Footer coin she still wore around her neck. It had brought her "good medicine" which all the Indians looked upon as gifts of the Spirits.

James, John and Black Crow stayed in the Paducah Village through the Christmas Season, the meaning of which was unknown to the Indians. John told the Indians the stories about Christ and his birth. To the Indians, the Great Spirit Father was all powerful, even if he was not exactly the one they recognized. They thought the story of the star and wise men very powerful medicine. John told them their English King, a King by birth, was appointed by their God, who was the father of Jesus. White Buffalo said, their Chiefs were also appointed by the Great Spirit and he could see they had the same fathers, and were in truth brothers. Mr. Grant had told James and John they must establish that the King of England was in fact a great father of the white man and would also be a great father to the Indians.

It was an emotional experience for them to leave White Buffalo and Yellow Bird behind, as they had become family. White Buffalo would take the furs to the trading post on Lake Winnipeg in the spring and establish a yearly trade with Mr. Grant's clerks.

James and John had received a letter the last time they were at the trading post on Lake Winnipeg. It was from their parents, sending the family news. Their sister Kitty was to marry a nearby neighbor, George Mackay of the Bighouse Mackays, who lived further up Strath Halladale in the north of Scotland. James and John were not happy to learn their darling thirteen year old sister planned to marry at such a young age. William was now in Petersburg, Virginia with their cousins Donald and Angus

MacDonald. They had opened a Commercial House for the trade of tobacco, furs and other items needed by the Colonists. It was hard to believe the young brother and sister they left behind had taken on the roles of adults.

With an agreement from White Buffalo to take the tribe's furs to the post on Lake Winnipeg, James and John were left with an opportunity to take the waters flowing down the Missouri River and along the Mississippi and Ohio Rivers. The route would take them close to where William lived in Virginia. Mr. Grant had wondered about the fur trade in the Spanish territory. They now had a chance to find out what was going on in the distant town of San Luis as well as make maps of the rivers.

White Buffalo and the tribe's elders had long discussions about the possible ways to get to Virginia. There were numerous trails used by the Indians. Some of the Indians were hostile and must be avoided.

Their final decision, was to go by water as much of the way as possible. They would go through the Sioux Nation who were unfriendly with everyone except Black Crow's people. The Assiniboine and Sioux often married into each other's tribe. Black Crow said he was happy to go on a great adventure with James and John. His tribe's connection to the Sioux would make it safe for them to travel along the rivers. On Tuesday, the first day after the first Monday of the year or First Footers Day 1781, James, John and Black Crow stepped into their canoes and paddled their way down the Cheyenne River where its waters flowed into the Missouri.

From the mouth of the Cheyenne, the group paddled their canoe south to follow the flow of the Missouri River to a well established trading town called San Luis.

They found the river continued to be dangerous with sticks, snags, uprooted trees and sand bars. They always kept a sharp look out for changes in the way the water rippled in front of them. It was one way of detecting a hidden obstacle in their paths. Game was plentiful as few of the fur traders had been this way. The river

and its destination to the ocean were well known by the Indians as well as a number of trappers.

The low hanging clouds kept the sun and moon obscured making it difficult to get the proper coordinates for their locations. They kept their journals in the best way they could, knowing that some of their notations would be incorrect.

At the mouth to the White River, they stopped their voyage for a couple of days, smoked the pipes and traded some goods with the Maha Indians. The Mahas had set up a small camp, where the braves were hunting for the tribe. The Mahas invited the group to stay with them and to hunt and return to their village which was located further down the Missouri River. One of the braves, *Young Blackbird*, the son of their Chief, Pajaro Negro, said his father would make them welcome. James explained they were on a voyage to San Luis but hoped they would have the opportunity to come again and spend some time in their village and smoke the pipe with his father, the Great Chief, Pajaro Negro.

James and John made notes in their Journals and drew their maps at each night's camp. They continued to have problems with low lying clouds obscuring the night stars. Black Crow was amused that they needed paper with marks on it to tell them the way they had been.

The group continued their journey down the Missouri River and didn't meet any more Indians until they arrived near San Luis. James noted there were quite a few settlers many miles up the Missouri before they reached the town owned by the Spanish. San Luis had a flourishing fur trade and was well established by Frenchmen who had settled there; many of the families there had originally been driven out of Canada by the English. James and John spent five days in San Luis. No one in the area seemed very interested in the business of the young Scotsmen and their Indian companion. It was a kind of come and go place where there was such a mixture of people that three strangers got no notice at all. They were always careful to speak in the French language. Black Crow only grunted even though he could speak some French also.

It pleased the people in town to think Black Crow was the servant of James and John. Black Crow, an important member of his tribe, simply showed them his natural haughty self.

James liked the area and made notes about its situation on the Missouri River and the junction it made with the Mississippi and lower down, the Ohio. It looked to be a profitable location. Many of the French Canadians said they had traveled the Mississippi River to San Luis for trade. James had not heard that any of the French Canadians had come to San Luis by way of the Missouri River, which ran through hostile territory. Most of the traders knew of the Mandan village but few had been to visit them.

James thought houses in the area were most interesting. They were built of logs in an upright position instead of the horizontal logs laid for most cabins. They also saw two story houses built with openings through their center. They were referred to as "dog trot" cabins. The cabins had long porches along their front. It was hot and humid during the worst months of the year. The people living in the cabins had the advantage of the breezes coming from two directions. The living quarters were on one side and the cooking area on the other. The arrangement prevented the heat, from the summer cooking hearths from spreading into the living area.

From San Luis they paddled their canoe down the Mississippi River. At the village of Kaskaskia, they sold their canoe and purchased three horses for a trip across country following the Buffalo Trace Road that would take them to Louisville, Kentucky.

They had hoped to see William on March 15th for his eighteenth birthday. The trip down the Missouri River had been much farther than they had understood. They estimated it was about 1800 miles from the Mandan Village to San Luis. February was well advanced and reaching Petersburg by March 15th would not be possible.

They hunted as they rode along and sometimes fished in the river. They had a net attached to a willow frame that made it easy to catch fish. In San Luis they had taken on some new supplies including ground corn. Fish coated with finely ground corn and fried in bear grease was a good change from roasted meat and pemmican. James thought some potatoes fried in the bear grease might taste quite good, but they didn't have any potatoes. The small black bears were plentiful in the area and easily killed. They never lacked for bear meat and grease.

When the group neared Louisville, they saw beautifully laid out farms and long legged sleek horses. From the standpoint of beauty, their horses didn't measure up too well. However; the short, heavy compact horses they were riding could be ridden all day without tiring and had served them very well.

The group sold their horses in Louisville to a local livery stable for a surprisingly good price. The local "horse farms" were more into breeding horses that could run fast, for the areas racing interest, rather than sturdy work horses. Strong horses were needed for transportation of goods along the Buffalo Trace road to Kaskaskia or San Luis and for work on the farms.

They purchased another canoe and started a long trip, paddling against the flow of the Ohio River. When they reached Cincinnati, they met a Welsh Minister named Morgan John Reys. He invited them to his home for conversation as he was anxious to learn what was going on in Canada. They told him they were going to Petersburg, Virginia to see their brother William. Their plans were to follow the rivers until they reached Petersburg. Rev. Reys advised the young men to continue along the Ohio until they reached Galipolis further up the river. From there they could take the Warpath Road to Petersburg. From there he said, "it is best to go across country because of the revolutionary activity in the area."

Wishing to avoid the battles of the revolution, the young men agreed it would be better to take the Indian trails.

Reaching Galipolis, they sold their canoe but were unable to find horses because all had been taken to use in the war. Like the experienced and seasoned woodsmen they were, they shouldered their goods and proceeded on foot along a section of the "Great Indian Warpath Trial." They were stopped several times by Continental Soldiers. They explained they were fur trappers going to see their brother who lived in Petersburg. The MacDonald's names were familiar to the soldiers and they were allowed to pass along the way. They spoke to the soldiers in a mixture of French and English which was acceptable to the soldiers who knew the French were friends of the Revolution.

The group reached Petersburg on April 21, 1781. The MacDonalds and William were easy to find. Donald had married a young Quaker girl, named Mary, and lived in a small cabin outside the town. William and Angus were staying at a lodging house in town where James and John stayed also. William had grown so much since James had seen him, he surpassed James in height and weight. He was not as tall as John, who showed more of the Norse ancestry of their mother. They all wondered if William had inherited his strength and size from their ancestor Murdoch Mackay. William had the light eyes of the Mackays and the red hair of some unknown ancestor, maybe Murdoch. While having a drink at the only pub in town, they noticed he was not short on the attention of the local female population, nor were James and John.

There were many Indians around the town and Black Crow made friends with some of them and left to stay at their village until James and John were ready to leave. The town was alive with America's Continental Soldiers.

The brothers and their cousins were allowed only two days of carefree visitation before peace in the area came to a halt. Petersburg was laid out along the Appomattox River and was the location of a large storage depot for the Continental Army. Twenty-five hundred British soldiers, led by their General Phillips struck the defenses in Petersburg, set up by General Peter Muhlenberg.

All the men in the area were rounded up to help with the fight. Black Crow brought in some of the Indian braves from the village where he was staying. The Mackays, MacDonalds and their group of Indians joined in to help General Muhlenberg stop the British. The fighting was very fierce and William was hit in his left thigh, by a mini ball. It didn't appear to be too serious, so he tied a cloth around the wound until such time as it could be treated. General Muhlenberg put up a good defense of the supply depot but was forced to retreat toward Richmond. The British took over the town destroying the depot as well as the commercial house of William and the MacDonalds, before they continued in their pursuit of General Muhlenberg. The Mackays and MacDonalds drifted into the forest, with their Indian friends and most of the other men and women of the town, upon the departure of General Muhlenberg.

There were a lot of wounded Continental soldiers left behind as well as a few British Soldiers. After William's wound was dressed, he was taken to Donald's home to be cared for by Mary. The Mackays, MacDonalds and their Indian friends picked up as many of the wounded soldiers as they could, to take them to the Indian Village for safety, until they healed. Some of the townspeople also took wounded into their homes. Three of the wounded soldiers were Scottish, one British and two Continental soldiers. There were no enemies among the wounded.

When the British had finished with their destruction, the townspeople returned to their routines. Seeing the destruction of their Commercial House, William and the MacDonalds knew they would not be able to replace most of their losses until the fall tobacco crop matured and they could purchase more goods to trade. It was fortunate that, at this time of year, there were no furs and tobacco in the store.

James and John stayed a few days to help rebuild the Commercial House for William and their cousins. It was time to return to Canada. William promised to write, addressing his letters to them, in care of Mr. Grant in Montreal.

Picking up their supplies the group containing James, John and Black Crow resumed their journey along the Indian trails until they reached a woodland path known as the "The Great Indian

Warpath," which took them to Hagerstown. From Hagerstown they took the "Old Trading Path of Pennsylvania" to Pittsburg. From Pittsburg it was, by a measure of their past travels, a short distance to Lake Erie.

At Erie on the Lake was a Scots family named Gunn, people they knew, so they passed a few days with them before joining a boat of Canadian Frenchmen taking their furs to Montreal. It felt good to be back with the boatmen, singing the French Songs and dancing around the campfires. James' violin was his constant companion and the night's camp and music brought comfort to the men who spent most of their lives in the wilderness.

Their canoe reached Montreal and the office of Mr. Grant on August 29, 1781. They brought him their Maps and Journals. They told him about William and the battle at Petersburg. They told him about the trip down the Missouri and across the country on the Ohio River. They told him about the Maha Indians they had met. They didn't tell him about their involvement in the Petersburg battle or the hidden soldiers. They were back in British held territory.

CHAPTER FOURTEEN

The White Rainbow

"GRAM, DID GRANDFATHER fight for the Americans in the Revolution?"

"No Johnny," Gram told him, "he wasn't really fighting against the English or for the Americans he was caught in a situation where it was necessary to fight for himself. Had he been captured by either the Americans or English he would have been imprisoned. He was fighting for his life as well as for his brother and cousins."

Gram thought, there was always that question, "whose side of the war had James taken."

Gram slightly shook her head and resumed her story:

September brought all the returning voyageurs back into Montreal with canoes heavily loaded with furs. There were long days of counting furs and seeing them properly bundled and packed for shipping to England. The English had stopped all trade with the colonies, now calling themselves "The United States of America."

Indians who formerly brought their furs into Montreal and Albany, New York to be picked up by the English now took their furs only to Albany.

There was a decided drop in the amount of furs coming into Mr. Grant's warehouses in the fall of 1781.

Another important event was in the making. The loosely formed company of Traders in the Northwest was formed into the

Northwest Fur Company. Their Employer, Mr. Robert Grant was one of the companies' partners. It was the plan of the company to break the monopoly the Hudson Bay Company had on the Canadian fur trade.

With the defection from England of the Colonial Americans, the Canadian people became less like their neighbors and took on a character that was both French and English and uniquely Canadian.

Many of the fur trading areas, previously trapped by the English and French Canadians, now lay in the territories claimed by the Americans. Without the furs from the Colonists, the English expanded their trade into the wilderness areas along the unprotected borders of Canada claimed by Spain. They freely used their superior finances to entice Voyageurs and their knowledge of the wilderness to trade in un-charted areas.

John had become quite dissatisfied with the long hours of work and the nightly carousing of the homeless men of the fur trade. In truth, he and James preferred the boats and wilderness to the questionable delights of Montreal. Drunkenness was so prevalent, it was impossible not to be accosted walking down the street. Whiskey and rum flowed as freely as water. The Indians of the area were so addicted to liquor, it was impossible to make a trade of furs without giving them enough rum to become intoxicated. Their taste for rum reduced their willingness to work trapping and trading for furs.

John met an *avocat*, recently arrived from France by the name of Paul Micheau. He also met his wife and their beautiful daughter Elizabeth. She was petit, with dark hair and large liquid, eyes and John was instantly smitten with her. Mr. Micheau had planned to set up a law practice in Montreal, but the French involvement in the American Revolution caused him to change his mind. He was now making plans to move his practice and family to the newly created states. He planned to settle on Staten Island, in the State of New York. There was a large fur distribution center there, where he planned to represent the fur industry.

John began making nightly visits to the Micheau home. Elizabeth and her parents made John a welcome guest. James occasionally went along for the visit, but he preferred the company of the men in town.

Mr. Micheau confided in John his plans for New York and asked John to join him in his firm as a clerk and study for the law. He welcomed John's courtship of Elizabeth and gave his consent for them to marry. John told James of the offer and asked him to go with them to New York and find a position there. James loved the wilderness and making maps and notes in his journal. He declined but promised to visit. John would not be far from William and that was good to know.

The spring and the time of departure of the boats to the Grand Portage and Lake Winnipeg were fast approaching. James took another contract with Mr. Grant which would keep him employed another two years. James and John had spent very little of their 1000 *liveres* per year salary. John had money in reserve to start his marriage with Elizabeth Micheau.

James planned to build up his accounts until he could go into the fur business for himself. The companies' owners were becoming very rich on very small amounts of capital or work on their part. It wasn't so much that James wanted to be one of the New Rich, but too often, success is measured by the wealth one has, and James wanted success and he wanted a home and security.

John's attention was completely focused on Elizabeth and James missed his companionship. He was also tired of being around all the drinking and merry making. James loaded his small one man canoe with some supplies and told John he was going into the wilderness and would be back for the wedding. He seated himself in the canoe and dipped his oar into the frigid waters of the St. Lawrence River. He wouldn't go far, just far enough to put humans behind. He needed time for thought and reflection and to be alone.

After a couple of hours rowing, with the river's water

gently lapping against his canoe, a peace began to settle upon him and the repetition of the dip and pull of the oar began to calm his spirit.

There was a mist in the air and an almost impenetrable cloud cover hung low over the river. The unseen sun did a playful hide-and-seek through the clouds sending small shafts of light onto the dark water where James' canoe glided along. To look ahead it seemed he was rowing into a bank in which he would disappear.

James had never played such a delightful game with nature. Then before him, he saw a sight he had never heard of, a rainbow arched through the mist. Rainbows had seemed a miracle to him since his father had showed him one arched over Loch Arichlinie at his home in Scotland. But this rainbow was without color, only shades of light. James didn't know what to think of such an unusual and glorious sight. He understood what caused a rainbow when the sun cast its rays against droplets of water setting off a rainbow of colors. He didn't understand how a rainbow was made without color. He felt the wonder of it deep within, like the time at Rosslyn Chapel. Here on the banks of the river beneath the rainbow without color, he decided to make his camp for the next week. He put his canoe into the closest bank, took out his supplies and turned the canoe over. He then hunted for just the right limbs to cut for supports to prop up the canoe, creating a lean-to for shelter. He built a fire and put on water to make himself a cup of tea. Hot tea with a little of his precious honey would sooth his restless spirit.

Taking his tin mug of tea with honey and a small splash of rum, he sought out a convenient log where he sat and gazed across the river. He sat while peace and quiet wrapped around him. He thought of home, of his mother and father and of Kitty and Jean, both married with children, and Robert and George his younger brothers. He thought of William in Virginia and his McDonald cousins. He thought of John who was not only his brother but his best friend. For the first time in his twenty years of life he would soon be without a close relative nearby. He cherished the feel of

solitude but wished for the warmth of a home and family. The lonesome call of a loon across the river echoed the loneliness of his thoughts.

James stayed at his camp for a week with only himself for company. He fished and hunted but little; it was not food for the body he craved but the richness of his own thoughts he sought to fill him.

As the day of John's wedding was fast approaching, he broke camp and made his way back to Montreal. He already felt the loss of his brother's presence. Elizabeth Micheau was a lovely young woman and James wished them a life of happiness, but sometimes, when he thought about it, he felt a great sense of loss that John would be leaving Canada.

At the lodging house James found John in a state of nervous agitation. He shouted, "Where have you been? Would you miss your own brother's wedding?"

James grabbed him and hugged him, almost hard enough to crack a rib. Fighting the sting of tears and the heaviness in his throat, he said, "I would not have missed your wedding, I wish you a wonderful life filled with happiness and many sons and daughters to keep you in your old age. We have been together, the two of us for so long that sometimes I think it must always be thus. I could not bear that when I returned, it would be to say goodbye. I love you very well, John."

John hugged James back. Both were filled with the emotions of the moment. Soon, the emotions had passed and excitement returned while they both got ready for John's life changing event. They brought out their carefully preserved tartans of the soft brown colors of the Strathnaver Mackay. Had James been taller, Elizabeth would not have known which Mackay she was to marry they looked so much alike in their Scottish dress. Looking extremely handsome, the two brothers headed down the street to the church not noticing the admiring and envious glances of all who saw them.

Elizabeth wore a soft silk polonaise gown of pale ivory, a

modestly altered version of the French court gown. The square neck was lightly covered with delicate pin and bobbin lace. The bodice came to a point below the waist, tightly corseted to create a waist that could be easily spanned by the expanse of a hand. The sleeves were gathered and puffed at the shoulder and ended just above the elbow where lace fell from the sleeves in delicate ruffles. There was just enough lace to enhance the beauty of the gown with out overpowering the wearer. The overskirt was pulled and draped showing a full underskirt of the same lightly creamed silk.

After the couple said their vows, the small wedding party returned to the Micheau home to partake of a late supper of roast venison served with wine and black currant sauce. There were ducks served in orange sauce and jellied salmon with caper sauce. There were plum tarts, sugared almonds and Madeleine's so delicate they melted in the mouth. James had never tasted such food and thought that if Elizabeth could keep a home and cook like her mother, John would surely be a wider man the next time they met.

A week later the Micheaus with John and Elizabeth Mackay prepared to depart Montreal. The family would take a ship to Cape Breton, Nova Scotia where they would stay until they could take a Dutch vessel to New York and Staten Island. The ship to take away James' only family in Canada also brought news from his MacDonald cousins in Virginia.

Petersburg, Virginia
May 28th, 1781

To: John and James Mackay
C/o Mr. Robert Grant
Northwest Fur Company
Montreal, Canada

Dearest Cousins:

With this letter, I had hoped to send wonderful news of William's coming marriage to Sarah Collier. Instead it brings news of a most terrible nature.

William our most precious cousin, and your beloved brother, is dead!

Some days ago the British Soldiers came back to our small town. They were constantly in and out our trading establishment. We had hidden all the gun and powder as soon as we heard of their approach. You know we have gone to great lengths to stay neutral in this whole war affair. Having a lifetime of our own taxation problems in Scotland, we paid upon command. In truth, the complained of taxes didn't seem so excessive to us. We laughed at the Colonial's "tea party" in Boston which some of the old relatives took part in. We sought only to live our lives and make enough money for the barest necessities.

My writing wanders, but our grief is great.

The lovely Sarah came into the store on the especially bright and beautiful Monday last. There were a couple of British Soldiers in the store, buying nothing, but handling all the goods, making disparaging remarks about "uncivilized Colonials" and in general being rude and arrogant.

William controlled his temper and said not a word but let the Soldiers have their way. That was a miracle in itself, for William surly did have a temper. The only answer must have lain in his love smitten state. He may not have noticed the soldiers at all.

Upon Sarah's entrance all thoughts took flight from his head and he forgot all except Sarah.

The Soldiers seeing their total concentration in each other thought to have a little fun. Moving next to Sarah, one of the soldiers, a bore of a fellow, "Prince Henry" we called behind his back, put his arm about Sarah and chided her for her attention to a "dirty Scotsman." Sarah was very frightened by the fellow and the other soldier did not interfere in the cruel display of Henry's behavior, but stood with a smile upon his face enjoying the harassment of the Colonials, as we are constantly referred to.

William, protectively, removed Harry's arm from Sarah, replacing it with his own and told Harry that Sarah and he were to be married, and to reframe from touching her person.

There was absolutely no provocation from William to incite Harry to raise his gun, although William was nearly purple with suppressed rage that the man had laid a hand on Sarah.

Harry raised his gun and shot William, an unarmed man, "point blank," into the chest. William barely lived long enough to tell Sarah he loved her. She is devastated in her grief as I know you will be also. My own Mary still weeps whenever she looks at me or Angus.

The English captain of course, held an inquiry into the incident. Samuel Brown, the other soldier as well as "Prince Henry" both swore William had accosted Henry. We received no justice in the matter. The captain proclaimed Henry shot in defense.

I don't have to tell you, the townspeople are angry. There is not one single loyalist left in Petersburg. The soldiers have now all withdrawn and I believe will not receive any welcome if they should come again.

One incident, I believe will bring you comfort. Old mother Schultz, that dear old German woman who was forced to cook for the British, has taken some revenge on the fellows. She added dried senna beans to their daily ration of boiled stew. Our grief was considerably lessened each time we chanced to see a soldier head for the bushes to drop his pants in his hurry to prevent messing himself. It was such a hilarious sight all the people found some reason to need goods from town.

When accused, Mother Schultz was very indignant that they would believe she would ruin a perfectly good stew. She very boldly told the captain, "Ya, the day will never come when I would ruin a good stew." She told them their own poorly preserved meats

were to blame for the cramping and flux.

Mother Schultz did not lie of course. The British soldiers were constantly complaining of the food they had to eat.

Let me caution you to do nothing, the time will arrive, I believe, when this part of the country will be free to be governed by the people who live here.

God willing, this letter will reach you before many months have passed. Let peace restore you and write of any changes in your circumstances, that we might not lose each other. Angus and Mary send their heartfelt condolences for all our loss.

> *Your most loving cousin*
> *Donald MacDonald*

There was no time to take comfort from each other over the loss of their brother; John was leaving on the ship and James must go back into the wilderness. They each let the rage they felt over the unnecessary death of their brother burrow deep within themselves to fester there.

James left for the Indian village to find Black Crow and to make the long trip back to Lake Winnipeg and two more years in the wilderness. James had an unshakeable numbness about him; even his ever-present violin could not lift the darkness of his spirit.

Days passed before the rhythm of the canoe and the singing of the Frenchmen, as they rowed the canoe, could at last begin to bring James out of the terrible blankness he felt at the loss of William. He wondered how long it would be before he would see John and Elizabeth again.

One morning just as the crew had set out for the day's rowing they came upon a most funny sight.

James told me, "A cow moose and her calf were swimming across the river and had just nearly reached the other side when the cow chanced to see our canoe coming toward her. She let out a loud bellow and turned to re-cross the river even though she had almost reached her destination of the other side. The calf, in its fright, continued in a very erratic way across the river and upon reaching the bank began to try to climb out. The bank was too steep and muddy for the calf to get a firm hold and the more it tried the more it slid back in the river. The men were all laughing so hard the canoe was almost upset. The calf not knowing what to do made a lunge for the boat of laughing idiots and would have surely smashed the canoe to bits had she not veered away at the last moment saving the men from losing their goods and an icy bath in the river."

The incident with the moose served to shake off some of James' moroseness and things continued to get better. At the night's camp, James joined in with his fiddle and the night was again filled with music, jokes and dancing.

The boatmen were met with unusual gladness upon reaching Lake Winnipeg with the supplies. Unknown to James there had been a great outbreak of Small Pox. There were no Indians bringing in furs for trade this year. Black Crow left to go to his tribe and see for himself the damage that had taken place there.

None of the men could go near the Indian Tribes. The Small Pox had spread to every tribe on the plains. Already the word received at the fort was that over a third of the Indians had perished. Some tribes had so few survivors they had joined neighboring tribes.

James did not know what had happened to his friends the Paducah. Were White Buffalo, Yellow Bird and their new sons still among the living? It would be a very long time before he could find out. Although he had experienced death many times the possible deaths of the young Indian twins and his friends was an another blow to his already aching heart.

James went to their little cabin on Pembina River where he stayed, alone. Black Crow found him there and joined him for the

winter. There was no good news from his tribe. It was one of the hardest hit by the Small Pox. It was believed one of the traders, who visited their village, started the outbreak. Black Crow had lost both Old Grandmother and his parents. After the winter with James, he would return to his tribe and move them to a location away from the traders. James told him in the future to never let sick trappers into their village. If one of their people got sick to put them away from the tribe and let only those people who had previously survived the sickness take care of them. Then, James told them, they must burn all the clothing and lodging of the sick to destroy the evil that made the sickness.

Over the next two years James thought of nothing but work. Work blotted out his pain and loss and dispelled the times of loneliness. The days were spent running traps and skinning the animals. The nights were spent by candle light stretching the furs onto frames. The time gradually passed and finally it was time to go back to Montreal.

Spring 1784

The boats arrived from Montreal, discharged their supplies, reloaded with furs and made ready to make their return trip. James would be returning with the boat crews.

With much difficulty James had trapped and traded for enough furs, but far less than he had hoped for. When he reached Montreal, James met Donald Mackay who was part of the Mackay Family who lived in the county of Caithness near where James' mother Elizabeth had been born. He did not believe they were closely related, but most Mackays were related to each other in some degree. James decided to join with Donald in hopes of expanding into rivers not yet trapped by the large fur companies. James was surprised to learn that Donald knew of the Mandan Village. They hoped there would be enough of the people left to trade with them. He would like to see his friends White Buffalo and Yellow Bird and their young sons again. However, he did not want to take the traders to the Paducah Village. He prayed his friends still lived.

Upon reaching Montreal and finishing his duties with The Northwest Fur Company, he told Mr. Grant he wished to join with a small independent trader for a time, and explore further than he had previously. Mr. Grant was agreeable and reminded him to always keep his maps current and that he would pay for any maps that James could bring him. He knew whatever furs were taken would eventually be brought to him for sale.

Mr. Grant said, "James, if you ever need to come back to the Northwest Fur Company, we will welcome your services. You know, I will retire in a few years and my brother Culbreth will take my place. I wish you well in your explorations."

CHAPTER FIFTEEN

Winter on the Saskatchewan

JOHN WOKE UP EARLY and decided to take a walk along the Gravois River which ran along Gram's house. Gram had talked late into the night about Grandfather. Sometimes she went into herself and related his life as if he were there with them. John worried the telling of his grandfather's story might prove to be too much for his grandmother.

The day was a beautiful summer day with light clouds of puffy white to enhance the brightness of the blue sky. It was a blue Gram would have said, "just like the blue of James' eyes when there was so much light the sky was nearly without color."

The mockingbirds were singing and the blue jays were scolding while the squirrels played on the branches of every tree. It was a most enjoyable day.

Upon John's return from his walk, he smelled the bacon frying. Gram had awakened from her sleep and was starting her day.

Yesterday, Aunt Maria, Uncle Zeno's widow brought fresh lemons from her shopping trip to St. Louis. Gram was making Yorkshire pudding to serve with the bacon.

Elizabeth poured the batter over very hot bacon drippings in her cast iron skillet, blackened and seasoned by many years of use. She sat the pan in the built-in oven, next to the fireplace, to bake. The pudding, when done, comes out all puffed and curled around the edges. Gram served the dish with the fresh lemons and finely powdered sugar. The pudding is heavily sprinkled with the sugar, and then the lemon juice is squeezed over the sugar causing it to melt. Served with home cured bacon from the smokehouse, the breakfast was fit for a king.

"Gram," John asked, "Will you feel like continuing Grandfather's story today. I worry that you will tire yourself unnecessarily."

"Johnny, the opposite is true I am more invigorated and alive with the memories than I have been since your Grandfather's death thirty seven years ago."

Gram continued, "The next few years of James' life were some of his most difficult and trying times. When we have finished with our breakfast and tidied the kitchen, I wish to continue."

Spring 1785 Montreal, Canada

John had now left Canada and James entered into an agreement with Donald Mackay, a fellow fur trader who had also worked for the Northwest Fur Company. Mr. Grant, his brother Cuthbert and the other partners of the Northwest Fur Company had in the past few years made deep in-roads into the fur trade, breaking the monopoly of the Hudson Bay Company. The Northwest Company went to the most remote areas to do their trading.

The Northwest Company, it was rumored, were taking unfair advantage of the Indians by plying them with rum until they became so intoxicated, that they sold their furs for far less than their value. It was a practice that reflected badly on the whole fur industry and made it difficult to deal with the Indians in a fair way. James had always had a good relationship with the Indians who had traded with him. Believing the rumors to be true was one of the reasons he had decided to leave, and join up with Donald Mackay.

James took a position as clerk and assistant to Donald. They outfitted two canoes for their two year trip into the wilderness.

James and Donald made a trip to *Trois Rivie`res* where they purchased the canoes. The canoes where called *Maitre Canots* in the French manner. They were forty-eight feet long and nine feet wide. Each canoe could carry up to four tons of weight. It took ten voyageurs, the steersman and the clerk to carry the goods and canoe across the portages.

The village of La Chine, resting about nine miles above Montreal, was the casting-off place for all the companies going into the wilderness. It was at this place the canoes were carefully loaded with the trade goods and supplies.

There was a most curious and unfortunate circumstance that La Chine came by its name. The explorer, Le Sieur La Salle, thought to find a route to China through Canada. He was murdered by his own men there. The village then became known as La Chine or China.

The trade goods in each canoe included a dozen English rifles. The rifles and other precious items were wrapped in the tough, thick skins of the loon, which had been smoked and dressed to make them waterproof. It was the same skin with which James wrapped his precious violin, maps and journals. In addition to the rifles the canoes contained: two kegs of gun powder and balls, two barrels of powdered rosin, four barrels of fat, one hundred pounds of pork sides, and ten barrels of rum, two iron cooking pots, hatchets, knives and sacks of blue and white glass beads. The canoes were so packed, it was necessary for the men to sit with their legs folded while they rowed.

In addition to the trade goods, the men had their own supplies which consisted of: One blanket, one extra shirt, one extra pair of trousers, two or three handkerchiefs, a twist or two of tobacco and a few other items, the men might want to take along.

James' equipment consisted of twice the amount of the goods of the men who would be returning with the furs. Men who wintered in the wilderness were required to take twice as many items or enough to last two years before their return. In addition to the required items he carried the compass he had purchased at the fair at Crief, when he went with his father George, and Brother John on the Cattle Drove in Scotland. James' violin was the most important equipment than any of his extras. Music was very important to the morale of the men. They sang their songs in French during the journey with the paddles of the rowers keeping time to the music. At each portage all the goods had to be removed and carried across the land on their backs. At the next river the goods were reloaded into their canoes until they reached the next portage, where they repeated the process of unloading, carrying and reloading the canoes.

Each time a portage was reached, according to its lengths, the men were given *pauses* or rest stops. The length of a portage was measured in how many pauses were needed to cross the land before the boats were put back into the water. Most of the time it was half a mile between pauses, or less if the ground was very rough or mountainous around rapids and waterfalls.

The two canoes, with the trade goods, started out on the usual route of the men of the fur trade. There were twenty canoes that started their trade trip on the same day as James and Donald. They would see them frequently along the way before they reached the Grand Portage.

Donald would head up the trip for the Company. James, as his assistant, would head up his group of men. He would receive a higher wage as an assistant and clerk than he had received before. They were a little short of men and some of the men were past the age that was usual for voyageurs and some were too young. Their canoes were under-manned and under-financed, but they were determined to get more of the profits for their labor. James and Donald were both seasoned fur traders and each had been in the business for ten years.

It took their two canoes more than a month to reach Michilimackinac, a staging depot at the juncture of Lake Huron and Lake Michigan. From La Chine to Michilimackinac it was nine hundred miles and thirty two-portages.

The goal of the traders was to reach the Grand Portage, which was situated on the North side of Lake Superior, a fifteen hundred mile trip from Montreal. At the Grand Portage James and his men would split into smaller groups and pick up smaller *"Canoes du Nord"* for their trip into the interior of Canada. One of these smaller canoes could be carried upon the shoulders of just two men and would carry about twenty-five hundred pounds.

James and Donald stored their large canoes and purchased four of the smaller canoes from Indians who had brought them to the Grand Portage for sale. Some of the trade goods were used to purchase the canoes.

Leaving the Grand Portage and the annual dance, they continued their trip along a seven hundred fifty mile route to Lake Winnipeg which at the time was called *Ounipique* or *Onipeg*. The men tried to pronounce the name of places like the Indians pronounced them.

There were seventy-two carrying places or portages to cross before they would reach Winnipeg. Sometimes the canoes had to be unloaded and carried a mere sixty feet around a rapid or other obstacle only to be reloaded and put in the water again.

James and Donald were headed to the Yellowstone and Missouri Rivers which flowed from the Rocky Mountains. This area was farther than had previously been trapped. James having already been to the Yellowstone River knew of the abundant furs to be gathered there. It would also afford him an opportunity to renew his acquaintances with White Buffalo, Yellow Bird and their sons. He hoped they had escaped the terrible outbreak of small pox.

In the fall of the year 1785, the men with Donald were forced to winter on the Saskatchewan River which had frozen before they could get to the better places of trapping. On the banks of the Saskatchewan they put together a cabin, midway from Cumberland House and the forks of the North and South Saskatchewan Rivers. They spent over a week, with their canoes trapped in the ice. When they were free of the place, James took some of the men to build a fort farther up the river and set out their traps. There was heavy snow and ice, and the men had to travel on foot using snow shoes. Donald and the remainder of the men stayed at the cabin.

James and his men arrived at the forks of the North and South Saskatchewan Rivers, the area was inhabited by the *Knisteneaux,* the French word for *Cree* Indians.

The lodges of the Knisteneaux were made by positioning long poles in a circle and tying off the top. Skins were laid around the poles to form a cone shape with an opening left at the top to allow the escape of smoke from the cooking fires. The skins do not seem to be sewn together as many tribes do, but laid loosely over the frame with poles spaced around the lodge on the outside of the skins, holding them in place. Most often these types of dwellings lodges were referred to as *tepees.*

James stopped at one of their villages and smoked the peace pipe with their chief. He asked permission to build a post a few miles from the forks of the river. James found that respect, fairness and kindness for the people of the villages brought him more trade than trying to get the furs for less than their value.

The medicine men of the tribe were highly esteemed men whom he treated with the highest regard. The traders depended upon a good report from the Spirits to the Shaman before they were allowed to do business with the tribe.

There were usually men in the group who needed some kind of medical assistance and James found the medicine men to be very good with herbs and tree barks of the area. It also gave them a good excuse to give the Shaman goods in payment for his esteemed services.

One of the old fellows of the group suffered from constant soreness in the bones and the Knisteneaux Medicine Man treated him with the bark of the *green tamarack tree.* A piece of the trunk was cut off near the top of the tree and chopped into small pieces, and from this a drink was made for medical purposes. The sticks were used again every two days to make drinks until a week had passed. The sticks were then buried in the earth. The old fellow's sore bones were much relieved by the remedy. Another of the men was given the roots of *sweet grass*, which numbs the mouth, to chew for a toothache and another was given the gum from a fir tree boiled in water for a bad cough. Placing a high regard upon the customs and medicines of the Indians was one of the ways that James maintained a good relationship with the Indians. He had learned much of the Algonquian language which was spoken or understood by most of the tribes of Upper Canada.

James asked the chief where would be the best location and if they would bring their furs to him for trade. The place being agreed upon, trade goods were exchanged and the fur traders left to begin building the fort, which they called Pine Fort. The location of the fort would allow the men to trade and trap on both forks of the Saskatchewan River.

Trees were selected to be cut and shaped into proper size and length. The first building was a storehouse, then a house for the clerk or, in this instance, a house for James. Next came the house for the men and then a stockade was built around the area of the storehouse and houses. When the fort was better established, more buildings would be added.

It was only after the winter was over that James learned that most of Donald's men had left to go back to Cumberland House, leaving only Donald and one old trapper to weather the hard winter alone. By good chance some men of the Hudson Bay Company found Donald and his companion and saved them from starvation by sending supplies back to their cabin. The old trapper was in such a bad way, only Donald's intervention had prevented him from taking his own life.

Donald joined James at Pine Fort on the Saskatchewan River. In the spring, James made a trip back to the Grand Portage to get more supplies and take in their furs. They had traded for a good number of furs from the Knisteneaux Indians in the area.

Donald's temperament had proved to be like that of a wounded bear, always unpredictable. James, with his canoes and his men, separated themselves from Donald as much as possible.

Upon James return from the Grand Portage, he found Donald settled into the fort. He learned there had been altercations involving Donald and the Knisteneaux living along the Saskatchewan River.

James with half of the men proceeded up the South Branch of the Saskatchewan River to its end. From the Knisteneaux Indians, James traded for dog sleds to take his group on to the Yellowstone and Missouri Rivers where they set their traps and did their winter trapping. Near the onset of winter, the Missouri froze solid enough for the men to continue with their dog sleds to the Yellowstone where there was much better trapping.

It was on this trip that James met with a tribe of Blackfoot Indians, so called for their moccasins which were dyed black. There were three branches of these Indians. The nation he visited was known as the Piegan Blackfoot Tribe. He did some trading with the tribe who had in their possession numerous articles made of the horns of the Big Horn Sheep. Their lodges were located at the foot of the Rocky Mountains. During the winter of 1786, he had a most interesting encounter with the tribe's Priest, or rather Conjuror that performed one of his miracles. They had passed several days with these Indians, and one night he and his men were invited into the tent where the Chief and his people were assembled to view the Priest's show. The Priest stripped naked and had himself tied hand and foot with Buffalo sinews. He was then wrapped in a shaved moose skin and tied all around with nothing in appearance but his head. He was then put behind a curtain from whence came noises of a struggle and voices of more than one person. The person, they said was the Spirit come to release him from his bondage. There was singing and shaking of the *Shee sheaquois,* which is made of raw skin sewn together in the shape of a gourd, into which small stones have been placed. The skin is then hardened by heat, and with a quick shake, the stones rattle around making noise. When the old Priest came from behind the curtain of skins, he was naked and glistening with sweat, but free of all his bonds. After he rested they smoked the Calument or Pipe of Peace. He related his vision of buffalo approaching the camp, that they were very fat, that the ill of the village would recover their health and that a courier from the Snake Indians was coming to make peace with the Piegan Nation. All these things came to pass and the old Priest was celebrated as a great and worthy man. Had all things not happened as he said, he would have blamed the Spirit for deceiving him.

After leaving the village and returning to the fort, the men talked about the magic of the old Priest and how impressed they were with him. To show them they were in error, James had them tie his hands with sinews. He then took a mouth full of water and slowly dripped it onto the sinews. Soon the sinews began to soften and get loose enough for James to remove his hands and free himself. He pointed out to the men he had offered to loan the old Priest some small rope which he refused. It was an incident James was most fond of telling.

By the end of November, the men had traded and trapped for all the beaver pelts their boats could carry. They made their way back to the Cree Nation and traded the dogs plus a little *lagniappe* back to the Indians for their canoes. They had traded and trapped for the biggest beaver they had yet encountered and were taking back close to three hundred pelts. They were to return to their Pine Island Post near the Indian village, before setting out to meet Donald at his winter post, built further down on the Saskatchewan River. They would then continue their trip to winter at Cumberland House.

James and his men spent the remaining months of the winter at Cumberland House on Moose Lake. In the spring they would again meet with Donald and his men before taking their furs into the trading post at the Grand Portage.

James and Donald discussed the Mandan Village and made their plans to visit the village and do some trading. They heard the village was greatly reduced in size since the small pox epidemics a few years back.

Some of the men were assigned the task of taking the furs on to the Grand Portage while James and Donald made their plans for a trip to the Mandan Village.

James remembered the Indian's love of the blue glass beads as well as the iron cooking pots. The cooking pots were hard to carry and very heavy. The pots were more for good will and future trade than for barter.

Leaving Lake Winnipeg, they rowed their canoes up the Assiniboine River which flowed down from the mountains, through beautiful and fertile valleys.

The Assiniboine branches into the River Catapoi, which is now known as the Q'Appelle River which they followed to its end. The Indian people of the Assiniboine tribes set up their camps to trade their horses for the use of the fur traders. James noted in his Journal, it would be a good place to build a fort. James asked after his friend Black Crow and was told, Black Crow was chief of one of the villages that had their lodges near the Turtle Mountains. Providing horses for the traders was very profitable for the Assiniboine tribe, and because the Mandan Nation was a well known place for trading with Indians of other tribes, all traders were welcome.

CHAPTER SIXTEEN

Carried on a Buffalo Robe

GRAM AND JOHN had turned in early the night before because today was a big day.

John woke up thinking today is the first Sunday following the day of my mother's death on Sunday, June 8th 1851. Every year on this day Gram ordered the carriage to be brought around to make a trip to the cemetery where his mother was buried. This year, because of John's visit, several of his cousins were going along. Uncle Zeno and Aunt Maria had four children, all much older then John. Some of their grandchildren, who were visiting Aunt Maria were his age and would be going along with him and Gram.

They packed a picnic lunch so they could stop on the way and turn a sad occasion into one of joy.

The day was a beautiful and bright sunny day for the outing. The trip to St. Charles and the Flint Hill Cemetery would take most of the morning. John, being "the privileged" guest was allowed to drive the buggy for Gram. As it was a four seat buggy, he was allowed to choose two of his cousins to ride with them. He chose two of his second cousins, who were closer to his age. He chose James Mackay named for his grandfather, who was always fun to be around. He chose Rowena Mead because she was such a lively and fun cousin. He did think it polite to include a girl cousin to ride with Gram, so when they had their debates they would not be a mismatched group.

They arrived at the cemetery and unloaded the flowers Gram had picked from her yard to decorate her daughter's grave. She was buried near the center of the cemetery. They took their hoes and spades so they could clean the grave before Gram laid out the flowers. It was always a sad occasion to visit someone they had loved so dearly.

Gram seemed terribly frail as she bent to lovingly place the eglantines, cockscombs and daisies upon the grave. For just a moment the terrible years of grief showed upon her face.

Finishing their time at the cemetery, they took a trip into the town of St. Charles and Gram showed them the house, now listed as 1017 Main Street, where she and grandfather started their marriage. The house was built of Burlington Stone in the old French manner. There were additions to the house that had not been there when Gram had lived there. They stopped the carriages and asked the present owners of the house if they might have a tour. Upon learning that Gram was the widow of James Mackay they invited them into the house and didn't hesitate to show them every nook and cranny of the place. The front room was thirty feet by twenty-five feet and there was a ten foot fire place at each end. It was a two story house with the stairs to the upper story on the outside. The front porch which ran along the entire front of the house was raised several feet from the street with steps at each end. At one time the under part of the house was used as a stable where the farm animals could be fed in the winter time without the necessity of going out into the cold. Although, the house was past the age of fifty years, the old place seemed to be in fine shape. Uncle Zeno, Aunt Lucie, Aunt Catherine and Aunt Julie were born in the house, so it was of special interest to the family. Gram said the happiest years of her life had been spent in the house. It was the first house she and grandfather had shared after their marriage.

The family of the house insisted they stay for tea and cakes. Gram consented and told them stories of the life they led when she and grandfather lived there. She told them about the people who came to visit. They entertained such people as the famous Col.

Daniel Boone. She would sit by the fireplace and play her harp while James played his violin. The more Gram talked of the old times the younger and more alive she became. Upon entering her old dwelling place, she shook off the sadness that had followed her from the cemetery.

Departing from the old family house, they drove back along Main Street where Gram showed them the Custom House where grandfather had received anyone traveling through the area. Everyone going into the Spanish area had to stop at the Customs House for inspection and receive a permit for travel. As grandfather was the Captain of the Militia for the district, it was he who granted the passports. Sometimes people stayed in the upper floor for the night. There was a blacksmith shop and large stable in back of the house for people who needed to re-shoe the horses and oxen that pulled their covered wagons. The Custom House was also built in the French manner of a two story rectangle with a half floor attic room.

When they returned to Gram's home upon the bank of the Gravois River, all the cousins wanted to stay the evening and hear Gram's continuation of grandfather's life. They could never get enough of the stories of grandfather's adventures.

The house's windows were all opened, letting in the evening breezes from the river and Gram continued her story about one of grandfather's trips to the Mandan Indian Village. The young people never tired of hearing the Indian stories.

February 1787

The trip to the Mandan Village from the end of the Q'Appelle River was one hundred sixty miles. The Assiniboine Tribe kept a camp of horses and mules where the river looped down toward the Mandan Village. The mules could be hired for less trade goods than horses and could carry more weight.

The mules turned out to be the most stubborn creatures, constantly causing loss of time and goods with their refusals to cross wet marshy places. The mules did not like the iron pots which were arranged to hang over their backs. They were comical in their attempts to dislodge them, but not amusing.

The trip took seventeen days, much longer than usual. Some of the natives were known to make the trip in less than three days in the summer.

Many miles before the group reached the village, they were met by the Mandans. The Indians were so happy to see James again, they put James and Donald on buffalo robes and four of the Indians carried each of them into the Chief's lodge, in the center of the village, before they let them down.

The pots and beads were well received by the women of the tribe. The women of the *Green Corn Society* took James all around their freshly turned gardens, showing him where they planned to plant the seeds he had given them. They had hills for beans, pumpkins, corn and squash. He brought with him seeds of water- melon and musk melon which he had found growing near St. Louis in the Spanish Territory. He told the women the melon seeds made plants with long vines and produced fruits that were very sweet and juicy and brought much pleasure when eaten. They all giggled, delighting in his attention and his company. James also explained the seeds of the watermelon he brought them could be used to make a tea for expelling excess water from the body.

On the first night of their visit, the Chief held a big feast and celebration for his guest. Before the meal, the men were cleansed with trips to the sweat lodge. While one of the women prepared the floor with sage, she very shyly told James he could make a tea of the leaves. She said she was happy to receive the seeds for the melons he had given them in the garden. The leaves of the sage bush, she told him, were used for the shaking sickness people got when they stayed in the wet river bottom areas. The cliffs where the Indian village was situated kept the area dry and

free of the shaking sickness. The air on the cliff was as pure and clean as any found in the Scottish Highlands.

James had known men who experienced the shaking sickness and who used Peruvian bark tea to control the illness. It was always good to know of a new remedy. Peruvian bark came from South America and was not always available.

James asked some of the Indians if his friends, White Buffalo, Yellow Bird and their sons of the Paducah Tribe had survived the small pox. Many of the people he had met on the previous visit had died of the pox and none could tell him of his friends. Not so many had died, they thought, among the Paducah.

The women never ate with the men but brought in beautifully made pottery platters of roasted venison and buffalo, baked fish and bowls of dog meat stew made to impress the visitors. James only hoped part of the stew was not the beautiful white sled dog he had seen playing with the children when they arrived at the village.

The women brought in bowls of beans, squash and corn as well as baked roots and boiled greens. They brought in plates of honey comb and marrow fat and platters of bread made from the wild oats growing in the marshes and fried in bear grease. Every dish must be tasted and proclaimed delicious, before the meal could end and the pipe smoking could begin.

The smoking of the pipe was a lengthy sacred ritual and the pipe was passed around the circle to each tribe member and guest in the Chief's lodge. The women did not take part in the pipe ceremony.

There were many different types of people in the Indian village, just as there are in all societies. There were women who dressed in provocative ways to entice the braves to show interest in them and walk with them into their lodges. The braves would give them food and trinkets. There were also young men who paraded around the village in the most wonderful costumes, impeccably clean and dressed in soft doe skin clothing decorated with beads and the down of swans and duck feathers. They wove sweet smelling grasses and flowers through their braided hair. Their apparel would rival the best dressed dandies in London or Edinburgh. They were called by the tribe "faint hearts" and "old women." The ponies they rode were decked out in a like manner of dress, with flowers and grasses in their manes and tails and the softest saddles made of doe skin. They neither joined the other braves in hunts or rough games, nor did they carry a bow with arrows, but fans made of turkey feathers. They appeared harmless in every way but were scorned by the chief and braves of the tribe. These men in the villages lived off the generosity of the others and added nothing in the way of work or the securing of food to the community. The entirety of their lives revolved around their dress and the care they took of their person.

In complete contrast to the dandies or fops, most men of the tribe adorned themselves with eagle feathers, bear claws and skins of the animals they had killed themselves. They were never without their bow and arrows, knives and hatchets.

The young women between the ages of twelve and fourteen were of the greatest value to their fathers, especially if they were comely and pleasing to look upon. The young girls of the better families would try to make a connection with one of the traders who would give her clothing, beads and other trade goods. She would bring wealth to her family. She would be the envy of other women in the tribe and exempt from the hard labor endured by most of the tribe's women. These women or young girls became very practiced in trading themselves for goods and trinkets. When one trader leaves, she and her father are free to make a connection with the next trader who comes along. There are no rules and laws in their society restricting the rights of the parents. When the people feel the passions of nature they do not deny themselves, or if a father chooses to sell his child, he is free to do so. The time period of the young girls' trade value is short as they soon lose their appeal. The girls enter into the trade business as young as eleven or twelve years old.

The *Gros Ventres* or Hidatsa who live in nearby villages do not have the same practices as the Mandan and hold their women to strict chastity. The fathers of young girls take great pride that when they send their daughter into marriage, she has not been touched by any man. These women also take great pride in their gardens and grow many types of vegetables for the food of the tribe. Other villages nearby were inhabited by the Arikara Indians.

On the following day, the guests were treated to the performances of the *Buffalo Dance*. The dancing lasts until the "buffalo come" which can be several days or even weeks. The men who do the buffalo dance are men who have proven themselves in the hunt and are sometimes quite old and revered by the tribe.

The men come out dressed in a buffalo head with its skin hanging over their backs. They make a circle and began their dancing, stamping and pawing the ground while making loud grunts, yelps and bellows in the simulation of the buffalo. The ongoing sound of the drums and dancing noises were enough to make a man wish for a little deafness. They have a belief in the tribe that the powers of these older men can be transmitted to the younger men through intercourse with the young men's wives. During the dance a young husband may encourage his young wife to seek out the most esteemed buffalo man and "walk the buffalo." That is to say she will choose one of the dancers at the urging of her husband and take him for a walk to a secluded place where they will enter into an act of mating. Through their copulation, it is believed she will take the power of the buffalo man into herself and transmit it to her young husband who becomes more powerful. These young husbands feel great honor when the old buffalo man gives his power to their young wife.

Should the dance not succeed in bringing buffalo within a reasonable time, then the *White Buffalo Cow Society* is called in to make their magic. The women, who have all passed the child bearing age, gather in a lodge dressed in deer skins dresses that are spotlessly clean. Their hair, braided the night before is carefully dressed and greased and let flow to its full length down their back and across their shoulders in undulating waves. Bands of white buffalo hide are used to hold the locks from their faces. They paint circles of red color upon their checks and down the part in their hair. During the chanting of the society's songs one of the women will have a robe of white buffalo lying across her shoulders. There are drummers there to make their music and keep tune with the chanting. The lodge is packed with guests anxious to see the success of the society's women. The women never fail in their endeavors to make the buffalo come. If a week or so has passed and the buffalo do not come, then all fires in the village are extinguished and no cooking is done to avoid warning the buffalo away. Scouts are sent out in every direction to alert the tribe of any buffalo sighting. Since the villages are on a large plain, where the buffalo constantly roam, then it is not long before they have wandered near enough for the hunters to go for a hunt. The Mandans do not hunt far from their village because of the constant threat of their enemies, the Sioux.

The white buffalo is the most sacred animal of these people. A white buffalo only occurs about once in a hundred thousand animals, so it is very rare. When such a buffalo is found the skins is treated with the utmost reverence. A white buffalo robe is owned by the entire tribe.

The buffalo has the most impact upon the tribe of any of the other animals. Their skins are used for clothing, mats to sit upon and covering for the lodges. The flesh and organs are eaten. They use the sinew for sewing together the skins for the lodges and clothing. The bones are shaped and used for making hoes and digging in the garden, the horns are used as vessels for drinking. There are no parts of the animal that go to waste.

While James and his fur traders were visiting the village, a large number of men and women and their children left for the buffalo hunt, which was not far from the village. The men rode their horses while the women, children and dogs walked, carrying and pulling the items needed to clean and preserve the buffalo

meat. The buffalo was the staple meat of the tribe, and the women were very industrious in preserving food for the winter. The daily feasts, which were prepared for the visitors, kept many women busy cooking and serving the food. The men never worked or exerted themselves other than hunting and playing games.

The dancing was enjoyed by the entire tribe as well as the guests. There was also, the Scalp Dance, Rain Making Dance, Beggar's Dance, Bear Dance, The Green Corn Dance and so many others that one trip would not suffice to see them all.

There were horse races between the Indians and their guests, who were no competition for the outstanding horsemanship of the Indians. Each time the Indians won, there was loud cheering, yelps, jokes and dancing to show off their superiority.

For ten days the visitors stayed at the Mandan Village which passed, some of the men thought, much too quickly. The group had made very good trades, and it was time to return to the rivers and the fort at Lake Winnipeg.

Trade with the Mandans had been better than when they traded with the Cree. The group headed back for the Grand Portage where they would transfer their furs back to the large canoes and return to Montreal and Quebec, where the furs would be sold.

CHAPTER SEVENTEEN

Canada Adieu

RETURNING HOME from their long outing they all sat around on whatever seating was available. Gram sat in her rocking chair by the fire while she related story after story to his cousins. The cousins were enthralled with Gram's stories about grandfather and always wanted to stay as long as possible.

It had gotten late in the evening, but Gram wanted to continue, as if there weren't enough time to tell it all.

James returned to Quebec where he made arrangements to send their furs to England. In August of 1788, he entered into an agreement with Donald Mackay to continue with him in the fur trade for a seven year time period. He then returned to Montreal to meet people with whom he had previously traded.

Donald returned from England and met his partners in Montreal in January of 1789. By this time the partners knew the agreement they made was not going to work. He had not fulfilled his part of the bargain. James wages from the years of 1785 through 1787 were to be his part of the money to start the new company with Donald. None of the men James had brought into the deal wanted to continue in the new company with Donald. James dissolved his part in the company, but found it necessary to file suit for the money which Donald owed him.

During the time he waited on the courts and his money, James worked for Robert Grant helping to prepare his convoy of canoes and trade goods for their departure into the fur country. He spent long hours with pad and pencil making lists of supplies and packing them in barrels to keep them dry. James worked until the

first of April, when he won his suit. However, Donald had no money with which to pay him.

He said his goodbyes to Mr. Grant and prepared for his departure from Canada. His future at this point was uncertain, but his first desire was to see his brother and family. He missed the long and easy friendship they shared.

Packet boats continually plied the waters of the St. Lawrence River to Halifax, Nova Scotia where ships could be taken to the country of one's choosing. James took an Old Dutch Trader, the safest way to travel, headed for New York. The vessel was slow and cumbersome and it took almost two weeks to lumber its way along the coast to New York. The trip could have been completed in a much shorter time had the English not blockaded the trade between the new United States and Canada. Otherwise, he could have taken a sloop down through Lake Champlain and down the Hudson River right into the harbor of New York.

CHAPTER EIGHTEEN

President George Washington

IT HAD BEEN VERY LATE the night before when the guests departed and Gram stopped telling her stories.

John was worried that she would make herself ill with all the unusual activity. She told him, "No, I have been so bored for such a long time that having you visit was an opportunity for me to relive my life. It is like being young again."

Over their morning breakfast and coffee Gram told of James' arrival in New York. It was during these moments, when it was just the two of them that John and his grandmother bonded with a special closeness that would influence his behavior throughout his life.

Gram sipped her coffee and continued with her story.

James arrived at his brother's house on Staten Island on April 15, 1789. The reunion with his brother, John gave him the feeling of being whole again. John's wife, Elizabeth and her father, Judge Micheau were also happy to see James. Judge Micheau immediately told him he could secure a job as a clerk, as they were always short of people that had a good hand with the pen. He could work on a temporary basis until he made arrangements to set up another business in the fur trade. He assured James that a young man of his experience would be sought out, and he had a number of friends who would be delighted to make James' acquaintance.

James was ready to leave the Canadian Fur Trade which was now completely controlled by large fur companies. There was

no future there for an enterprising young man. The next month he would be twenty-eight years old, but not too old to start anew. At the moment he had no prospects; however, he had his experience in the fur trade, and his maps and journals of the areas he had traveled. It was these items and his experience that he intended to use to find a position that would secure his future.

New York was a city of lively interest. James had arrived in time to see one of the greatest events in American history. On April 23, 1789 General George Washington, now the first President of the United States of America, would arrive on the shores of New York in a barge especially built for the occasion. It was in New York that Washington would be sworn into office as the new country's first president.

The whole city was awash with excitement. Every man, woman and child in the city of New York and every person for all distances around that could, came to the city. They were there to witness the historical occasion, and see their General. They came to convey well wishes with their presence, as he came into town. A great ceremony was being prepared for his arrival.

There was not, at the time, an official residence for the new President. Temporary arrangements were made for him to reside at No. 3 Cherry Street.

General Washington left Mount Vernon on the 16th of April with his Secretary, David Humphreys and Mr. Charles Thomson. Mr. Thomson had delivered to the General his Certificate of Election. From Elizabeth Point, New Jersey the General was taken onto a barge and conveyed across the Hudson River to New York. The barge was hung with red moiré curtains to create a beautiful and festive atmosphere. Other barges and boats which crowded the river were also beautifully and elaborately decorated for the occasion.

For seven days General Washington had been in route to the city. All along the way there had been speeches, and hordes of people had come to wave their hands, flags and handkerchiefs in good wishes and expressions of joy.

There was a program of events to take place when he reached the New Jersey shore.

A salute was fired when he reached the Battery, another fired when he had passed the Battery. In his barge, just below the Battery, the Spanish Ambassador, Don Diego Maria de Gardoqui, saluted the New President with a round of rifle fire. The General stepped from the barge onto steps which had been erected and covered with carpet to ease his way to the Wharf. He wore a white shirt under a blue coat with buff colored trousers and vest.

There was a contingent of men, including the Governor of New York, Mayor and State Officials, to meet him when he arrived at the Wharf to accompany him along the route to the house on Cherry Street.

A full dress parade featuring the Legion of Malcolm's Brigade and Bauman's Artillery also accompanied Washington.

The crowds were impossibly large even though it was raining. As the foreign Ambassadors passed along the route behind General Washington, the Spanish and French Ambassadors nodded their heads in recognition to Judge Micheau. James, John and Elizabeth standing with her parents were all scrunched together in the great crowd. They were just as anxious to see their General, the President of the United States as anyone else.

For the new President, the day was not yet over. After a brief rest at his new residence, he was conveyed to the home of Governor Clinton for dinner.

James, John and their entire group retired to the home of the Micheaus for dinner and interesting conversation. There was one conversation that was quite amusing. It seems there was quite a discussion as what to call the New President. Was he to be called His Highness, The President of The United States or His Mightiness the President of the United States or what? After all, they certainly didn't want another King. The House refused any suggestions except the one outlined in the Constitution, which was

"The President of the United States." The entire group agreed it
was just the right title for General Washington.

A salute was fired from the Battery, at sunrise on the
morning of April 30, 1789, to commence the morning services. An
hour long service was held at all the churches to pray and give
thanks before beginning a day filled with festivities.

At 12:00 Noon, the Congress assembled at Federal Hall to
form a procession and meet their New President at his home on
Cherry Street. The President joined the procession in a carriage
drawn by four horses and returned with them back to Federal Hall
and the Senate Chamber to receive his oath of office. To please the
thousands of people standing in the streets below the balcony of
Federal Hall, General Washington moved onto the balcony so all
could witness the ceremony. The people in the Senate Chamber, or
as many as could, also crowded upon the balcony. The Chancellor
of the State of New York administered the oath followed by his
emotion filled cry of *"long live George Washington, President of
the United States."* President Washington then repeated the oath
of office with a strong, solemn and steady voice:

> *"I do solemnly swear that I will faithfully execute the
> office of President of the United States, and will, to the best
> of my ability preserve, protect, and defend the Constitution
> of the United States."*

Upon completion of the ceremony, he reverently bent and
kissed the sacred volume of the Bible upon which he took his oath.
A new Country had a new President, and it was simply the most
moving moment anyone attending had ever witnessed. The whole
chamber was rent with shouts of joy and hats thrown into the air.
All the cities' Church Bells began to ring. James and John,
together with the crowds of people in the street, cheered until their
throats were dry and tears of emotion slipped unnoticed from the
moist eyes of most of the people gathered there. James was

overcome with longing to be a part of the new United States of America.

There were many minor celebrations going on in the city. Dinners and Balls were held in great profusion. The little group, which included James, spent many hours during the evening going from one house of friends to the next and meeting more people than he would be able to remember. It was open house wherever they went with an air of joy and thankfulness for the ending of the war with England and the beginning of a new era.

The following morning, May 1st was James' 28th birthday. He awoke with the throb of a hammer in his head, for he, like all the others, had over indulged with the immense amounts of beverages they had been presented to drink the night before. He forced himself from his bed, as he could hear the household coming to life. Fully dressed, he presented himself in the breakfast room. After a cup of strong Jamaican coffee, he decided he would survive for the day's entertainment. To celebrate James' birthday, a boat trip around the Island of Manhattan was planned along with lunch at *Fraunce's Tavern*, already famous as the house where General Washington had said goodbye to his troops.

The food served was divine. James ordered rack of lamb with his favorite morel mushrooms, Naples macaroni sprinkled with Parmesan cheese, buttered parsnips and creamed onions. The meal was followed with all being served a *Triffle* soaked with wine, covered with whipped cream and decorated with candied fruits.

While the happy group enjoyed their meal at the tavern, the new House of Representatives of the United States was preparing its reply to Washington's Inaugural Speech.

Arriving back at the Micheau home from their outing, the group was served a light supper of lobster salad. After the men enjoyed their port, James picked up one of the small *Betty Lamps,* hanging on a sideboard, to light his way to the upstairs bedroom which had been allocated for his use.

On May 6th, President Washington made his first official appearance and on the evening of the seventh he gave his first ball. Invited guest included members of the Congress and Senate and many other city officials and distinguished guests. The ball was said to have been a great occasion. Only Thomas Jefferson was heard to make ill remarks about the three hundred guests who had stayed until two o'clock in the morning before taking their leave. James of course didn't know, as he was not there.

The French Ambassador's Ball was given on May 15th and was also said to have been a grand affair. Judge Micheau and his wife had been guests and were very effusive about its elegance.

For James, the greatest occasion was an invitation to attend an especially elaborate ball given by the Spanish Ambassador, at No. 1 Broadway on May 22nd. Judge Paul Micheau was a personal friend of the Ambassador and his invitation included all the family and their visitor James Mackay.

James purchased a new suit with a white shirt and white satin breeches, white satin waistcoat and silver blue velvet overcoat. He wore white silk stockings and soft black pointed-toe leather shoes with highly polished silver buckles. He refrained from buying shoes with the high heels that some men wore and chose shoes with flat heels that hardly added to his height. His hair was queued back with a black ribbon which allowed his hair to hang conservatively between his shoulders. He was more than glad that powdering the hair was no longer necessary to be in style.

John, not to be outdone by his brother, wore a coat and breeches of uncut golden brown velvet. The waistcoat was of butter cream corded silk, scattered with small flowers embroidered with yellow silk thread. The shoes were black like James' with ornate filigree silver buckles. His stockings were of pale golden brown silk.

Elizabeth too, dressed in keeping with her escorts, the two most handsome men in town. She wore a burgundy silk gown with a flowing skirt and long sleeved bodice. A bouffant muslin kerchief covered with Belgian lace wrapped her shoulders and was tucked into the front of the dress. Her hat, puffed at the crown was of light burgundy silk faced with a lighter shade of the burgundy silk. Her beautiful dark hair was dressed in loose curls which hung down her back. Her stockings were of a sheer burgundy silk. On her tiny feet she wore small pointed slippers of silk dyed to perfectly match her dress. The heels of her slippers were two inches in height, somewhat reducing the disparity between her and her husband, John.

Madame Micheau's gown was more in keeping with the current French fashions. She wore a Mauve silk gown looped over panniers. The underskirt was of pink silk flounced around the bottom with tiny pleats of the same color. The bodice was of mauve silk embroidered with tiny pink flowers and dipped to a deep "V" between the panniers. The neck line of the bodice was squared and the sleeves were puffed twice before they ended at her elbow. She wore a kerchief of pink silk edged with lace around her shoulders and tied in front covering the low neckline of the bodice. She wore stockings of pale pink silk and her slippers were of mauve velvet embroidered with the same pink flowers as her bodice. Her small stature was also enhanced by the addition of the two inch heels on her slippers. She wore no hat upon her head but pulled the hair back, puffed upwards and circled with a cord of mauve silk. The curls gathered at the back of her head and hung down to bounce upon her shoulders. The natural silver strands of her hair were enhanced with a fine coating of powder.

Judge Micheau wore a coat and breeches of black uncut velvet lined with a discreet shade of mauve silk. His waistcoat was a mauve stripped corded silk. His stockings were of black silk and his shoes of black leather very pointed and without heels. He wore no buckles upon his shoes as did James and John.

Looking upon their finery, James could not help but be glad the festivities were taking place before the heat of the summer. He was also thankful an ordinance had been passed, just two months before, to fine owners who let their pigs, chickens and other cattle roam freely about the streets.

The fullness of the ladies gowns required two carriages to convey the group to number one Broadway and the lavish party.

The street was crowded with horses, carriages and joyous people. Upon reaching their destination, they found a walkway of wood covered by carpet that had been laid to the front door to protect the finery of the invited guest.

The mansion was one of the grandest houses in the city and had escaped the fires of 1776 which destroyed so much of New York. It was a large two story brick house with an attic. The entry way was in the middle of the house with two windows on each side. The house was built upon a lot with a fifty-six foot frontage. Guest could be seen through the lighted windows, creating a picture of beautiful elegance. A butler showed the group into the grand hall where James was introduced to his host, the Spanish Ambassador, Don Diego de Gardoqui, as a fur trader recently arrived from Canada who had made trips into the Upper Spanish Territory. The Ambassador was most interested in the activities of the Canadians and the area claimed by His Majesty, the King of Spain. He asked James to call upon him in June when he would have more free time and could speak with him at length about the territories.

James asked the Ambassador to send word to him at the Micheau home where he was presently staying and thanked him for the invitation to join in the night's celebration.

The Grand Hall was crowded with guests who were slowly making their way through arched doors beautifully draped with flags and emblems, and opening into the garden set to serve supper to a large group of people. Torches lined the perimeter of the grounds casting a romantic light over a profusion of flowers in their beds and decorating the tables. Flowering shrubs perfumed the air and a trio of violin players played soft and lovely melodies to flow through the air and enhance the conversations of the guests.

Tables groaned under the weight of numerous dishes of roasted beef, geese and ducks, pickled tongue and fish in caper sauce, boiled lobsters, crabs and clams and fresh oysters to be eaten out of the shells. There were vegetables, fruits, jellies and preserves with biscuits and breads made of several kinds of flour. There were cakes and pies with apples and cheeses, nuts and melons and ice cream.

The drinks were so many that one only had to choose which he preferred, Madeira, French wine, cherry brandy, champagne, beer, cider and other drinks as well.

Two of the people James met were John Pintard, a man he found to be a very fine and industrious gentlemen. The other, a relative he understood of Mr. Pintard, was Thomas Hutchins. Mr. Hutchins he learned was the Geographer General to General Washington in the past war. He had explored the territories of Spanish Florida and his brother, Anthony, lived in the vicinity of the Mississippi River. It was with Mr. Hutchins he spent most of the evening in an engrossing conversation of explorations. They made each other a promise that they would continue their discussions at another date.

The occasion presented a wealth of writing material for James' Journal, which he had neglected of late. But certainly, he would write of all he had seen in New York and of the people he had met.

CHAPTER NINETEEN

Spanish Ambassador Gardoqui

THE PREVIOUS DAY had been one of close companionship between John and his grandmother. The short time John had been visiting, Gram had gotten quite lively and in tremendously high spirits. Late in the evening Gram had sought her bed and John had taken a walk along the river. Chirps of crickets and the buzz of cicada playing their music along with the differing croaks of frogs, big and small all together produced a pleasing symphony of country harmony. The stars were so bright it felt as if you could pull one down from the sky, simply by stretching out your hand. John thought of his grandfather and wondered if the soul of a person after his death could in some way see what was happening to his family. He wondered if Grandfather truly was somewhere waiting for Gram as she believed.

The following day brought Aunt Catherine Guion and several of her children to visit with Gram and Aunt Marie. Aunt Catherine lived in the close-by Cardonlet area. It was her custom to visit Gram at least once per week bringing goodies from her own kitchen.

It was a wonderful occasion for all the cousins to be together. For the entertainment of the younger cousins, they played games such as Tag, King of the Mountain and Blind Man's Bluff. John and his older cousins made jumping boards and a see-saw for the children to play upon. Gram and Aunt Catherine served up a hearty meal of fried chicken, potato salad, Gram's tasty yeast rolls, Aunt Catherine's sweet cucumber pickles and blackberry cobbler.

After supper Aunt Catherine and the children gathered around as Gram renewed the telling of her story of grandfather.

James thought waiting for an invitation from the Spanish Ambassador, Don Diego Maria de Gardoqui, was like waiting for First Footer's Day when he was a small boy back in Scotland. It seemed there were far too many hours in the day, and most of James' time was spent in writing entries into Court books for Judge Micheau. There was always so much paper work to be done, Deeds to be recorded and filed, surveys to check for errors and wills to be written into the Will Books and then returned to the families of the deceased. The work was tedious and tiresome. Wills and Deeds must be copied into the records exactly as they were written. He was glad to have the work but was most anxious to continue with his life. He was not accustomed to the indoor life and he missed the rigorous life and campfire talk of the fur trade.

To relieve the boredom of his indoor job, James read any and all newspapers he could obtain whether they were in English, French or Spanish. Studying the translations stimulated his mind as well as taught him what was going on in the different countries. James read the numerous notices in the papers concerning the household accounts of the first family as well as the accounts of running the new government.

President Washington gave notice that regular hours would be kept and he would only receive "visits of compliment" on Tuesdays and Fridays between the hours of two and three in the afternoon. He discouraged any visits on Sunday.

The household accounts were published for the public's information. The liveries of his white servants each cost twenty-nine dollars and they received seven dollars per month in pay. The black servants received an allowance of forty-six dollars per year for clothing. The President's housekeeper received eight dollars per month and her three helpers each five dollars per month. Including the President's valet, secretary and steward his household expenses amounted to two thousand dollars per year.

James, who had never had a servant, thought the whole arrangement of the President's household and the working of the government extremely fascinating.

It was during the second week of June that James received the anticipated letter asking him to call upon the Spanish Ambassador. He was asked to bring any records he might have of his travels in Canada and into the Spanish Territory.

There still were a number of days until James' appointment. He decided he would move into the city from Staten Island where he was staying with John and Elizabeth. He took a room in Widow Bailey's boarding house at No. 22 Broadway, which was on the same street with the Spanish Ambassador he was to call upon. James wanted to explore the city and visit the taverns where a person could learn all manner of events being planned. It never hurt to keep ones ear to news around him.

Broadway was a diverse and interesting street of commerce, where he could purchase anything he needed. There was Jacob Morgan, an attorney he had met at a previous occasion. There was Robert Dodds, the silk dyer who dyed all the ladies shoes to match their outfits. There was a blacksmith, hairdressers, grocers, cake shop, saddler, shoe maker, tailor, tobacconist, a pewterer, William Allen the gunsmith and in addition there was Ephraim Ross' Tavern next door to his boarding house room which was so close he could often hear the conservations of its occupants.

The gun shop's owner, Mr. Allen, was part of the Allen Clan, which was a Sept or associated small clan, connected to Clan Mackay back in Scotland. James thought he would be welcome to drop in for a chat and check over any new weapons that might be on the market. He could find out when William had come to America and maybe some news from Scotland. It would be good to have some up to date news from home. Perhaps he would find a pistol to purchase if he could afford one.

James, just before his departure from Canada had received a letter from his sister, Catherine, telling him of the terrible forced evacuation of home sites in the Kildonan area of Scotland where he was raised. This was news he could share with William Allen and maybe gather further information.

In the evenings, when James retired to his room at Mrs. Baileys, he re-read and corrected his journals and poured over his maps. He had traveled from the mouth of the St. Lawrence River to the mountains at the far side of Canada. He had traveled most of the known rivers as well as some that had never before been traveled by civilized man. James remembered the Blackfoot Indians, along the river Rochejaune and their fascination at the color of his skin and hair. They had never before seen a white man.

The day before James was to meet with the Ambassador he walked into the establishment of William Allen. He had guns for sale as well as a gun repair shop. There were a number of small pistols in the shop he found very interesting. In particular there was a pair of Scottish made pistols which really caught his eye. He had seen a pair at the fair when he had gone on the cattle trip in Scotland. They were all metal, flint lock pistols with engraving all over the butt and barrel. Just 12 inches long, they were a perfectly matched pair. They were meant to be purchased by a wealthy man. James didn't think he would ever have the kind of money that was required to purchase the guns.

James passed most of his day in the shop talking with William Allen, the gunsmith. They spoke of Scotland as William had come from the Coast near John O'Groats, high up in the Caithness area. He was a tall and broad shouldered man with the white blond hair and icy blue eyes of his Norse ancestors. It was some of the same distant ancestry which had, no doubt, been also a part of James ancestry.

At the end of the day they adjourned to the Tavern at No. 15 Broadway owned by Hercules Wendover, who, according to William, kept a good stock of spirits as well as served a plentiful supply of good food. It was also a place where many of the shopkeepers as well as important townsmen, gathered.

James ordered the cream of squash soup and lobster pie. He ended his meal with a chocolate mousse cake. William chose the goose with turnip greens and potato dumplings and for dessert he chose the rhubarb and strawberry pie. The food was well prepared and they noticed a variety of dishes being served to the other customers. One man was enjoying a bowl of onion soup with a dollop of country cheese on top. A glance into a secluded corner revealed the French Minister, Marquis De Moustier having dinner with the great American General, Henry Knox who appeared to be enjoying a dinner of minced pie of beef and braised fennel. James also noticed a dish of "Scottish haggis" listed on the menu. Before he could give his order, the haggis was brought to a neighboring table. It failed to resemble in any way that he enjoyed in Scotland. Upon seeing the dish of haggis on the menu, James had felt a little homesick, but not for the type of haggis being served here. After their supper the men lingered over brandy discussing the politics of their new government. James told of his plans to open a commercial house on the junction of the Mississippi and Missouri Rivers to handle furs. He thought there would be a good market working with the Dutch who had warehouses on Staten Island. Through his brother John, married to the daughter of Judge Micheau, he had already met a lot of people.

James discussed the possibilities of a source of guns for the Indians who preferred the English Rifles to the French Rifle which was undependable. Perhaps the new American made rifles were good and dependable. He thought the coming years would present possibilities for trade with those Indians with whom he had become well acquainted. It was very important to keep their friendship intact.

When they finished their brandy, the new acquaintances parted to go their respective ways. William returned to his living quarters above the gunsmith shop and James returned to Mrs. Bailey's boarding house.

June 25, 1789

James woke before any morning sounds could be heard from below his room. He knew it was the anticipation of today's meeting that had awaked him much too early in the morning.

In the corner of the room was a water pitcher and bowl sitting upon a small chest. Along side the chest sat a chamber pot for his use and convenience. James washed himself, shaved and dressed his hair. He clothed himself in buff colored knee pants with white stockings, a conservative stripped vest and blue broad cloth coat. There were no buckles on his shoes today. He wanted to make the impression of a man of some success but not a man of too much excess and leisure.

Mrs. Bailey served a fine breakfast of sausages, eggs, biscuits, cream gravy and fried potatoes. She did not stint on the quantities served each guest. After breakfast, James returned to his room and reviewed his journals and map. He would leave the journals behind and take the map to his meeting with the Ambassador. He had become accustomed to holding back that which was not needed at the moment. The map would speak for itself, any other information to be shared would be decided upon at the meeting.

It was just a short walk to No. 1 Broadway and James paused a few moments to view the lovely home of the Ambassador before going up the walk and presenting himself at the door.

An elegant looking butler, nattily dressed in a scarlet coat and a severely powdered wig, opened the door. Upon learning James' business with the Ambassador and his statement that he was expected, he was shown to the room the Ambassador used for his office.

The room was free of other guests and James could see that it was to be a "private" conversation.

"Mr. Mackay," the Ambassador said, "Come let us talk of your explorations; I am most interested in what is happening in our outer territories. Please if you would tell me about your beginning and experience in the fur trade up until you left Canada."

Ambassador Gardoqui had come right to the matter at hand, there was no small talk as one might expect between gentlemen. But then James was sure he was not viewed by the Ambassador as a gentleman. He thought Gardoqui was asking for a lengthy story. He began with his leaving Scotland because of the lack of opportunities for young men. He recalled his employment with Mr. Grant and the breadth of Canada that had to be traversed to get the furs out and back to England. He recounted his experiences with the Indians and his many journeys into the outer territories of Canada.

The Indians, James said, could be persuaded to trade furs for goods and they were very much in need of supplies. He told of his friendship with White Buffalo and Yellow Bird of the Paducah Tribe and Black Crow of the Assiniboine Tribe. He told him of the Arikaras, Mandan and Hidatsa Indians who lived near the great curve of the Missouri River, which flowed from the east from the Rocky Mountains and lay in the territories, claimed by His Majesty the King of Spain.

James talked about the Yellowstone or *Rochejaune River* where the beaver were the largest he had ever seen. He told the Ambassador of the English settlement only 150 miles from the Mandan Village in the Spanish Territory. He told of his numerous trips into the area to take out furs for the English Traders. He told him he had left Canada and was planning on opening a Commercial House in Cahokia, to trade with trappers along the Mississippi River and, he hoped, in His Majesty's territories of the Illinois and Missouri Rivers, if a license for trade was granted.

James laid his map upon the desk of Don Diego Marie de Gardoqui and said, "Your Grace, this map will show you where I have been." The Ambassador was astonished as he had no idea of the breadth of Spain's own territory. James explained his "Table of Distance" and how he measured from one point to the next and calculated the distance in leagues.

The meeting lasted three hours before there was a discreet knock upon the door announcing luncheon. James was invited to stay for luncheon, which he was honored to accept.

The Ambassador asked for permission to have the map copied so he could send it to the foreign minister of Spain through a secret communication. It was understood the source of the map would not be revealed for the protection of all involved. With the understanding of some future position for him, he granted the Ambassador the few days he asked to copy the map.

Communication and plans could be quite lengthy and James told the Ambassador he planned a trip back to Scotland to see his family which he had not seen in many years. He again stated he could be contacted at the Micheau home on Staten Island and he expected to be gone until the spring of the following year when the weather allowed for calmer seas.

James left the Ambassador's residence feeling quite good about the prospects of his future. He didn't know at the time that his visit would start such a chain of events that would make drastic changes in his life and perhaps the new nation he had just begun to call his home.

The Spanish firm of Gardoqui and sons was the primary source of secret communications of the Spanish. Immediately upon Mackay's departure, Ambassador Gardoqui wrote to Don Jose' de Monino Redondo, conde Floridablanca who was the foreign minister to King Charles III of Spain. He wrote the secret communication with great excitement describing in detail the meeting he had just had with the young "Englishman" and the years he had spent in Canada working for the fur trade. He related his visit to the Blackfoot "Piegan" Indian Nation that lay east of the "cordillera of mountains" that divided the waters of the rivers of the Missouri River and those of the Pacific Ocean. He said he reached a divide in the mountains where it would be difficult but not impossible to travel carrying goods, from the rivers running east to the Atlantic to the rivers running west to the Pacific.

Gardoqui told the Spanish Minister and advisor of all foreign affairs to Charles III, King of Spain, of the remarkable map he was already in the process of copying and which would be in the packet containing his communication.

In less than a week from the time of James' visit the secret communication between the Spanish had left the residence of Ambassador Gardoqui and was on its way to changing his future, bringing him years of unbelievable adventure in exploration, wealth in lands and devastating problems.

Before returning to Staten Island, James thought it would be an enjoyable undertaking to hire a carriage to take him around the city. In a rented carriage, which was regularly used to show visitors around, James was taken the full length of Broad Street, around the Battery and along the wharf on Front and Water Streets. They wove through the city up and down the streets looking at the architecture of the buildings. On Wall Street, the most fashionable place of residence and the center of political life in New York City, he passed the house of John Pintard, the fine intelligent gentleman he met at the Spanish Ambassador's Ball. Finally they found themselves at Cherry Street near the home of the new President. When the carriage tried to make its turn onto the street they found it blocked by a chain. The next morning James learned over breakfast the President was suffering a painful carbuncle and had to lie upon one side. The heavy traffic which continually passed his residence had to be stopped so he could get a little rest.

Although his time in the city had been exciting and interesting, it was time to return to the home of his brother and make plans to journey to Scotland.

CHAPTER TWENTY

Cuivre River

IT WAS ONLY GRAM'S FATIGUE that caused Aunt Catherine to put a halt to the story telling, much of which her children had heard before, but which was all new to John. The children were all gathered together with all their shoes, which had been removed to be packed into the carriage, when they headed for home. John was sorry to see them go, for it had been a wonderful day. Aunt Catherine promised she would return with the children before he left to go home.

The rest of the day was quiet and peaceful and James put on water for tea, which he and Gram took out to the bench overlooking the Gravois River, one of Gram's favorite places to find contentment.

After the evening was over and they had a good night's sleep, Gram and John did the morning chores, had breakfast and retired to the little arbor which was always so lovely in the morning. As they sat to continue the story of grandfather, a shower of eglantine blossoms fell upon their heads and perfumed the air around them.

Gram continued her story:

At a pre-appointed time James returned to the Ambassador's residence to retrieve his map. He learned the Ambassador had already sent a communication and attached a copy of his map to the foreign minister Floridablanca in Spain. After picking up his map, he returned to his brother's home on Staten Island. James remained in New York to the end of June.

In the next few days James made arrangements to travel with one of the Dutch trading vessels on its way to Nova Scotia where he would change ships. In Nova Scotia he found a fast sloop on its way to the Orkneys, just off the tip of northern Scotland, with a load of trade goods. The months of July and August were the most favorable to travel by ship, because the weather was usually mild. He knew his parents would be overjoyed to see him again. John and Isabel had planned to go on the trip with him, but they were expecting a child and Isabel could not travel.

All had gone quite well with the trip, not enough sea turbulence to even mention, until they reached the waters off the coasts of England. A British *Man of War* bore down upon them and they were asked to bring about to be boarded. The ship was brought to and boarded by officials from the British Military Ship. All passengers on board were brought up on deck and questioned as to their nationality and loyalty. It was a very tense moment and many of the passengers were noticeably frightened, some of the women and children were crying, for they feared their young sons or husbands would be taken for the English military. James, when questioned, stated he was an employee of Robert Grant and the Northwest Company in the fur business of Canada. Being a Scotsman, they didn't question him further. Had the officials known he had been in America, he would surely have been taken aboard their vessel for further questioning and possible imprisonment.

Without further incident, they neared the coast line off the Orkney Islands. He looked out over the water to see the "Old Man of Hoy" stone welcome him home. James found a fishing boat on its way across Pentland Firth to Scrabster on the coast in far northern Scotland.

The captain said, "around this time of day, they play the pipes at Strathy Point, would you be wantin' to hear them again?"

James was delighted. Music from the pipes played on the moors and promontories overlooking the waters were particularly haunting and beautiful. He was anxious to get home, but this was a treat to be enjoyed.

It was a very short time after the point came into view that James could hear the bagpipes. The player stood tall and erect on the point, outside the old castle ruins, with his tartan flapping in the wind and the music flowing over the waters in a beautiful and haunting melody. Was the music reaching out to the ones that had left or welcoming home those who were returning? James had not anticipated the impact hearing the music would have upon him, and he let the tears flow unchecked down his cheeks.

For the conversation and news of America, the captain had wanted to take James around by Strathy Point and then to Melvich Bay near Portskerra, where he would drop him off. He could then make his way home to Scrabster.

Upon his departure, the captain looked at James and said, "Hearing the pipes again does something to a man's heart, doesn't it?"

"That it does" James replied.

James hired a horse at a local livery to begin his trek down the Strath Halladale to Loch Arichlinie. The distance was just over twenty miles, but being late in the day, he could make an overnight visit at the longhouse of the Mackays of Bighouse. James sister, Kitty, being married to their son George, was living there and he knew he would be most welcome.

A new keg of ale was broken open to celebrate his return, as all wanted to know the events transpiring in the new world, the immigration destination of so many Scots. The smell of the peat fire brought rushing memories of James childhood back to mind. The food and ale were the best he had tasted in many years. Tales of adventure and loud bursts of laughter rang far into the night before the company of relatives sought their beds.

Rising early the following morning, James planned a two hour ride to get home in time for a breakfast of oatie cakes cooked by his mother. At his father's longhouse all had changed; all his brothers and sisters had become adults and sought their own lives. But still, nothing seemed to have changed. He had come home.

James' mother was just crossing the short walk from house to barn when she spied him coming around the corner. She dropped the empty buckets she was carrying to milk the cows. She let out a scream that brought forth all the family from inside the croft, as well as Da from the sheep pens. She moaned and cried as tears dripped from her face, and she held out her arms to welcome him home.

It was some time before his mother, Elizabeth left off her joyful weeping and was able to stand back and give him the inspection that showed her son to be a man and not the young boy who had left so very long ago. George, James father immediately instructed his grandson, Angus, Jean's oldest son to find a nice lamb and dress it to roast for a home-coming celebration. He was also instructed to carefully remove the stomach so *Haggis* could be made of the leftovers.

James, on his second night home, spent most of the night by the hearthstone, smelling the peat fire and talking with his father and mother. James' plans were to stay through the winter months and leave in the spring. He never liked sea travel during the *terrible gale* months of the year. He did not suffer from *mal de mer* but he was a cautious man by nature. He laid his plans with the best possible advantages to himself whenever possible.

James quickly fell into the mode of the farmer, helping to bring in the corn and oat crops, shearing sheep and bringing in the cattle to be sent to market. Farm chores did not wait upon visitors for any reason. Fall in Scotland was a time of preparation for the long cold winter months ahead. The nights were spent around the peat fire smoking their pipes while his mother spun and wove the wool into new tartans. The ban on the wearing of them had been lifted just a few years past. They laughed amongst themselves as they had never really given them up anyway. If nothing else it had irritated the English. They joked that it wouldn't surprise them if the King found himself dressed in one someday in the future. The Scots were stubborn people. If they couldn't win on the battlefield, well then, time and persistence would get them their way. It had always been thus.

During the winter months the Mackays stayed near their hearth. James was dressed the part of a relative come to lend a helping hand. Only the closest friends and relatives knew he was home. For almost twenty years now there had been a steady stream of the Highlanders departing for foreign places. The difference now than in centuries past they were taking their families. Some of the families were going to the Americas: Virginia, Georgia, the Carolinas and Canada. Others were going further to Australia, New Zealand, Africa and any other country that would welcome them. The friends and relatives talked of all the conditions which were being forced upon them in Scotland. They told James about the increase in rents and about how hard it was to raise enough cattle and sheep to pay the prices. They told him some of the Clan Chiefs were spending all their time in London and some even selling their kinsmen into servitude. James encouraged his parent's friends to send their children to places where they could own land and build their future. Skilled men and women were needed in the colonies; there was a good future to be found. The educated Scots had a distinct advantage over many who could not read or write. Many people of the new country had to sign their names with their mark. Such people were very naïve to believe they wouldn't be cheated when even the educated had to always be wary in their business dealings.

Living with James' parents were two of his sister Jean's children. She had died five years before leaving a houseful of orphans. Angus and Margaret had come to live with their grandparents and help on the farm. The death of William in Virginia was not discussed. It was no use reviving the fermenting anger he still felt over such an unnecessary death.

The winter months passed and before the heather could come to bloom again, James departed and was on a ship on its way to Liverpool, England. While in the port he chanced to meet a

Frenchman, Pierre Fouchet on his way to New Orleans. James had not thought to head for the Spanish territory just yet but, why not? He found the company of Pierre to be entertaining and took passage to New Orleans instead of Canada. Pierre was looking for adventure and he certainly had chanced to find it with his deepening friendship with James Mackay.

The crossing was a terrible one. The spring gales had caused high swales upon the ocean. The rocking of the ship caused all the women and children aboard to become very ill from the constant motion. The crying of the children and the smell of their illnesses kept James and Pierre topside, taking in the fresh salty air during most of the trip.

Upon arriving in Point Chalmette, a few miles below New Orleans, James wrote to his brother telling him to send any letters and mail to the post in Cahokia for he was continuing his plans to open a trading post there, provided he was granted a trading license. When he heard from Ambassador Gardoqui and received a license to trade in the Spanish territory, he would move his operation to the west side of the Mississippi River.

James and Pierre visited the trading establishments on the river and purchased all the necessary items they would need for their trip up the Mississippi River on their way to Cahokia. They purchased a pirogue to carry them and their supplies. A small ship containing a party of pioneers, heading up the Mississippi, was getting ready to leave from the area. James and Pierre asked if they could join up with the group. The group consisted of three families: The Muellers, a family of German immigrants, the Grays a Mississippi family of five boys and the LeRoches, a couple from France who were joining their children, already settled in the Spanish Territory. James was sure they would feel at home because most of the territory was inhabited by French speaking people.

The group spent several weeks in extremely hot and humid weather. James and Pierre often set their pirogue into the water and made side trips up the many rivers to hunt. The camps at night were jolly occasions if one could beat off the mosquitoes. They would build a center fire with smaller smoke fires around the edge of their camp to help keep the mosquitoes away. A hunting party would be sent out to bag the night's supper. Fresh meat was preferred over their stores of dried food. When supper was over, James brought out his violin to play or fiddle a few songs. There were women in the group who not only prepared the food but provided some lively camp fire dancing. The Mueller family did not participate in the dancing as they were *Black Dutch* and didn't believe in such behavior. There were three girls and two boys in the family. The girls were of an age to be married, but when James and Pierre tried to include them in conservation, their father would not permit them to talk to the young men. The boys were polite enough, but the family did not encourage friendship. James thought their black voluminous clothing must be extremely uncomfortable in the heat and humidity of the area.

The Mississippi family was descendants from several generations who had neglected any form of proper education while living in the backwoods. The boys were excellent shots with their long rifles, but could not read or write. The family reminded James of the Indians; the men hunted, talked and ate while their mother did all the work of cooking and setting up the camp.

When the ship arrived in St. Louis, James and Pierre parted company with the pioneers to continue their trip to Cahokia which was across the river from San Luis, to the east, in the Illinois territory belonging to the United States.

Crossing the Mississippi, in their pirogue, the young explorers set up camp on the banks of the river. They spent several days visiting with residents of the town, checking out the fur trade, gathering information on Indians of the area and in general finding out all they could about the place and its prospects. Cahokia was the busiest place of the area and had been a place where people lived for many centuries. James let it be known he was looking for a site to set up a fur trading post and commercial house. He was

told there was stiff competition from the Chouteau brothers, Auguste and Pierre across the river in "San Luis."

During the following weeks. James and Pierre went on many forays up and down the area's rivers and into the uninhabited lands along the waterways. Pierre was still building up strength for their longer journey up the Ohio River. There were numerous small rivers flowing into the Mississippi as well as the big muddy Missouri that emptied into it from the west above San Luis and across from Cahokia.

On one of these forays they banked, tied up their pirogue and climbed to the top of a small bluff overlooking the river. It was here they chanced to find the remains of a very old furnace. Shifting through the old ash and debris around the tumbling rocks Pierre found pieces of molten copper. *"Cuivre"* he said to James, "Some one many years ago smelted Cuivre here." James pointed to the extremely beautiful and clean river and answered. *"Cuivre,* the river of brass, thus do I christen thy rippling tides."

It was James' habit to name places discovered in a descriptive way. He made notations of the new *Cuivre River* in his journal and on his map.

James decided this was the place where Pierre would trap for his fur hat. He had explained the tradition of making a hat from your first trapped animal. A hat marked a man and made him recognizable like nothing else. James still wore his red fox hat, which now contained two of the tail feathers of the bald headed eagle, a few dangles of trading beads and pieces of silver. Hidden in the fox's ear and held in place with pine rosin, was a nugget of gold from the Yellowstone River; something no one ever saw. For a person who could read the signs, the hat told the story of a man of the wilderness, his knowledge of the fur trade and the Indians. The hat spoke of his years in the wilderness and where he had been. If he had taken an arrow through his person, the arrow would have gone on the hat too. Pierre would have to earn his own decorations.

Pierre learned to set out traps and make his shirt and leggings from a deer he killed himself. After a couple of days when the traps had not yielded a suitable specimen for a hat, Pierre lost patience and shot a raccoon. Pierre didn't know, but that impatience along with his unskillfully made clothes would mark him as an inexperienced woodsman. The coon was fat and already taking on his winter coat. From the skin, James showed him how to make himself a hat. The hat completed his woodsman uniform of fringed deerskin shirt, britches and moccasins, an American long rifle, a very sharp hatchet, skinning knife, flints, and powder and balls for the rifle. Except for the newness of the clothing and articles and his own unique style, he was dressed like James. The exception, James' clothes showed the signs of a skilled woodsman, a man of experience and the tailoring showed he had made many skin suits to cloth himself. James also still carried his *dirk*.

The young men had roamed the area for the past month and the heavy beginning of the coon's winter fur told James it was time to continue with their business. Winter would be early and cold.

James, with Pierre, headed down the Mississippi toward New Orleans but took a turn onto the Ohio River and headed east to see his MacDonald cousins in Petersburg, Virginia and conduct some business in Cincinnati.

The fall weather was warm during the day with enough *nip* in the evening air that their nightly camp fires were welcome and cozy. Every night, James made entries in his journal and consulted his maps. Pierre was forever fascinated with all they saw; he had been raised in Paris, and this country was vast, beautiful and new to him. The nights were passed in easy companionship. Traveling the Ohio was a far different journey from the wild and freezing waters and rough terrain of Canada.

James wanted to stop in Cincinnati and call upon John Robertson, a fur broker Thomas Hutchins had told him about. He and Pierre tied up their pirogue and found a room in a nearby tavern. They needed to clean themselves up after spending weeks of travel on the river.

James and Pierre spent a couple of days checking out the town and listening to local gossip at the taverns. Mr. Robertson was easy to locate. Early on the third day in town James presented himself to Mr. Robertson as a friend of Thomas Hutchins. Mr. Robertson said he had been expecting him, as he had received a letter from Thomas.

While in town and in the company of Mr. Robertson, James and Pierre had the opportunity to meet with several men of the town who were acquaintances of Mr. Robertson.

James and Mr. Robertson came to an agreement to join into a partnership to buy furs and sell trade goods. James was to set up a trading store in Cahokia. The business would be based on the trade of furs for necessities the pioneers needed when heading into the Spanish Territories. They could buy their goods with furs. Many of the pioneers were coming from Virginia and Kentucky and most of them were experienced woodsmen. Actual money was hard to come by and furs were often used as currency. If the word went out that a pioneer or traveler could purchase the needed equipment before crossing into the Spanish Territories with furs, then they could get a ready supply from all across the country. It would be a different operation than the one that was being practiced by the fur companies. This manner of business would give them access to home-trappers, who over the winter months could gather a large number of furs without the expense of outfitting trappers to go into the wilds just for the occupation of trapping.

Mr. Robertson would ship the goods from Cincinnati and James would set up a trading post to receive them and in turn ship the furs back to Mr. Robertson in Cincinnati to be disbursed to buyers.

As more people moved into the areas, it became more difficult for individuals to become involved in the fur trade, unless they were willing to expend large sums of money to outfit crews to spend the winters in the far outer fringes of society. In the business

James and Mr. Robertson had agreed upon, the possibilities of buying a few furs at a time were endless.

James and Pierre took their leave of Cincinnati, and since the winter months were coming along earlier than usual, a trip to visit his cousins had to be put off until another time. The young men started back down the Ohio River for Cahokia. Following the pair was a large keelboat of goods to be traded and the beginning of James' new enterprise.

The flow of the river brought them back to Cahokia in less than half the time it had taken to row up the river. It would take the keelboat a week or two longer. In that time James could, with the help of local men, put up a building to house the goods upon their arrival.

James and Pierre, along with some hired local help, built a store of squared logs, stuck upright into the ground and mudded in between the cracks. This was a French method of building as opposed to the English way of stacking logs one on top of the other. A high pitched roof of shingles was laid over the building. The roof extended several feet from the building supported by log columns which rested upon a split board porch. The room of commerce was a large room extending the length of the building. A table was set up at one end for counting the furs and completing the trades. One end of the room contained a fireplace and a few assorted chairs and benches where people could warm themselves, take a cup of coffee or sit around and gossip during the cold of the winter. A section, separated by a cloth curtain behind James' desk of commerce, was to be used for his living quarters. The area contained two home constructed beds, strung with ropes and covered with mattresses of moss. There were furs to soften the beds and the new blue and green plaid, from his mother, to cover him at night. He had a small table, candles and an oil lamp for light when he wrote in his journals. The floors were of rough split boards that he and Pierre would smooth during the winter months. A small shed was built behind the house to be used for cooking.

The completion of the building took less than a month. It was a most satisfactory undertaking.

Pierre stayed the winter and shared the sleeping quarters with James before he departed for France in the spring of 1791. He had, as the French would say, made the "grand tour" of America, which was a fashion of the time for young gentlemen of means.

The word spread that there was a trading house in Cahokia on the Mississippi that would trade goods for furs and the spring brought a steady stream of pioneers into the Spanish Territories, many needing supplies and bringing furs to trade for them.

CHAPTER TWENTY-ONE

Cahokia Trading Post

WHEN JOHN RETURNED from a short walk along the river, which he enjoyed each evening, he suggested that perhaps Gram should seek her bed. There had been another day of story telling and she was always so excited when reliving the past. Gram insisted on continuing her story even though the evening had gotten late. John could see the shine of stars through an open window and a small breeze blew in from the river. He felt quite sleepy but Gram seemed to sleep only a few hours each night. Sometimes she took a small nap in the afternoon after dinner. Gram consented and they snuffed out the oil lamps and banked the fire in the hearth to prepare for the night's sleep. The beans they had picked earlier in the day from the garden would keep until tomorrow.

The following morning, Gram said she needed to go into town and ordered the carriage to be brought around. She had seen an advertisement in the newspaper of a new shipment of things she needed. Each summer she made up batches of Ague tonic which she used to dose the family at the first signs of chills or fever. She said it was grandfather's recipe used in the wilderness. The recipe consisted of two ounces of Peruvian bark, one ounce wild cherry tree bark, one dram of cinnamon, one teaspoon of capsicum, one ounce of flowers of sulphur and two quarts of port wine. All the ingredients were pulverized and added to the wine. It was allowed to set for a week before it was used. The tonic was to be taken, in a small glass, two or three times per day until the fever had broken or until the entire tonic was used. The cinnamon, John thought

must have been to hide the terrible taste of the Peruvian bark, which was quite bitter. There were also a number of other items that had been advertised. Gram needed turmeric for yellow dye and cochineal for scarlet dye. Sometimes while she told her stories she worked at her spinning wheel, making cotton thread that she used for knitting bed covers. She was planning a particularly colorful bed cover of yellows, browns and red. For the brown color, she used the green hulls from the nuts of the black walnut tree.

When they reached the city of St. Louis there were a number of other items Gram purchased in addition to the things she needed for her threads and tonics. She purchased the herbs of jalap, tamarinds, bark of camphor, ground red wood and some Venice turpentine and bees wax to use in her ointments. It was a great outing and always exciting for John to go into the city. The stores carried a most amazing amount of goods from every part of the world.

Returning home, Gram spent the rest of the day making up her tonics and ointments. Dying cotton to use in the bed cover she was making would wait until another day. Gram had put on a vegetable soup to simmer by the fire before leaving that morning, which she and John had for their evening supper. Relaxing with a cup of tea after a long and productive day, Gram continued her story.

The spring of 1792 brought in more furs than James had thought possible. There were muskrats and mink, beaver, otter, raccoon, grey squirrels, buffalo skins, deer skins; all of which were traded for the goods James had brought from Cincinnati. He took in fewer beaver than he had hoped, for they were getting scarce near the long established settlements. He stocked calicos and linen, gun powder, lead balls for pistol and rifle, boxes of beads, shawls, and hanks of worsted wool and large *carrotes* of tobacco. He also stocked flour, sugar, rice, oats, salt, peppers, and a large variety of herbs and other items pioneers might need to take on their journey.

One of the most popular items James had to sell was his Ague tonic. It was made without the use of Quinine which was often hard to secure. His tonic was made with Peruvian bark, wild cherry bark, cinnamon, capsicum, sulphur and added two quarts of port wine. He warned people of the necessity to treat the ague at the first signs of fever and chills and dispensed the recipe for his Ague Tonic or sold it to them in bottles.

When James returned from his trip to Cincinnati, he discovered that the Germans who had come up the river from New Orleans with him and Pierre, had come back to live in Cahokia. After they arrived in San Luis, they had been refused residence because they would not take the oaths to become members of the Church of Rome, which was a requirement to live in the Spanish Territories. Often referred to as *Black Dutch*, people of the *Reformed Churches* were as strict in their devotion to the teachings of Calvin and Luther as the Catholic to directions from Rome.

Mr. Mueller was a blacksmith, and immediately applied for property next to James' trading house. He said he would build a house and smith shop and also a flat boat to ferry people across to the Spanish territory. He did not seem perturbed about his change in direction. He was a hardworking and industrious man.

On a daily basis, pioneers were trying to get across the river into the Spanish territories, which had hampered James' forays into the country. James hired the oldest of the German boys, Johan to tend to his trading house while he continued his exploration in the country. He needed to acquaint himself with the rivers and land of the area and to get acquainted with the local Indians and other people settled there. He also told them they could trade furs for goods at his trading house. It made for a good trade relationship for the furs they trapped during the winter months. He told them some of the things he carried, which could be traded for their furs. He explored the east and west sides of the Mississippi as well as the rivers in the Spanish territories.

Several Osage Indians had come into the trading house with their furs and James had become acquainted with an Indian brave he called *Mis-cum*. Mis-cum was a Cree word meaning "to find" as James had learned when in Canada. Because Mis-cum's friends had said he liked being out in the canoe and in the woods, where he brought back all manner of things, the name seemed to suit him. He also liked hunting, fighting and fishing the same as the other young braves. His ability to find things, was what interested James the most. He took Mis-cum on as a companion in his travels around the rivers of the area, all of which Mis-cum knew very well.

Their first trip was up the Mississippi to the Cuivre River, which James wanted to visit again. It was "one of the most beautiful areas he had ever seen." The water was clear, running over a rocky bottom, with the sun filtering through the trees. The river was peaceful and quiet and altogether lovely. He thought it would be a good place to build a plantation. The woods were abundant with wildlife and there were a number of Osage Indian Villages scattered through the area.

James found the Osage to be industrious like the Mandans he had met far up the Missouri River. They had gardens where they grew pumpkins, squash, beans and corn. He always liked to take along some seeds for the squaws to plant. Most of the Indians didn't know about watermelons but were happy to get the seeds. The men were hunters and kept good supplies of buffalo and deer meat. The woods around the villages were teeming with small animals, such as rabbit, squirrel, possums and raccoons. They also gathered a number of plants and roots to supplement their diets.

The Indians paid in furs for the beads James brought, which they used to decorate armbands, leggings and moccasins. The men had their heads shaved with a scalp lock extending from the forehead to the top of the neck in back. The women wore deerskin dresses with belts decorated with beads. Some of the women had numerous tattoos on their bodies and wore earrings, bracelets and necklaces made of fresh water mussels that were found in the area's waters. They also had strings of multi-shaped pearls hanging from their necks and ears. The mussel sometimes yielded up a large pearl, some a beautiful grey in color. James told them he would take mussels and pearls as well as furs in trade for merchandise at his trading house. The mussel shells were excellent for making buttons. The pearls would be well received by people in Cincinnati and New York.

Houses of the Osage might be described as similar to the croft houses in Scotland. They were rectangular in shape like a croft and the saplings which held up the roof were curved over and covered with skins as opposed to the heather used in Scotland. But all in all, they had a similar look, except that a Scottish croft had walls of rock which extended from the ground to about four feet high before the bog fir was curved to make the heather covered roof.

Mis-cum and James were teaching each other their language, and James felt he had made a good friend. He made a list of items he thought the Indians needed and would make some gifts to them. He found it was the best way to begin a friendship as well as establish a trading partnership.

James and Mis-cum stayed in the woods for a month, following rivers and making a wide circle around San Luis, until they reached the Mississippi. They then made their return up the river back to Cahokia.

Upon his return, James found that his trading house had been well tended by Johan. Mr. Mueller and his family had made a lot of progress getting the smith shop built and working. By the time winter set in, they would have their land cleared and their house completed. Mr. Mueller was already doing a brisk business in his smith shop, complete or not. He was working, in spare moments, to build the flatboat. James knew he was lucky to have such a fine neighbor. He still did not talk with the young women of the family.

It was now late summer of 1792, and time for James to be receiving a boat load of supplies from Mr. Robertson in exchange for the furs he had sent before he left on his journey with Mis-cum. He was gaining a reputation for fair trade and was settled into his store with some comfort. He made many forays around the area and went into San Luis on numerous occasions. He listened to all the gossip. He especially listened to news of what was going on in the territory. He had heard of the new Governor, Baron de Carondelet and his Lt. Governor Zenon Trudeau. There was a lot of talk about a trip of exploration, headed by a man named D'Eglise. His expedition was going up the Missouri River with the intention of reaching the Mandan village. He met the Choteau family, and contrary to what he had been told, they didn't seem to care at all that he was running a store that was something of a competition. They did such large volumes of trade, perhaps they didn't notice the small amounts of furs he took since they came from the east side of the Mississippi.

James did whatever he could to make himself known in the area. He attended the meetings at the community house and discussed the business of the day with anyone that was in attendance.

In the spring of the following year, 1793, James had a chance to meet with Zenon Trudeau who seemed very surprised when he found James to be a man of education who did not come to his office dressed in dirty buckskins. They found many common topics of interest. Mr. Trudeau was favorably impressed and talked to him about a future trip on one of the expeditions. James and Zenon talked extensively about his fur trade days in Canada and the explorations he had made in that country. Zenon asked James to move to the Spanish Territory as he would have to be a citizen for at least a year before he could receive permission to head an expedition up the Missouri. It would also mean he would have to take an oath to become Catholic. James recalled to mind his trip to Rosslyn Chapel in Scotland and the oaths he and John had made and the wonderful reverence they both had felt. He knew it did not make one *shilling* of difference what he proclaimed to be as long as, in his heart, he kept his communication with God. He thought of the Order of the Knights Templar and the holy mission they had hidden for so many centuries. No, it didn't matter at all what his religion was called; he was still his Father's servant.

In July of 1793, James moved into San Luis leaving the Mueller family to tend to his store until such time as he could make the necessary arrangements with Mr. Robinson to dissolve the partnership, if he were allowed to head an expedition of discovery up the Missouri River, he would be gone several years. It was always the same, a position was promised but the politics of the day were slow in happening.

In June of 1794, before James could be in the Spanish Territory for a full year, another expedition left St. Louis led by schoolmaster, Jean Baptiste Truteau. He was to join the earlier expedition headed by D'Eglise who was still somewhere up the Missouri River.

The trading store was being run by the Mueller family who were honest, thrifty and fair to the customers. James discussed the tonics and ointments with Mrs. Mueller and found her to be very knowledgeable in the use of herbs. She had an ointment of her own that she made and added to their supplies. It was an ointment made with pine rosin, bees wax, lard, honey and Spirits of Turpentine. It was used for bruises, cuts, burns, scalds or any kind of putrid flesh. It was used on animals as well as humans and was gentle enough to be used on a baby. The ointment was especially helpful in the care of horses that were always finding someway to harm themselves. Pioneers coming through Cahokia were anxious to buy Mrs. Mueller's topical ointment as well as the Ague tonic made by James for shaking sickness. There was a fear in the women that they would be in the wilderness without the knowledge to treat their families.

In July, James left for New York to see his brother and take care of business in that city. He also took a trip to Cincinnati to make arrangements with Mr. Robertson for the Mullers to take

over the store as he had received confirmation that a third trip would be made the following year up the Missouri River, and he was to lead it. It would be a far larger group that he was to take than had previously been attempted.

After James returned from New York, a letter from Zenon Trudeau arrived at his door one morning in October. He stated he had a houseguest, Antoine Soulard, a young surveyor that had a bad case of the Ague and Zenon knew of James' tonic and wanted him to bring some to his home and show his wife Julia how to administer the dosage. He said he had become quite fond of Antoine and also wanted James to make his acquaintance as he thought they would have a lot in common. Zenon and James had become fast friends, and James was happy to grant the request. He gathered up several bottles of the tonic to take to the little fort in St. Genevieve. Antoine was a couple of years younger than James. Zenon Trudeau was about twenty years older and liked the company of the two young men. He became advisor and mentor to both of them. James and Antoine were many miles from their birth places without family. The three of them fell into a natural and easy friendship. James' excellent command of the French language erased any problems of communication.

James' Ague tonic for shaking sickness was a popular item in the area and its effectiveness became well known. Chills and fever were common ailments along the shores of the river. He didn't know what caused the Ague, but it seemed to him it was much more prevalent in low lying wet areas than in the dryer climates. He had not seen any cases of ague in the northwestern areas. Just after Christmas, William Arundel, a fellow merchant in Cahokia, came into the trade store and asked James for some of the ague tonic, as he had taken in a young Welshman who had been very ill. During their conversation James mentioned he would be leaving for an Expedition up the Missouri the next summer. As it was to turn out William Arundel's guest was a young Welshman named John Evans. John had been financed by some Welsh businessmen in London, to come to America and seek out the *White Indians* who legend told were descendants of the Welsh. James gave the tonic to William and asked him to convey to Mr. Evans that he would enjoy getting acquainted with him at a more opportune time.

CHAPTER TWENTY-TWO

Missouri River Expedition

A LOUD CRASH coming from the direction of the kitchen brought John out of bed and running to the source just as Gram said a very loud, "Drat!" The strongest word she used in her "frustration vocabulary." It was amazing that she was up preparing breakfast after the long hours she had kept the day before.

"Johnny, I dropped the pan, I meant to surprise you with your grandfather's favorite current scones and raspberry preserves this morning. There is fresh cream and honey just squeezed from the comb, but put your pants on before you come into breakfast."

Red to his hairline, John immediately returned to his bedroom to get properly dressed, washed and hair combed, before he presented himself for breakfast.

There was a light shower of rain this morning, keeping them inside. The windows across the front of the house were open letting in the rain cooled air. The roof over the porch kept the wet from coming into the house.

After a delicious breakfast of scones, preserves and honey and coffee from fresh ground beans that filled the room with a delicious aroma, Gram and John retired to the rocking chairs before the hearth. She picked up a bowl of green beans and started her story of grandfather, all the while shelling speckled beans into a bowl. John set up the churn with fresh cream and began to work the dash in the up and down motion that turned cream into butter.

Gram continued her story.

It was several weeks before John Evans could regain strength enough to meet with James. He found him to be an honest and sincere young man. A dreamer, who believed the American Continent had been settled by Welshmen sometime in centuries past. If John Evans could recover his strength from the illnesses, he had the intelligence and necessary skills to be a good Lieutenant.

James mentioned Evans to his friend Zenon Trudeau as a possible assistant for the coming trip up the Missouri. Much to his surprise he learned that Trudeau had imprisoned Evans on suspicion of spying. James interceded on Evans behalf and explained that he had often been asked of the White Indians, which he personally didn't believe were the Mandan Tribe as Evans had been lead to believe. He had received a list of Welsh words during the last trip he made to Cincinnati from an acquaintance named John Rhys, a Welshman, who believed the legend of the White Indians as did John Evans. James had accepted the list and told Mr. Rhys that he would certainly see if any of the words sounded Welsh.

In James' talk with Evans, he learned he was a well educated man, and decided to hire him as an assistant. Trudeau relying upon James' good judgment granted permission for Evans to assist James on the upcoming expedition.

James was pleased for he would need someone to help with writing down coordinates when he was making his map. There were many details to attend to while they planned the trip up the Missouri River. James' plans were to begin his journey in the late summer. There were boats to build, supplies to be gathered and men to hire. James had already become acquainted with a number of men seasoned in the fur trade and used to the hardships, which a lengthy trip up the river would require.

With James as the leader of the expedition and John Evans as his Lieutenant, there were thirty-three men for the trip. The purpose of the trip was to establish the northern boundaries of the

Spanish territory, to chart rivers flowing into the Missouri River, build forts, and establish communication with the Indians.

During the summer he had received a visit from the young Blackbird, an Omaha Indian, who had learned from the man D'Eglise that a Jacque Mackay was now residing in the territory. The young Blackbird had come to San Luis to see if it was the same Jacque Mackay whom he had met several years before. He found the man to be the same. James told him of his own expedition, leaving later in the summer, and he hoped that he could spend some time in the village of his father, the great Chief Pajaro Negro or Blackbird. The young Blackbird told James they had met with a man named Jean Baptiste Truteau who had also come up the river. The Chief Blackbird had not communicated well with Truteau. The young Blackbird told James they would be watching for his voyageurs to come up the river, and that the Omaha would make him welcome.

For the trip, there would be three *berchas* and one *pirogue*. The berchas were to be eight and one-half feet wide and fifty feet long and made of planed boards. For added strength on the berchas, metal strapping would be applied to the bow and stern. The boats were to be sealed with melted rosin over the entire surface. At one end there was to be built a shelter for merchandise and sleeping areas for the men. The boats would have a slightly converse bottom but generally flat. There were to be runners laid around the inside of the boats so they could be poled when necessary. They would have one square sail which would be put up whenever a breeze could be caught to help push them up the river. The smith shop of Mr. Mueller undertook the building of the boats. He also undertook the building of the pirogue. The pirogue would be built fourteen feet in length with the beam amidship to be thirty-six inches wide. It would have three bench seats and have the capacity to carry six rowers and a man fore and aft.

One of the berchas would carry all the goods meant for the Poncas, Omahas or Mahas as they were sometimes called. The

Arikaras and the Mandans would receive one boat of goods. One boat would be used to pay the Sioux for permission to proceed up the river unmolested. The pirogue would be used for the convenience of the hunters to get into the smaller streams to seek game.

While Mr. Mueller was building the needed boats, James was busy gathering the supplies for use as well as for trade. Mrs. Mueller was making two barrels of the Ague tonic. She furnished a barrel of tincture of the *herb de la laque* or herbs mixed in liquor which was used for colds and pneumonia. She also furnished two small wooden tubs of ointment consisting of a mixture of *blood root, yellow dock and jalap root*, used for putrid flesh as well as the *old German ointment* she made. These would supplement the other items he would need on the trip for accidents and illnesses. The leaves of the jalap plant could be eaten along with a number of other plants and roots during the spring and summer. The berries of the jalap plant could be used for ink. The jalap is also known as *Poke Weed*. In addition he took pulverized Peruvian bark, flowers of sulphur and turpentine and a large supply of molasses and rum.

James took his new Lieutenant, John Evans into the woods to teach him about plants that could be used for food and those plants to be used for medicine. It was knowledge a man must have, if he hoped to survive. James had some concern that the illness John had recently, was the illness that affected those people who lived in wet and swampy places. He knew it could come again when least expected. He had plenty of the Ague tonic which should take care of the illness problem should it occur again.

James bought knives, hatchets, hammers, guns, awls, musket balls, and gun flints as part of the trade goods. He took carrotes of tobacco for the men, blankets for warmth and trade and hooks and string for fishing. Mr. Trudeau had sent flags and medals as gifts for the chiefs. These items were cherished by the Indians and were jealous if they did not receive as great a flag or medal as had another chief. He took beads and cooking kettles for the women. He took yellow ochre, vermillion and Prussian blue

that the Indians could use when decorating themselves. The Indians were very vain when decorating themselves with colors and fancy beaded animal skins.

Food supplies, taken for the trip, included barrels of salt, pork bellies, flour, ground corn, oats, barrels of hominy and enough rum for the men to have two or three allotments per day as well as some for the Indians. James had the experience to use the rum sparingly with the men as well as the Indians.

An advertisement was placed in the San Luis newspaper seeking men to take an extended expedition trip up the Missouri River. The trip was planned for six years, only men without family obligations need apply.

James had hired John Evans and the next man to apply was John Lefleur, a Frenchman, whose family were long time residents of the territory and who had many years of experience hunting and trapping on the rivers. He also hired *"Jolly"* or Jollibois, *"Scarlet,"* a very redheaded Irishman and Augus McAy, a Scotsman who was generally known as *"I."* The two oldest Gray boys, Daniel and Thomas from Kentucky who had first come up the Mississippi River with him were hired, primarily for their skill as hunters. He also hired an experienced voyageur named Pierre or Peter Cruzatte, who played the violin and fiddled as well as James. Having spent many years in the wilderness, James knew the importance of music and Pierre was an entertainer. The rest of the voyageurs were men who had experience in the fur trade both from Canada and the Louisiana territory.

The small caravan of boats headed by James Mackay, left St. Charles the last of August, 1795. After months of preparation, the boats had been built, supplies gathered and stored aboard the boats and the men assembled. As was the custom, the boats left at noon. Perhaps because it gave the townspeople time to come down and see the men off, or perhaps it was to give the men time to get over the effects of the celebration the night before. In any case, the trip advanced a short way up the river on the first day.

Only two leagues were passed before reaching the first night camp at *Habitation* where two homes sat upon the river's northern bank. The following day, being the Sabbath, no travel was planned. The Sabbath camp was always a time for rechecking their equipment and supplies. Soon they would be beyond a distance where supplies could be easily obtained.

The hunters of the group, Daniel and Thomas Gray brought in fresh meat, always using their bow and arrows, as they were instructed not to use guns unless it was absolutely necessary for safety. The meat was stripped for drying before the camp fire during the entire day of the Sabbath. No supplies were taken from the stores aboard their berchas.

During the week following, the weather remained pleasant with the heat abating during the first week of September. The greatest problem was the clouds of mosquitoes hanging low over the waters. Smoke from the camp fires helped during the sleeping hours.

James and his expedition reached the River Gasconade to camp for their second Sabbath. The river flowed into the Missouri from the south bank. The river was navigable for a considerable distance by pirogues. The land was good and could support a sizeable settlement. Game, on both sides of the river, was abundant.

A small party of Osage Indians came into camp. With the weather still warm, the tattoos decorating their bodies were in open view. They had great pride in them and welcomed the group to a close inspection. It was from them James learned the distance a pirogue could travel up the river he called *Gasconade*. The river which invited you to take its waters, but when you were on the river you knew its invitation was insincere, for it was not a good river for travel. The Gasconade River had its source near the *River des Argues* or the river of disputes. James always held to his habit of naming rivers after their character or location.

There was plenty game along the riverbanks which kept the supplies of the expedition intact with the exception of salt, of which they had an extensive supply.

James spent much of his time with his Lieutenant, John teaching him to measure distances for the time when the expedition would be split and he would be in charge of some of the men. Often they walked along the banks of the river with James showing Evans the plants that could be eaten from the wild to supplement their diet. He showed him the nettle which grew extensively and could be added to soup or stew much the same as Scotsmen had eaten during his youth in the country of his birth. He showed him the plantain, which grew, he thought, all over the world, and explained the uses of the plant. The leaves crushed and rubbed on mosquito, ant, spider or any poisonous bite would neutralize the poison.

Halfway during the second week of travel, the river of the *Great Osage* was reached. An overnight camp was made, but the following day heavy rains necessitated a day of delay on the trip. The Great Osage flowed from the south. It was a beautiful river that could be navigated for almost 100 leagues by pirogues. The villages of the Great Osage and the Little Osage Nations lie eight leagues up the Great Osage River which had its source near the River des Argues.

The third Sabbath was spent in camp upon the banks of the Mine River which flowed into the Missouri from the south. The river was very broad at the mouth and could be navigated a considerable distance with canoes. There were several lead mines along the river.

Grand River was passed during the following week. The expedition set up their camp on the eve of the last Sabbath of September, on a hill upon the bank of a small river. There were so many snakes the site had to be abandoned, and a late camp was made near two old villages of the Little Osage and the Missourias Indians. Behind the village on the south bank stretched a beautiful plain. The two nations had abandoned the area because of their constant wars. The lands would be good for settlements and hunting.

Cold rains, during the week, slowed the expedition and an early Sabbath camp was made upon the south banks of the beautiful Kansas River. The river was deep and wide and flowed through the Nation of the Kansas Indians. Canoes could navigate its waters for at least sixty leagues at any time of the year. The village of the Kansas Indian Nation was eighty leagues from this river. Hunting remained good and only the rain had caused the men to dip into some of the supplies. An extra ration of rum was passed out to warm the belly and sooth the morale of the men. Music had to be played under the tents and there was no room for the nightly dancing. Sails from the berchas were removed at night to form tents when the rains were this heavy. The canvases were large enough to form tents which could sleep ten men. A smaller tent was shared by James and John Evans. Jolly, the camp cook could be depended on to furnish a hearty meal even in rainy weather. He had brought a large quantity of mix he referred to as *pocket potage*, and with the help of assorted wild greens and maybe a little meat, he could make a tasty stew.

At Nordaway River, one hundred thirty-two and one half leagues from St. Louis, the expedition made camp for their sixth Sabbath. The Nordaway came from the north bank and could easily be navigated by small canoes. There was an abundance of many different kinds of animals. At this river four deer and a bear were killed. The weather was becoming cold.

James calculated that by the next Sabbath the expedition would have a camp near the Platte River. This was to be the site of the first trading house he would build. Being the first part of October, he expected they would experience their first snow fall before reaching the Platte River.

A league before they reached the Platte River, the expedition came upon a path and small river which led to the Oto Nation. A camp was made for the night. The following morning

they struck camp and moved a half league further up the Missouri River at a spot they determined to build a house.

Camp was made on the south bank and a log house was constructed where James left two of the traders who had come with him. Thomas and Daniel Gray and a small hunting party brought back a number of ducks from the river, several deer, two black bears and a number of squirrels and rabbits. The bear and deer meats were dried and the fat of the bears rendered. The arrival of the expedition to this point was a matter of celebration. Jolly made a thick stew of the rabbits and squirrels, oat flour dumplings and some dried plumbs. The cold weather had driven away the pesky problem of the mosquitoes. It was no longer necessary to smear themselves with bear fat and smelly herbs to help repel the insects. Nightly doses of the Ague tonic had kept John Evans well and healthy. John thought the tonic unnecessary as he was now well. James knew the nature of the illness was to return with a vengeance when it was least expected. The tonic was extremely bitter and only the allotment of rum following the dosage rendered it acceptable to the taste.

James traded with the Oto Indians for fresh supplies and called a council with the chief members of the tribe which numbered sixty. He chided them for their bad behavior and evil conduct toward the whites, referring to their treatment of D'Eglise and his expedition. He told them he had been sent by the Spanish Father for the purpose of furnishing them with goods that would make their lives easier. They gave only weak excuses for their past evil ways and told him all the traders they had commerce with had told them lies and cheated them of their furs. James told the Indians the Spanish Father wanted only to see them happy. The company he represented wanted to build a fort in the area where there would always be merchandise for their use without their having to trade with the English who had cheated them.

The Indians seemed much affected by James' speech, which was given to them through an interpreter, and gave their word they would quit their evil ways. They had come to pillage the boats containing goods for the Arikara and Mandan Tribes. However, they did not touch any of the boats and took only those goods James gave them.

James remained with the Otos for eleven days and through honesty and mildness won them over to the side of the Spanish. He promised the following year a boat of supplies would be sent to them if they refrained from doing evil to the traders coming into the area.

From this post James sent letters back to the Missouri Company in St. Louis telling them of his promise and urging them to make a boat of supplies ready for the Oto Indians.

Upon resuming their trip up the Missouri, James met with some of the traders in one of their berchas, who were returning from a previous trip of exploration. Some of the men wanted to go back up the river with James' expedition. Two of the men were Antonio Breda and Pierre Antoine Tabeau. Thus James replaced the men he had left at the trading house at the Oto Nation.

By the time the expedition reached the Platte River, news of the expedition had reached the Mahas and the *young Blackbird*, with whom James had visited in San Luis. They came to meet the expedition with a band of young men. Blackbird the younger, told James he was sent by his father to keep him safe.

It was now November and James, fearing they would not reach the Mandan Village before the next summer, sent John Evans and a party of men on to the village.

James traveled overland with the group for two days in a heavy fall of snow. The boats were slow to come up the river as ice was forming along the edges. On the eleventh of November a point on the Platte was reached where they made their camp. It was a day's journey to the main village of the *Maha* who are also called *Omahas* where *Chief Blackbird* kept his lodge. He came to meet James at the river and set up guards to watch the boats so nothing could be stolen.

The two days following James' arrival at the Maha Village the weather was so cold and bad the men could not unload the berchas. The days were spent inside in council with the great chief, smoking the pipe of peace, and discussing matters of the government and the Missouri Company. James found Chief Blackbird to be a man of great experience, wisdom and intelligence. The Chief was also a despotic ruler with the pride of any European Prince. His reputation had far preceded him and James knew him to be a sly and cunning man. The braves he commanded were seven hundred in number and all staked their lives on his orders.

The story that was told about Chief Pajaro Negro or Blackbird was that he had a number of braves who were dissatisfied and not following his orders. Those dissenters he invited into this lodge to discuss their problems. He fed them all, about 80 of his braves, with the great *Indian delicacy* of dog meat. Into this he placed a crude form of arsenic. After a lengthy speech, he told them because of their disobedience they would all die before morning. They all died during the night. After this he could count on absolute loyalty from his braves. On the first night when dinner had been served and James found it was dog meat, without hesitation he took a bite while looking the old chief in the eye. He wanted the old chief to know that he put his trust in him and wanted to be friends. The old chief, with a twinkle in his eyes, told James he was a man of great courage and he counted him among his true friends. He promised to escort him personally to the village of the Arikaras so no harm would befall him.

James spent several days in the large earth lodge of Blackbird. When Indians from other tribes came in with their complaints, he joined in with the Great Chief, the soul of the village, in meting out justice or awards as were warranted. James presented him with flags and medals which he had brought from the Spanish Government. They preferred the silk flags brought by the English to the ordinary ones sent by the Spanish. Blackbird told James about this and hoped the next time he came he would bring larger medals and silk flags. After the presentations they smoked the calumet of peace. Blackbird, being the most important chief of all the areas they would travel, was given the most important of the medals.

On a large plain on the banks of a small river between the village of the Maha and the Missouri River, was the site James chose to build his fort for the protection of the Maha Nation. The fort was built to have a number of cannon, promised to be sent by the Government of Spain and the Missouri Company. The fort was named Fort Charles for His Majesty, the King of Spain. The location of the fort could have been purposely prepared by nature for the building. The plain was elevated about one thousand feet with a commanding view of the area. The fort, although some distance from the Maha village, was easily accessible with the horses the Great Chief had provided for James' use. By the end of November, the tribe was running short of supplies and a hunting party was sent out with Daniel and Thomas Gray to bring in fresh provisions.

During the month of December the weather was so cold the waters on the river were completely frozen. In the shelter of the fort the winter was passed in some comfort despite the cold weather. The hunting was adequate and their supplies took care of their needs. They had no illnesses that could not be readily treated with the medicines and herbs brought along for that purpose.

Evans and his party had been gone two months when they returned to Fort Charles. They had come upon a hunting party of Sioux and they ran, fearing for their lives. The Sioux had given chase but had finally given up and the party got safely back to Fort Charles on January 6, 1796.

James sent a message to the Sioux Chiefs, asking them to come and meet with him. He had to sooth over the misunderstandings caused during the last expedition as well as the aborted trip of Lieutenant Evans. The chiefs did finally come to Fort Charles, where James won them over with an excessive amount of gifts to get their permission for Evans to start another trip to the Mandan Village.

On the eighth day of June 1796, the expedition made its second attempt to pass through the Sioux Nation. John Evans, with a crew of men and two loaded berchas began their journey up the Missouri to reach the Mandan Village. From there they were to proceed to the Rocky Mountains in search of a route to the Pacific Ocean. James gave Evans explicit instructions as to his behavior with the Indians. He told him to keep very detailed journals and maps, and to make notations on plants and animals and bring back specimen's when he could. He was especially interested in receiving a specimen of the animal, mythical he thought, which was reported to have a horn growing from the middle of his forehead.

When the building of the fort was completed, James, leaving a number of men at Fort Charles, consented to go with a large hunting party of Mahas, across the country, to hunt buffalo and other game. He traced their route on his map, which by horse covered nearly a thousand miles. Leaving in late June they did not return until September in time for the harvesting of the green corn.

Leaving Breda in charge of Fort Charles, and taking John Lefleur, Angus McAy and two of Breda's party, James' left the fort in the pirogue. He began their assent up the Missouri River to join Evans at the Mandan Village. The party reached the mouth of the Cheyenne River on the eighteenth of October. The weather was holding mild and James, who remembered with affection his friendship with White Buffalo and Yellow Bird of the Paducah Indian Tribe, wished to reacquaint himself with them. It was also an opportunity to catch up on the numbers of Indians in the area and make notations on the rivers. He hoped the many epidemics since he had seen them had not destroyed their family.

The Indians knew of the coming of the white men in the pirogue days before their arrival. Two days before James thought they would reach the village, camp was made and the men were enjoying their evening meal of roasted squirrel, when they were surrounded by a party of Paducah Indians. In the forefront was James' long time friend White Buffalo.

A hearty and happy reunion it was, and the friends visited long after the men of the party had gone to sleep. White Buffalo brought in his canoes and accompanied the party to his village, which they reached on the third of November. Yellow Bird had birthed four more children, in addition to the twins, John First and James Footer, who were now seventeen years old. She still wore the First Footer coin that his brother John had given her around her neck. She said, "The lucky coin saved her family from the small pox which had killed so many people of the tribes." She said they had moved their village and had entertained no strangers as soon as they heard of the pox, just as James had told them to do.

James asked of news from the Mandan Village and was told that John Evans had arrived there, and the white traders who had been living in the village for a long time were not happy to see that he had come.

James sent a message to Evans at the Mandan Village by one of the Paducah runners, letting Evans know that he was now at the village of the Paducahs and that he would go across country and meet him at the divide in the mountains. James had clearly instructed Evans in the way to go to get through the mountains to reach the river that flowed down to the Pacific.

James stayed with the Paducahs until the middle of February of the year of 1797. Before he could leave on his trip to the mountain divide, word came from the Mandan Village that Lieutenant Evans had become ill. James immediately made plans to leave the Paducah's village to retrieve Evans; he feared it was the return of the old sickness he had experienced in Cahokia. The only relief, if the tonic was not available, was to drink oneself into a stupor.

Yellow Bird wanted to travel to the Mandan Village and have a reunion with her family, or what was left of them. So many people had died of the pox. James, White Buffalo, Yellow Bird and their twin sons, leaving the smaller children behind, left the village of the Paducahs on horseback. James instructed his men to

return to Fort Charles and he would return with John Evans and his men.

Arriving at the Mandan Village, now called Fort Mackay, the 15th of March, James found that Evans was indeed ill and had been receiving threatening letters from fur traders in Canada, some of whom James knew. He also knew it was only a matter of time before John would be so ill, the traders could take severe advantage of him. He ordered the berchas loaded lightly with just the necessities they would need to reach Fort Charles.

James, in a private conversation with White Buffalo, advised him to move further across the plains for the protection of his tribe and if possible make an alliance with the Apache or Cheyenne. He told him he feared there would be many white men bringing the small pox and the venereal diseases which had spread very rapidly throughout the country where the white men visited.

After only three days at his namesake, Fort Mackay, James smoked the calumet with the chief and the most important members of the tribe. The following morning, James said a fond good-bye to his friends. Some of the men had moved in with the Indian women, against his instructions, and were not anxious to leave.

James made a comfortable bed for Lieutenant Evans on his bercha. It was an area protected from the weather to ease his trip as they made a rapid descent down the Missouri River. Due to the runoff from the melting snow the river was particularly swift and great care had to be taken to keep the boat from colliding with limbs and other debris.

It was the same old illness of chills and fever that had grabbed hold of Evans again. During his long stay with the Mandans, he had used all the Ague tonic James had given him. James immediately began to dose Evans with the tonic and he began to recover, but the illness had such a hold upon him that he was a long time in doing so. By the time they reached Fort Charles, seeing that his Lieutenant would recover given time, James made his preparations to return to San Luis.

John had not found his White Indians and James knew there was no water course that went all the way to the Pacific without a lengthy portage. The trip had not been a complete success but they had learned valuable information about the country and made peace with the Indians. He knew this would be the last long trip of exploration he would make. He had not reached the Pacific; however, he and Evans had made maps and kept journals that would be an invaluable contribution to the next expedition to come this way.

James left part of the men with Lieutenant Evans until he could recover completely from his illness at Fort Charles, and began his trip back to San Luis.

With only half the number of men that had left on the expedition, James reached San Luis on the first day of June 1797. James hoped the Spanish Government would honor their promises of land and he could begin a life with a future.

CHAPTER TWENTY-THREE

Elizabeth Long

GRAM FINISHED SHELLING the beans and John had churned the cream into butter. Both rose from their chairs, Gram to put the beans on to cook over the open hearth and John to press the butter into a wooden mold with a rose on top, which left its print in the butter. John took the butter along with the buttermilk, left from the churning, out to the well house to keep it cool.

Outside the rain had stopped and a wispy colorful rainbow hung over the Gravois River. John stood as if in a trance, gazing upon the rainbow, until Gram touched his arm.

"Rainbows are God's promise; I always feel special to have seen one. Don't you think, Johnny, they're one of God's wonders?"

"I do Gram, every time they come out, just after a rain. I remember you're telling me of the strange colorless rainbow grandfather saw in Canada, and I wish I could see one too."

The heat of the summer quickly dried any water left clinging to the yard's foliage. Gram and John made a lunch of leftover breakfast scones, fried bacon and fresh buttermilk. Without the honey and preserves, the scones were very much like a breakfast biscuit except cut in a triangle shape instead of round.

John picked up Gram's pillows and they retired to the arbor where the rain had washed everything clean, and there was a breeze coming from the river.

Gram continued her story.

"Johnny, I have been remiss in not telling of my own parents' arrival to the Louisiana territory. My papa, John Long, was a sea captain and fought in the American Revolution. He was born in Port Royal, Caroline County, Virginia in 1752. He fought in the battle of Brandywine with the great General LaFayette. After the war, he was captain of a ship named the Liverpool, for about five years. While on a trip to London in 1782, he met my mother, Elizabeth Bennett, who was the daughter of James Oliver Bennett, Rt. Honorable M.P. of Cardigan, Wales and Elizabeth Trenton of Camarthen, Wales. They had a very whirlwind courtship and mama's parents did not want her to marry an American sea captain. It, I am sure, was very scandalous, but mama eloped with papa aboard the ship Dolphin, which was bound for Philadelphia where they were married on June 15, 1782. After I was born the next year on September 2, 1783 in Philadelphia, my parents moved to Port Royal, Virginia. It was the birth place of my brothers, William and John, Jr. and my sister, Nancy. Papa stayed in the shipping business for several more years. We moved to Kentucky where Uncle Lawrence lived with his family but did not care for the place. Papa persuaded Uncle Lawrence to return with him to Port Royal and move to the Spanish Louisiana territory. Papa needed to live near the water where he could keep a ship. The blood of a sea captain was in his veins and without a ready conveyance he felt very lost.

Papa heard the restrictions upon taking the Catholic faith had been lifted, somewhat, in the Louisiana territory, for they were in great need of immigrants and were offering a considerable amount of land to families that would move to the area and build their homes. There was the added benefit of raw goods such as lead, tobacco, cotton and timber growing in the area that could be shipped to countries which needed them. Papa was an asset to any new young country.

Papa and mama packed us and all our belongings aboard our little sloop <u>The Elizabeth</u>. Going with us was Uncle Lawrence Long and his family. His two boys Gabriel and John were great company for my brothers but were a constant tease and nuisance to me. Together we left our homes in Port Royal. We sailed down the Rappahannock River, saying a sad farewell to all the people we knew, the beautiful old homes along the river and everything that was familiar to us. We passed wharfs stacked high with cotton and tobacco ready to ship to places that would pay high prices for the goods. Leaving the Rappahannock we sailed down the Chesapeake Bay and finally out into the Atlantic Ocean. We sailed past the coasts of the states of North and South Carolina, and Georgia. We sailed around the end of Florida, a territory owned by the Spanish and along the way we watched the porpoises play and the little flying fish skim across the water, sometimes flying over the bow of the ship. We continued our trip along the coasts of Alabama and Mississippi until we reached the mouth of the Mississippi River at New Orleans. From New Orleans we continued up the Mississippi.

We arrived in Kaskaskia in the spring, but the Mississippi River was full of ice and we had to wait until the thaw before we could proceed safely up the river to San Luis. There Papa met with Monsieur Zenon Trudeau and received a grant of land near the little settlement of Bonhomme where we built our house.

From the day we arrived in San Luis, there was constant talk about the expeditions that had left to explore the Missouri River. The last expedition to leave was that of your grandfather and his Lieutenant, John Evans. Everyone wanted to know what they would find in the way of new territories and if there would be problems with the Indians they encountered. Was there really a river that flowed all the way across the continent to the Pacific Ocean? There were rumors that it was not the first trip that Monsieur Mackay had made on the river, and in fact had explored areas of Canada and the Rocky Mountains. You can imagine that Papa and Mama as well as I were anxious to meet these adventuresome men. My brothers started making hats from rabbit fur and pretending to be explorers. They had hatchets and guns made of wood. They made bows and arrows like the Indians and their sling-shots were never far from their sides. They were constantly scalping each other in imitation of savage Indian attacks they fantasized were taking place.

When your grandfather returned from his expedition in the spring of 1797, there was naturally a big to-do about his trip and the forts that were built. People wanted to leave immediately and "go up the river."

Monsieur Zenon Trudeau gave a grand party. Mama and Papa were invited. We had been in San Luis for a year and Papa and Monsieur Trudeau had become friends. I, of course, was considered too young to be invited to the party. I was so envious of Papa and Mama for their invitation. Everyone was talking about Monsieur Jacque Mackay, and I was just dying of curiosity to get a look at him and his young Lieutenant John Evans, who I had been told was from Wales. It was mama's place of birth. Mama and Papa were already concerned about the type of man I would find to marry. I overheard them talking about this John Evans as a likely candidate, as he was the right age and well educated. I did not know about that, I did not feel ready for marriage even though some girls my age were already wives.

There were many marriageable men in the area. However, they were unschooled, unwashed, too old, or just plain unsuitable for a gently bred young woman. Of course, there were the young sons of the French and Spanish, but they didn't seem to have a lot of interest in girls from America. I heard Monsieur Mackay was a fine looking man as was Mr. Evans, even though he was often ill. Papa and Mama were very impressed with Monsieur Mackay and I think secretly wished I were a little older, but in that case, I am sure I would have already been married.

There was a nice little group of people who had become Papa and Mama's friends over the past couple of years. There was the Lieutenant Governor of the area, Monsieur Trudeau and his

wife Eulalie Delassise Trudeau who seemed to be the center of the group. Some of their other friends were: Antoine and Julia Cerre' Soulard, Charles Gratiot and his wife Victoire Choteau Gratiot and Charles De Hault Delassus. There were others of course, but Papa and Mama, who both spoke French, had been invited into the circle of the old French families of the territory.

Julia Soulard and I had already become friends and I considered her to be my best friend, even though she was married. She was very little older than my age of 15, and we suited each other well in our friendship. It was my friendship with Julia that eventually brought about my introduction to your grandfather, James Mackay. Julia sent a note to Mama asking that I be allowed to come to their home and spend some time with her, as her husband, Antoine, was going into the country with a survey crew, and would be gone several days. She wrote Mama that she would enjoy my company in his absence.

It was the month of December that I went for my visit, a perfect time for talking before the fire as we quilted or spun thread upon the spinning wheel. I did feel sorry that Antoine and his crew would be spending so much time in the cold weather.

Hearing our carriage, Julia met me at the door. It was a happy reunion for both of us. Sometimes weeks went past before women had a chance to meet together. It could be quite lonely alone at home with only servants and a child to keep her company. Julia had only her small baby, James Gaston for company. Antoine, Julia said, with a sly twinkle in her lovely dark eyes, was in his study with Monsieur Mackay. They had been closeted in that room, behind closed doors, for the better part of the morning. Antoine, who had a map of the Spanish territory, was updating his information with the information Monsieur Mackay had acquired during his explorations from Canada as well as the new information he had gained from his recent expedition up the Missouri River and the rivers that flowed into it.

It was past the hour of dinner and now that I had arrived, Julia decided the men had withheld themselves from her company too long. She sent one of the servants to bring the two from their den of hibernation and take a break for dinner.

My first meeting with James, was quite a shock to my system. I had been prepared for an untidy man dressed in the buckskins of a woodsman. However, before me stood a fine specimen of man not dressed in buckskins but dressed in clothing as fine as any Papa imported from England or France. He didn't look old at all, and I think perhaps, I didn't breathe for several moments. I learned that he was thirty-six years of age, not old at all. I knew immediately, even if he didn't, that he would be my husband, that there would be no other man for me.

I had no wit whatsoever; he must have thought I was a dunce or worse a little girl. Although, I spoke French fairly well, it was a bit of a strain to keep up with the rapid conversation. Antoine was completely excited with James' map and information on the Missouri River and Indians. The Missouri Company, in which they both had a share, had spent considerable amounts of money and the expenses of the expedition had ruined them as a company. However, the prospects of future gains far outweighed the company's loses. Spanish officials were, I think, a little overwhelmed with the size of the country they owned and for which they had far too few people to manage and protect it.

By the time supper had begun, I was much more myself and able to join in the conversation. Julia had teased me unmercifully all during the afternoon when the men had returned to Antoine's office. James too, was spending the night with the Soulards. They departed the following morning for their survey trip. Monsieur Trudeau had appointed Antoine "surveyor general of the Spanish Upper Louisiana," and upon James' return had hired James and John Evans as part of his survey team.

Julia was up very early the next morning supervising the packing of food supplies for the survey crew as well as seeing to breakfast for them to eat before their departure. I was up as well, dressed with hair combed and tied back with a yellow ribbon which went very well with my brown woolen dress, cut to flatter and also to keep me warm on these cold winter days. We had a large breakfast of bacon, eggs, biscuits, hominy grits and several different kinds of preserves, honey and country cheese. We all drank coffee and the men had poured a liberal amount of brandy in theirs. When I looked surprised, Monsieur Mackay told me it would help keep the cold away. They all laughed, when I said, surely they must take extra bottles with them while they worked.

I spent a wonderful week with Julia while the men were gone into the wilds. She taught me some of the finer points of playing chess. We worked on our embroidery as well as weaving, spinning and quilting. We played with the baby every moment he was awake. It was far more enjoyable than playing with dolls. There was an endless amount of different activities that must be done. Each morning Julia directed the servants in what they were to do for the day. Since it was winter time, there was no cotton or tobacco to care for, but there was wood to chop, animals to kill and preserve, as well as cows to be milked and hogs to feed. The chores were never finished, and Julia directed the house help as well as gave the instructions to the overseer who directed the people who worked outside the house in everything they did. I wanted to learn. I had not taken a lot of interest in the workings of our home as Mama did all the directing there. It was while staying with Julia, that I began to change from a young girl into a woman.

In a few years I was determined to be just as skilled as she in the running of a home or plantation.

Soon after the return of the men from their trip, I had to return to my parent's home. I regret to say, it was some time before I had the opportunity to see James again.

James was appointed captain of the militia and the commandant of San Andre` in the community of Bonhomme where we lived, which was just west of San Carlos. It was during this time that he became a regular visitor to our home. There was always some reason to stop by and talk with Papa. However, he paid little attention to me. I am sure he saw me as a little girl, no matter how

I fixed my hair or what clothes I wore. It was quite frustrating to not be able to attract his attention. He was a serious kind of man, but he was quick to pick up his violin at any party. He was very popular with the women. Many women of the day were married long before their sixteenth birthday. At my sixteenth birthday I had not a single prospect for marriage, except for the one I wanted who didn't even see me.

The fort at St. Andre` was well maintained and James had earned a reputation of being fair and keeping order in all his work. He impressed the French and Spanish officials. He petitioned for land which the Spanish had promised as payment for his expedition. He received grants of land amounting to more than thirteen thousand arpens on the Cuivre River. It had hardly any monetary value, but land was the only currency the Spanish had to pay for their employee's services. The grantees still had to spend considerable amounts of money to survey the land and cut any timber from it that could be exchanged for cash. But it was a start, and James felt that his prospects for a future were good and he could now think of acquiring a wife and family.

I had reached my seventeenth birthday before I got any notice from James. I shall always remember that harrowing August day. I was looking my very worst. I had been picking the last of the beans from the garden and was dressed in the most faded and worn dress I owned, my hair was limp and wet from the excessive heat and humidity. I started into the house from the garden, laden with a large basket of beans. I heard a lot of yelling and commotion coming from the nearby river. There were always a number of people about, as the river was a very busy place with people coming and going. One of the young Negro boys, who was *cat-fishing* along the banks of the river, had waded out into the water to bring in the fish he had on his line. In his excitement he had not looked around him and when he stepped into the water, he disturbed a large water-moccasin, the poisonous snake we most often refer to as a *cottonmouth*. It sank its fangs in the child's calf, just above the ankle. James had just tied up his boat when the incident happened. The child was extremely frightened and screaming with pain. Blood was running down his leg and foot and dripping upon the ground. James took out his knife and quickly made two slashes across the bite and began to suck out the poison. He then lifted the child and was bringing him toward the house and at the same time calling out for me to bring the *Sinakle.* I had no idea what he was talking about, but I did know about Snakeweed which grew around the house and in the garden. Immediately, I ran to the garden and pulled off leaves and told the child to begin chewing them and directed the other children to go pull as much as they could find for me. I took the chewed leaves from his mouth and placed them over the wound and asked James to bring the child into the house. I put a kettle of water over the fire and put on a pile of wood to get the fire going good. I then dumped in all the snakeweed the children brought. The other children were sent outside and told to run and get John, the blacksmith while James and I took care of Simon, who was the blacksmith's child. I made a large container of snakeweed tea to feed him a small amount every few minutes and took the cooked leaves and roots to make fresh poultices every ten minutes. The snakeweed is a powerful antitoxin and I thought, thanks to quick treatment, he would survive. John came soon enough and took his son off with a supply of snakeweed and white willow bark. He was instructed to keep poultices on the wound and give the child the tea to drink as often as he could and white willow bark tea if he became feverish.

Papa and Mama had gone into San Luis, the boys and Nancy were off, heaven only knew where, and I was alone at the house. Mama was the real healer in the family and learning the use of herbs was one of the lessons she taught me. Even though it was not proper to be alone with James, I invited him into the house and started some coffee to boil.

"James," I said, calling him Monsieur Mackay seemed much too formal after what we had just been through, "what is Sinakle?"

"I believe it is the same weed you have just taken from the garden. I didn't know the name other than the one I learned from the Indians."

"In Virginia, it is referred to as Virginia Snake Weed or more commonly just snakeweed. It is one of the herbs Mama taught me how to use. It is also good to take the sting out of any kind of insect bites. I believe it is also referred to as Plantain."

When the coffee came to its boil, I removed it from the fire and strained us both a cup. Taking Papa's brandy from the shelf, I poured us both a good shot into the coffee. I thought I needed the brandy as much as James.

At the same time I also became very aware of my old faded dress that was much too small and my hair that was in such disarray. I began to feel very embarrassed and wished he could just finish that coffee and leave.

"Elizabeth, what you did for the child was very grand, *dinna fash yaself* about your attire."

I had heard James' Scottish expressions enough by this time to know he was telling me not to worry myself about the way I looked.

It was at that moment, when our eyes met, that I knew he saw me as a woman.

James stayed until Papa and Mama returned and explained what had happened with Simon and he praised me very highly to Papa for my quick thinking and actions. When he left, he asked Papa if he could call upon me, and thus he began his courtship. Asking Papa if he could call upon me, in those days was almost the same as asking Papa if he could marry me. James had committed himself to me when he accepted my invitation into the house, knowing when he came in, I was alone without a chaperone.

CHAPTER TWENTY-FOUR

The Commandant Takes a Wife

GRAM SAT IN THE ARBOR a moment, with a dreamy look upon her face, recalling loving memories of a time more than a half century past.

It was late in the evening and time for Gram and John to return to the house and prepare a light supper and the continuation of her story.

Gram made corn pones over the open hearth while John returned to the well house to bring in some butter and the fresh buttermilk. The beans, which had been cooking all afternoon, were now ready to eat. Their supper consisted of corn pones dripping with fresh creamed butter, beans and buttermilk. It was a most satisfying evening meal.

Gram took her chair before the now cooled hearth, picked up her knitting and took up her story where she had left off in the arbor.

James came every Sunday for dinner, after our family returned from church. He had long talks with Papa while Mama, Nancy and I prepared the dinner. There were often others there for Sunday dinner as well. My younger brothers, William and John, Jr., were usually around somewhere too.

Mama kept a well stocked chicken yard, and it was William and John's chore to catch a chicken or two, wring their necks and prepare them for Mama to cook. Sometimes we had chicken, pan fried with bacon drippings. Sometimes she placed the chicken in an iron oven that sat atop the wood-coals with coals scooped to lie on top of the oven. The oven had a special lid with a lip that kept the coals in place. Doing this, the chicken could be put on to cook before we left for church and ready when we returned. She also laid the bread to rise, so it would be ready to bake upon our return. There was always something nice Mama made for dessert, such as *bear-claws* fried in bear fat and sprinkled with sugar.

After dinner I was excused, so James and I could walk along the river and have a little time to ourselves. My sister Nancy was not too happy to be left with the kitchen cleanup; however, she had a young romantic heart. We were never entirely alone. My brothers were always somewhere in the vicinity, more often than not being a nuisance. William adored James and considered him to be the hero of the day, which was much to our advantage as he was willing to retrieve anything James might have forgotten to bring along on our walks. When we went riding, William old enough to know we would like to be out of his ear's range, usually rode a little ahead. This was the extent to which I was left alone with my suitor. We talked on every subject and I pestered him with questions about his travels, his home in Scotland and his fur trading days in Canada. I wished that I could have attended the inauguration of President Washington. It must have been the event of the century.

We passed the fall with James coming to our house almost every Sunday. I was allowed to accompany Papa and Mama to social functions in San Luis and San Carlos where we would meet James and other friends. Occasionally at these gatherings, I was asked to play the harp, and James was always asked to play his violin, for he was an accomplished musician and he enjoyed fiddling.

Papa and James discussed properties of the area at great length. Where were the best places to apply for grants and the costs of surveys and the Indians willingness to allow settlers?

James claimed four thousand four hundred and sixty arpents of land on Wild Horse Creek in the District of San Luis where he began to establish a farm with a mill house to serve people in the area. He built a cabin for the people who would live there and work the farm. He put in corn, cotton and tobacco fields. He planted an orchard and a large garden for the care of the workers on the farm. The yard was fenced with split rails to keep out the stock. He also made claims for land on the Cuivre, Sabine and Bonne Femme Rivers. The Spanish governments were without funds to pay for surveys, military services and other things the country needed. They could only pay in land. James received over 13,000 arpents of land on the Cuivre River for his expedition and mapping of the Missouri River to the Mandan Village. It would take a lot of time and expense to survey his grants.

Papa had his claim on the Rivers Dubois and St. John for ten thousand arpens of land. If James and I had not loved each other, it would still have been a good marriage of convenience. Mama never forgot to remind me to be a good wife, and that I had caught the attention of the most sought after and eligible man of the area. It was a blessing that he was also fair to look upon. None of these things did I spend much thought upon. It was my heart that did flips and flutters when he was around, the other meant little to me. Some of the older women, whom he had not asked to marry him or with daughters that they hoped he would marry, had spiteful things to say within my hearing. I tried not to let these things hurt, but they did anyway.

James came on Christmas Eve. We decorated the house with branches of pine and holly and threw pine cones on the fire to scent the air and hear the pop of the resin induced fireworks. Mama was making a cranberry relish over the hearth while we roasted peanuts and sweet potatoes and stayed in out of the cold, except for trips to the privy and to feed and care for the animals. While Papa and James were doing the chores, James asked Papa if he would allow us to marry before my eighteenth birthday.

Papa said, yes, he would welcome James into the family as his son-in-law.

Christmas Eve James stayed overnight with us. He and I were allowed to bundle, now that we were soon to marry. It was rather a quaint custom, one that is much practiced in the east. A man who has spoken for a young lady is allowed to share a bed with her, provided there is a board along the length of the bed to separate them. It is a method used to accustom innocent young ladies to the proximity of a man without fear of loss of virtue. The whispered sweet words between then can only enhance the day of their marriage and the life they will begin together. The board was not so high they could not hold hands, but certainly too high to allow further intimacy, especially with parents or siblings in the same room. It is quite a proper thing, but it did not prevent the pounding of my heart, nor quell the excitement to know how close we would lie together all night.

Finally it was time for all to go to bed. Our bed was separated by hanging a quilt between us and my parents. I put on my toe length flannel night dress and crept into the bed. I had taken the long handled heating pan, filled with hot coals and smoothed it over the sheets to make them warm. If James did not linger in talking with Papa his sheets would be warm too. All the candles were extinguished and the only light was from the wood coals on the hearth. I could see just enough to tell that James also wore a long night shirt.

"Are you scared of me then?" he whispered.

"No, I don't think I am." I answered in the thinnest voice that sounded not at all like me.

"Well, then, maybe you could be putting you hand on top of the board, so I could take it in mine." I could hear the laughter in his voice and it spared me the nervousness that I felt. After all, Papa and Mama were just the other side of the quilt.

There was a comfort knowing he was there, but I was asleep long before he finished telling me about Christmas in

Scotland. For the first time since he left, he said, "he had a family again, and the feeling was very good."

When I awoke Christmas morning, the room was alight with a fresh fire upon the hearth and the busy-ness of Mama around the hearth was homey and familiar. James had already left our bed. In the near future, upon my marriage, I would be doing as she was doing now. I heard the old cock crow outside and hastily rose, washed and dressed to start the day. I made the bed and removed the divider board. I set the table for our breakfast.

"Where is Papa," I asked. I was a little shy to be asking about James, but wondered where he was.

"Doing the chores as usual and this morning he has a nice strong back to help. You wouldn't want a husband who didn't offer a helping hand," she said.

In but a few moments the men returned from the chores. The boys and Nancy were up, wanting to open their presents. I was anxious to open mine too. James brought presents for all of us, if I could judge by the amount of boxes. There were also packages from Papa and Mama.

We had a special breakfast of Maple syrup just received from Vermont, little thin pancakes and lots of crisp bacon. The pancakes, Mama said, were from a recipe that James learned from the French in Canada. James called them "Flatjacks." They were delicious, and William was rolling his around a large scoop of strawberry preserves and soft farm cheese before covering them with syrup. Before breakfast was over, we all tried the pancake rolls with preserves and cheese. James pronounced the rolls to be an improvement over his pancakes. Of course, William would never let us forget "his invention."

Once the table was clear and the dishes put in the tub to soak, we went at the packages with all the excitement of small children.

My gift to James was a warm wool scarf I had knitted myself, and a pair of soft leather gloves lined with rabbit fur. I wanted his hands to stay warm when he did his survey work.

James's gift to me was a wedding veil ordered from Holland months ago by his brother, John, through a Dutch trading company in New York. It came from the city of Bruges, where the women made fine lace in a style called *pin and bobbin.* It was the finest most beautiful piece of material I had ever seen. I could not speak, and tears filled my eyes, it was so fine and lovely. There were also several lengths of the pin and bobbin lace to decorate my wedding dress.

"After you," he said, "then our daughters, in their time, will find the veil useful." It was truly an heirloom to be passed from generation to generation.

Such a comment caused a fair bloom upon my face, but I expected to have a number of children.

From Papa, I received a bolt of white china silk for my wedding dress and soft leather shoes and gloves from Morocco. Mama had bought soft colored muslins, for dresses, to make my trousseau and silk for my underclothes and night dresses. She also purchased a short bolt of blue velvet for a cape. We would be busy sewing before my wedding in February. From James' family, I received a writing set, so that I might write to them and get acquainted, else they would all come and live with us. I did write to James' sister Kitty that very afternoon. Kitty was James' only living sister, just a few years older than me. James' older sister Jean had died some years before.

James gave my brothers, William and John, wooden whistles carved by his brother John in New York. Nancy and Mama received handkerchiefs and collars made in Bruges and trimmed with the same delicate pin and bobbin lace that adorned my wedding veil. Papa bought the same soft Morocco gloves and shoes for all the family.

For Papa, James' present was a new rifle from the shop of William Allen in New York. I think it was a lucky thing for us that

James' brother John lived in New York and had access to all the finer things that were hard to get in our area.

After all the excitement of the gift exchange, James and I bundled up in furs and boots to take a walk. Today, Christmas Day, we would not have a chaperone; it was just the two of us.

There was snow upon the ground but not so deep as to make walking difficult. Each time we spoke puffs of frozen breath escaped in little clouds, and I could feel the warmth of him through his new gloves. When we were far enough from the house and the spying eyes of my siblings, we took off our gloves and he opened his coat so that I could step inside and share his warmth and he mine. The feeling was very nice when I slid my arms around his waist and over his back under his coat. I could feel his muscles big and hard across his back. They moved and hardened wherever I touched. His hands were drawing pictures over my face and I wanted him to kiss me more than anything. Light as a butterfly his lips touched mine, warm and soft and so exciting that I felt faint and fluttery in my stomach. He touched my chin, with a slight pressure pushing it down so my mouth opened and his kiss was no longer soft and warm but divine.

After Christmas, I was not to see James for over a month, as his duties called upon all his time. At the first of February the banns were posted for our marriage upon the door of St. Charles' little Catholic Church. Papa had given James his formal consent, as I was still a minor, only seventeen on my birthday the 2nd of September the year past. Mama and I sewed every day on my trousseau and wedding gown which were almost finished. Nancy, my little sister demanded to be allowed her part in the sewing. She embroidered, with great skill and patience, *love knots* around the hems of all my night dresses and petticoats. We received well-wishing visitors, almost daily, as weddings were the grandest occasions for celebration in the country.

February 24, 1800, my wedding day had finally come.

My wedding dress was made in a style with a scoop neck, trimmed with tiny lace that matched my wedding veil. The skirt was gathered under the bodice and banded with a ribbon of white satin before it fell straight to the floor covering all but the smallest amount of my shoes. The sleeves were puffed to the elbow and then tight to the wrist, there was a small train that attached to each shoulder and fell away to the floor and for several feet behind me. My hair, which fell below my waist, was always a problem. My hair to me was muddy brown, which I detested, but James called it "rich chocolate," either way there was still too much of it. Mama fixed my hair in braids and wrapped them around my head to form a coronet with tiny little curls falling around my face and neck. The hair style was most flattering and grown up. The beautiful lace veil was then attached to the top of my hair and floated down almost to the floor. Mama loaned me her little pearls to wear around my neck. I hoped James would think me the most beautiful bride he had ever seen.

Uncle Lawrence Long, Papa's brother, with my aunt and cousins, came by and picked up my two brothers and sister to take them to the church. I was to come with Papa and Mama. I was so very nervous, I thought I would be sick and ruin my beautiful gown. Mama kept putting her handkerchief soaked in lavender water up to my nose for she was afraid I would faint.

The church was very small, not at all grand, just one room with a little steeple and made of logs, but it looked beautiful to me.

After Mama made a few adjustments to my clothing and hair and was satisfied with my appearance, she went into the church. Papa was to walk with me to the front, else I could not have made it on my own.

As I walked through the door, I could see our good friends and family and many people I did not know. The church was very full with just enough room for Papa and me to walk down the isle.

James stood so tall and handsome with the Parish Priest, Brother Leandre Lusson. He was dressed in his Spanish military uniform. The coat was white with blue cuffs and collar. There was a silver epaulet on his right shoulder and a row of silver lace at his cuffs and more ruffling from his cravat. The turned back tails of his coat were also of blue. He had on blue knee pants and vest, the style still being worn by the Spanish but discarded by most other militaries. He wore white silk stockings and black shoes with silver buckles. His lovely red and gold hair had been powdered and queued in the back as was the military style for a captain. He was the most handsome man I had ever seen.

The Priest asked us many questions, which we answered. James was asked, who he was and from where he came.

He answered, "I am James Mackay and legitimate second son of George Mackay of Arichliney, Judge of the County of Sutherland in Scotland and Elizabeth MacDonald. I am Captain Commandant and domiciled in the Post of St. Andre` of the Missouri."

Brother Lusson asked us, "Do you James Mackay and Isabella Long make this marriage of your own free will?"

We both answered together "yes."

For the first time, I realized I was not only changing my last name from Long to Mackay, but I was no longer Elizabeth but had taken the French and Spanish name of Isabella. It felt very strange, but not enough to make me want to discontinue the marriage. James already called me *"Bella"* when no one else was around.

Brother Lusson asked us, "What religion do you profess?"

James answered, "I profess the religion Catholic Apostolic and Roman."

I answered, "I profess the Religion Protestant."

Brother Lusson asked us, "Are you willing to bring any child or children of this marriage to the Church nearest your dwelling and send them for instruction?"

We both answered, "Yes."

Brother Lusson asked my father, John Long and my mother, Elizabeth Long, "Do you consent to the marriage of your minor daughter?"

They both answered, "Yes."

Brother Lusson asked James, "Do you have permission to marry or is there any reason you can not?"

James answered, "I am the Captain Commandant of the Post of St. Andre` and have received permission from Monsieur deHault de Lassus, Lieutnant Governor of the Western Illinois as he received a letter that the said Lieutenant Governor had written to us under date of the 23rd instant that he knew no legitimate reason that James being of age should not take a wife."

Brother Lusson then asked, "Is there any constraint by authority, menace or violence to this vow of marriage?"

We both answered, "No."

The Priest then gave us our vows according to the ordinance of his Majesty, the King of Spain, under the date of 30 November 1793 and in the presence of our family and friends, Laurence Long, Peter Rock, Gabriel Long and John Long, Jr., who signed with

James and me and my parents John and Elizabeth Long who all signed our marriage record. Our additional witnesses were Priscilla Long, Nancy Long, Sally Caulk and Saley G. Lewis.

After the ceremony and Brother Lusson, Priest Recolet, Cure` of San Carlos had duly signed our Certificate of Marriage, we were all dismissed to journey to the home of my parents where we enjoyed a wedding feast and the many good wishes of our friends.

CHAPTER TWENTY-FIVE

The Summons

JOHN WOKE WITH A START, and realized he had dozed off while Gram was telling her story and hoped he had not missed much. The warmth of the hearth and the night air had lulled him into taking a little nap. Gram had dropped her knitting onto the floor and had dozed off too. John carefully picked up the knitting and laid it back into Gram's knitting basket. Lightly lying his hand upon her arm brought her awake.

"Gram, we need to go to bed now, we will talk more tomorrow."

John's stay with Gram was fast running out, and in a few days he would have to return to his home. His time with Gram meant more to him than he could repay in his lifetime. He made a silent promise to tell his children about Gram and his grandfather so they would know the kind of people they were fortunate enough to have for their ancestors. He didn't think being proud of one's ancestors meant that a person should be prideful and not fulfill their own lives. They would, one could only hope, be a guiding influence for lives well lived.

John fell into a peaceful sleep seeing grandfather in all his Spanish Military grandeur and Gram a youthful young girl in her wedding finery. He had seen Gram's wedding dress and veil, so carefully preserved, still beautiful even with the touch of age upon it.

The following morning brought another beautiful June day and the early arrival of Aunt Catherine. She brought wonderful things to eat as she usually did. Gram and Aunt Catherine were

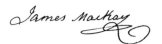

very close, as Aunt Catherine was constantly checking on and worrying about Gram. Gram didn't mind at all, but she did enjoy her own small house and the privacy to read, knit and dream without the interruptions of an active family and many small grand children.

Today was the day that Aunt Catherine and Gram usually brought down the quilt frame and worked on their quilts. The work would not interfere with Gram's story. As soon as needles were readied and the quilt tightened upon the frame, I was given a large basket of *hanks of wool* to roll into balls and Gram continued her story.

We moved into the house James had purchased on Main Street in the nearby town of San Carlos, which of course is now known as St. Charles. It was somewhat different than it was when we went to visit last week. That is where I started my first days of marriage. It was a grand house of Burlington Stone with ten foot wide fireplaces at each end of the great room. Our marriage was ideal in every way. James went to work at the little settlement of San Andre` which was situated close to the Missouri River for the convenience of the trade boats which plied the river. As was the custom of the day, the living and cooking facilities were at one end of the room which measured twenty-five feet in length. Our bed separated with curtains, was on the other end of the room.

The remainder of February and the month of March were very cold, and not a lot of building could be conducted at the San Andre` Post; there were days when James stayed home with me and we worked before the fire. We kept a cow and chickens in the barn below the house. It was a great convenience to be able to milk the cow and gather the eggs without going out into the cold. I did all the chores like Mama had done at home. I cooked over an open hearth and spun wool by the fire. We roasted peanuts and shelled pecans and walnuts in the evenings. It was a very fine life. James sometimes brought out the great plaid tartan his mother had made for him and we wrapped it around ourselves and cozened together upon the bear skin that lay before the hearth. We had many visitors on Sundays, sometimes Mama and Papa, sometimes Antoine and Julia Soulard with their little boys, James and Henry and another child on the way. They would come on Saturday and stay until after Church on Sunday, before returning to their home. In the evenings we had music. James played his fiddle and I, my harp. More often than not there were others there to join in the music making and share our company.

In the spring a terrible thing happened. When the snows far up the Missouri River began to melt, the little post of St. Andre` was swept away by the treacherous and unpredictable flood waters of the *old muddy river*. What had seemed like an ideal situation for the placement of Saint Andre` for trade along the river, was completely swept away when the Missouri over-ran its banks. All the people and their goods were moved into San Carlos, and until homes could be built to replace the ones lost, we had other people living in the upper story of our home. It was a difficult time for all concerned. Cabins were hastily constructed around the town to make places for people to live. The post was very small and contained not so many people that San Carlos could not care for them.

The work of building cabins was very hard, and James came home sometimes weary and discouraged about the loss of his post. By the end of summer our house was again our own. All James' correspondence he now did from his desk in our great room. It was sometimes very crowded during the day, but at night we were alone.

On Christmas, Papa and Mama came to our house, and we had a grand dinner and exchanged presents. Mama said she was much impressed with the improvement of my cooking. I surprised her with a plum pudding from the recipe her mother had used since she was a little girl in Wales. Many of my recipes had come from

Mama and Grandmother Bennett or James' mother Elizabeth or his sister Catherine. I also received recipes from my friend Julia Soulard and from James' German friends, the Muellers. Recipes, the making of clothing and children were the biggest parts of conversation between the women folk. We also discussed the use of herbs and what illnesses they could be used to cure. James had spent so many years trading with the Indians he had learned about many of the plants that were used by them. Only the very largest cities had doctors, so we all had to depend on the knowledge gained from each other. Many times James was called out to help someone that was ill, most of the time taking me with him.

James was the Captain Commandant of the mounted Dragoons. He was referred to by the Spanish as "Don Santiago Mackay." He also took over the duties of Commandant of San Carlos, as well as the area of Saint Andre` in the spring of 1801. James territory covered all the land north of the Missouri River with the exception of a small area called Portage des Sioux. The Custom House, just down the street from where we lived, became available for his use. He moved all his books, maps and survey equipment there, to conduct the area's business. Anyone who came into the area must first stop at the Custom House and get a passport before continuing into the territory.

I passed the summer of that year being ill and pregnant with our first child, who made his appearance on the 18th of August, a most terrible hot and humid day. We named him Zenon John, but we have always called him "Zeno," as he was named for James' good friend Zenon Trudeau. He was perfectly formed without the usual redness and malformed head of so many infants. What little hair he had was of a pale gold, and I could tell that he was to be the image of his papa, who, like all other proud fathers I had met, took all the credit for his production. During the summer, James had visited the village of his Osage Indian friends and brought back herbs of Squawvine, Holy Thistle, False Unicorn, Red Raspberry, Black Cohosh and Lobelia, which when mixed together would, they said, "make an easy delivery." I drank the tea from those nasty tasting herbs two times a day for six weeks prior to the time Zeno was born. I can only tell you Mama said, "It was the easiest delivery of a first child she had ever attended." I, of course, was very thankful for it and would never again complain of the vile taste of herbs. Mama came to stay with us for two weeks leaving only Nancy behind to care for Papa and my two brothers.

I think every one in San Carlos came by to see the new baby and bring small gifts in celebration of his birth. After all, James was their commandant, and to him they must all come for the resolution of their problems.

San Carlos was a friendly and close knit community. James was always fair in his dealings with the people under his care and tried to help their lives in any way he could. In a sense he was much like a clan chief in his native Scotland. Like his father, he acted as Judge for all disputes and granted permission for any buildings or passage into the territory under his protection.

The next year, 1802, James mapped all the area and supervised the building of a road between San Andre` and the settlement on Femme Osage Creek, built by the famous Indian fighter Daniel Boone. James had a salt works in the area called "Mackay's Saline." The road was often referred to as "Mackay's Salt Lick Road" or "The Great Salt Lick Road." Everyone knew the main reason for building the road was to get to the precious salt deposits near the Femme Osage settlement. Col. Boone also owned a saline works and came to our home on many occasions. He was a giant of a man with a look of great strength and a full head of white hair. He also possessed great charm and carried himself with a presence that all would notice. We had, on special occasions enjoyed his company overnight, where he stayed in our bedroom upstairs. He and James spent many hours entertaining me and other guests with their hair raising tales of the Indians, the back woods, wild river runs, deaths of friends and the fur trade in Canada. Col. Boone related the incident of the death of his brother who failed to return home from a hunting trip. When he went to look for him, he found his brother lying where the Indians had killed him. Although, it was a common sight to see Indians in the town of San Carlos, we did not experience the problems that some areas seemed to suffer. James spoke with them most of the time in their own tongue. He knew several of their different dialects and some of the Indians could speak a little French and Spanish. Very few of the people of our settlement could speak anything other than French or Spanish, and James was the only Spanish official who spoke the English language.

By spring of 1803, we had begun to hear rumors that the French had sold the Territory of Louisiana to the United States. This we couldn't believe as it was owned by Spain. Naturally we had heard that Spain was in negotiation to trade the territory back to France, but no one had heard that the feat had been accomplished. Even secret communications were not very secret in this country. James was very careful of what he did or said, for any mistaken communication could have dire consequences for our family.

In May we learned that indeed, we had been sold to the United States, and on the 26th of that month, I gave birth to our second child, a girl we named Eliza Lucie. This child was obviously to be mine, as she had dark hair and deep blue eyes. My life was full of happiness, and I tried not to listen to territorial rumors that would bring concerns. James took all of the happenings in stride, but he was nonetheless, worried for our future.

In December, Captains Lewis and Clark came to San Luis. There was no longer any doubt that we had now become part of the United States. James continued his duties, as no officials had come to relieve him. Until his official release, he was still commandant of the territories north of the Missouri River.

Captain Lewis was denied permission to leave on an expedition of discovery up the Missouri by our lieutenant governor, Carlos deHault Delassus, because he had not, as yet, received formal confirmation of the territories purchase. Captains

Lewis and Clark set up their headquarters at a place we now call Camp Dubois on the *Rivier` du Bois,* or Wood River, to wait for the formal papers of their claims to reach us. We were all forbidden by our lieutenant governor, Delassus, to in anyway consort with the Americans until all legal papers of confirmations had been received by him.

Captain Lewis spent much of his time in San Luis trying to hire crews to take the river journey. Captain Clark, so we heard, spent most of his time at their camp on the Wood River.

The winter was a very hard one, with the Missouri being almost frozen solid. It was not a good time to be leaving the house, but James continued with his duties. On a very late night, just after the beginning of the New Year, we received a visitor, Private Joseph Fields, who said, he had been sent by Captain Clark to bring James to him.

It was a meeting of great secrecy. Private Fields brought a summons to James to make a trip to the Wood River camp and speak with William Clark. Their Intelligence network knew of James' Missouri River Expedition or they would not have sent Private Fields to bring Captain James Mackay to them. I was terribly afraid. The consequences of his meeting with Captain Clark were just too terrible to think about. It could very well mean the loss of all our lands if the Spanish or American officials saw reason to turn against us. Many of the grants of land James had received had not yet been surveyed. Private Fields spent the night with us, and assured James and me that there would be no consequence to his visit, as the confirmation of purchase was expected to arrive any day. The sale of the land was a feat already accomplished. We were Americans now, even if the papers had not arrived.

James had not responded to Captain Clark's previous invitations to meet with him at his camp. James had in fact been forbidden by Lt. Governor Delassus, who was also our good friend, to do so.

"Captain Mackay," Private Fields said, "The Captains have given me every assurance that those who cooperate with them, by imparting the knowledge they have learned, will be given every consideration as American citizens. You have information they desperately need to make this trip a success. You are the only man in this territory who has been to the Rockies and know what is there. They already have your maps, but the rivers are not joined."

"The rivers are not joined," James nearly shouted at Private Fields, "because they do not exist!"

"Captain Clarks says President Jefferson is convinced there is a water-way all the way to the Pacific. If this venture fails, Sir, you will be the one to take the blame, even if you are not there. They will accuse you of withholding information that would have showed them the way. Captain Mackay, Captain Clark would not have sent me for you, in this freezing weather if it was not of great importance that you meet with him. Captain Clark says to assure you that you will be well rewarded for your cooperation."

"Very well," James responded, "We will leave in the morning."

That night, Elizabeth said, "I cried in our bed," I knew Private Field was right, that James had no choice whatsoever but to call upon Captain Clark. But, I did not believe James would be rewarded for his cooperation. It had been Papa's experience with politicians that they had little control of the things they promised. At the Spanish request, James' made promises to the Indians to supply them with goods, but when the time came to send the promised items, the Spanish did not send them. The Indians would not have forgotten the promises of their "Great Spanish Father" that were unfulfilled. Politics were tricky business and best to stay away from anything that involved promises.

For several days prior to Private Fields appearance at our home, I had suffered from the chills and fever of a winter illness. Zeno and Eliza had also been very fretful and feverish with the cutting of their teeth and the discomforts of winter. I did not want James to leave and be away from us even for one night. I felt a sickening foreboding about this trip. Nevertheless, it was my duty to be a good wife and I prayed he would be back without encountering any of the terrible incidents that happen so frequently to people who venture out in unsuitable weather. The reasons for this trip were even more fearsome. He was the Spanish Commandant of our area. Was it possible he could be tried and shot for treason before the confirmation papers of the territories sale even arrived?

The next morning I made James and Private Fields breakfast consisting of a large pot of black coffee, ham and eggs and all the biscuits and gravy they could eat. I packed two large sacks of food and put into each sack a bottle of whiskey. For most of their trip, they could ride horseback, which would be the best way to go because of the freezing weather. There was a family named Lloyd, whom we knew, where the horses could be left while James and Private Fields made their trip across the Mississippi to the camp of Captain Clark. Private Fields had left his boat near their homestead and could easily retrieve it for his crossing. I insisted James also carry his plaid, as it could stand up to any cold. The ice on the river was not strong enough to hold their weight and chunks of ice would destroy a canoe. How they would cross it, I did not know. James, always prepared for the most dangerous and tedious task, brought out the old buffalo skin and ribbing which he used to make a coracle. It had not been used in a long time and had to be thoroughly rubbed with melted fat to make it waterproof again. The old skin, smoked and cured and rubbed with numerous coats of wax and fat was thick and hard. A canoe was too fragile for the river, but "the coracle would make it just fine," James assured me.

As soon as the men had departed, I sat down and wept. It was not so much that I was afraid for their safe return home, but of the consequences of this journey. We knew from a letter James had received from John in New York that the territory had been truly bought even if we did not have official confirmation. We still lived under the Spanish flag and James' trip to talk with Captain Clark might constitute treason. On the other hand, it was only a matter of legal confirmation, we were now completely part of the United States and not to cooperate with its officials might also constitute an act of treason. In my mind the horror of it was more than I could comprehend. It was like experiencing the death of one you love while celebrating the birth of another. How can one experience the intensity of both emotions at the same time without being split apart?

I dried my tears and fixed the children their breakfast. To please them that morning, I made Bannocks like their Aunt Kittie in Scotland. She had sent me the recipe in one of her lovely letters.

When James returned from his meeting, he would tell me about Captains Lewis and Clark and this trip they were taking where no white man, they said, "had ever been before."

CHAPTER TWENTY-SIX

Winter Meeting with Capt. William Clark

THE STORY OF GRANDFATHER'S LIFE was most interesting to John; however, he had just about rolled all the balls of wool he could tolerate. He begun to think about all the goodies Aunt Catherine had brought in her basket.

"Aunt Catherine," John asked, "what wonderful things have your brought for lunch? I wouldn't be complaining if you brought some of your sweet lime pickles."

Gram and Catherine, who rarely thought of eating when they were working on a quilt, remembered the appetite of a growing young man. They set aside their needles, and with John's help set the table for lunch.

Aunt Catherine employed a wonderful Creole cook, who was raised in the French areas of New Orleans. Her cook, Maria Charbonneau, made the most delicious and strange things a person could imagine. For our lunch, Maria had sent a large kettle of *Jambalaya* which was made with ham and sausages, rice, onions, peppers, tomatoes and I didn't know what else, but it was good. All Gram had to do was set it over the fire for a while and it was ready for us to eat. To drink, there was *Cherry Bounce,* with just a touch of the normal amount of whiskey. We had *Cole slaw* and *plantains* fried with butter and sugar. Maria had once sent a soup called *Bouillabaisse,* which was a fish soup, ready to eat just as soon as I could catch the fish to be cooked with the soup.

While Gram and Aunt Catherine took their afternoon rest, John thought he had to go work off some of the lunch he had consumed or he would be taking his own nap. Fishing and skipping stones along the river bank seemed a good way to be outside.

After a couple of hours outside in the heat of the day, John was ready to return to the coolness of the house. He had rolled all the yarn, so Gram would have to give him another chore while he listened to her stories. One thing for sure, he was not going to do the quilting, which he considered "women's work."

Entering the house, John found that Gram and Aunt Catherine had already resumed their quilting. He found that Gram had gathered all the dull knives she owned and laid them out with a whetstone to be sharpened. This was much more in keeping with work he preferred, than wrapping balls of yarn.

Gram was most anxious to continue with her story.

"I think," she said, "I have not worried so much as I did during the time James was gone on his visit with Captain Clark. He left on the morning of January 10, 1804 and did not return until after dark of the next day. For two days, I fretted more than the children and could find nothing that would take my mind off the trip he had embarked upon. Surely James would be accorded a warm place to sleep for the night by Captain Clark.

It was already late in the evening, when I put a kettle of water over the fire for hot tea, which would be laced with whiskey and lots of honey. The fireplaces at both ends of our great room were built up so that, in fact, the room was a little too warm. I kept a steady watch so that his tea could be made the moment he came through the door. I also had a large pot of spicy Creole chicken and rice stew over the fire, keeping it hot. Blankets had been laid by the fire to warm. It was so terribly cold outside. James would need the nourishment of hot food and drink, as well as the warmth of hot blankets when he arrived.

Finally James came through the door, not the front as I had expected but through the woods and the back door. He had already put his horse in the stable, put a blanket over him and given him oats and water. His condition was as bad as I had anticipated. I quickly poured him a mug of whiskey to drink, straight from the bottle. I pulled away his plaid and took out his dirk, always sharpened to a razor's edge, and began to cut away the ice incrusted skin clothing he wore. The clothing removed, I wrapped him with the warm blankets and began to massage him with hot linens and put his feet in warm water to slowly begin the thawing process. He had stood there shaking, drinking that mug of whiskey and not speaking, while I removed his clothing. Now the tea and honey were ready. I added another healthy dose of whiskey as nothing warms the body from the inside out as well as whiskey. After he drank three cups of the tea and whiskey, he was warm enough to eat some of the hot stew waiting for him.

The children were still awake and clamoring for his attention. They were good children and although Zeno was barely out of his nappies, minded his father with a single word of command. As soon as he had finished the stew, Zeno climbed upon his lap and snuggled against him under the blanket. Perhaps the next most comforting thing is that of a small warm body.

Eliza was just beginning to fret, as it was time for her to be fed and put to bed. I sat before the fire and opened my dress so she could nurse. Zeno was soon asleep in his father's arms and Eliza was too full to stay awake; we rose and put the children down for the night in their little beds.

I very quickly ran the heated bed irons over the bed sheets to warm them so James would not chill again in bed. The fires in the hearth had now died down; I banked them and put away the food. I joined James in our bed where we could now join the heat from our bodies to sooth and warm one another.

As soon as the chills had passed and he was warm and comfortable, he began to tell me about his visit with Captain William Clark.

James and Private Fields rode their horses with a pack horse to carry their goods and the coracle James was taking. When they arrived at the Mississippi River, James left the horses with the Lloyd family until his return. The coracle was easily and quickly put together with leather bindings to its ribs.

Private Fields retrieved his small wooden boat to cross the river with James to follow when he had finished putting his coracle together. Private Fields appeared a little concerned with the reliability of the coracle.

James thought he would have liked it better if Private Fields had left his boat and gone with him in the coracle, which he thought the safer of the two. However, it was best if the two were not seen together, as Private Fields was a soldier in the American Military while he was an officer of the Spanish Militia. He had also not received orders to cooperate with the Americans.

When James arrived at the Illinois side of the Mississippi at Wood River, Private Fields had already landed and had his meeting with Captain Clark.

Upon James' arrival, he was taken to the tent of Captain Clark. He found that Private Fields had informed the Captain of his imminent arrival and had then immediately departed to resume his duties.

Captain Clark had slipped through some icy water earlier in the day, before James' arrival, and was already suffering from the icy dunking which had almost frozen his feet. He was not in the best of conditions for a visitor. However, he greeted James with sincere thanks that, "he had accepted his invitation." The long trip through winter weather and crossing a river partly covered with ice did not render James in the best condition for the visit either. Nevertheless, he discarded his misgivings. Captain Clark had been gracious enough to allow James a small drink of whiskey and a little time before the fire to warm himself. They then began their discussions which continued for the best part of the afternoon.

James found Captain Clark to be a man of quiet control and obvious experience in his knowledge of the Indians and maps he had laid before him upon a table for James' inspection. You can imagine James' astonishment to see his own map and the maps of

John Evans from their trip of 1795 and 1797, lying on the table. It was not only the maps but also other correspondences that he had made with Spanish officials.

There was a large sheath of his correspondences with the Spanish that had been translated from the originals into English. The Americans network of Intelligence gathering had been most thorough. Some of the correspondence, Captain Clark told him had been translated by John Hay, as neither he nor Captain Lewis were fluent in French or Spanish.

Captain Clark had James' Indian Notes, his Table of Distances and his instructions to John Evans as to what routes and rivers he was to use to cross the Rockies. They also had instructions from President Jefferson as to the way they were to conduct their *Corps of Discovery*. Their main concern, it seemed to James, was not the impossible hardships of the trip they were planning but how the Indians would receive them.

James pointed out to Captain Clark, "Sir, you have put me in a most precarious situation. I have always, in every country I have called home, been loyal and faithful to that country. You have commanded me to cooperate with you, when you know I have been strictly forbidden to do so by the country for which I hold the position of Captain of the Militia as well as Commandant of an area of their territory. If you thought it strange that I did not arrive with Private Fields, you must recall that he is an employee of the American Government while I am an employee of the Spanish, therefore, I have made every effort that we not be seen together for fear of future consequences."

"Mr. Mackay," Clark replied, "we have waited all winter for the confirmations of purchase to arrive. The spring will be upon us and our expedition must leave at the first possible moment the weather allows. The knowledge you have of the areas we are to traverse, must be shared with us. You are an American Citizen! Confirmation or not, you are no longer an employee of the Spanish. The Treaty of Cession was signed April 30, 1803, nearly a full year ago. We have tried in every way to make the transition an easy one. There are only a few Spanish Officials who have not cooperated with us. If you are to continue as an American Citizen, I can grant you no further time to come around to help us. Regardless of the lack of confirmation papers, I am now your commanding officer and I expect your help and explanations of the maps and notes which have already been turned over to us by the French and Spanish."

James understood this was no simple request but a direct command. "Captain Clark, I have worked for the past ten years in the Spanish territory, taking their commands, and being a faithful servant. I have taken land for work that I have done for them. I have many acres that have not yet been surveyed. The finances of my life depend on the whims of politicians. Can you assure me that my cooperation will be appreciated to the extent that all will not be taken away from me?"

With strong conviction Captain Clark said, "The Second Article of the Treaty of Cession guarantees that all private properties and Spanish Land Grants will be honored and will not be taken by the United States, that they will be confirmed and given proper title. Only those public lands and common grounds are subject to seizure by the government of the United States."

James accepted this and replied, "I witnessed the Inauguration of President Washington in New York, and at that time, I felt there was nothing I would rather happen than that I could be part of the building of a new nation. I will do my best to tell you all that I have learned from nearly twenty years of exploration through the territories where you are headed. However, you must know your intelligence in this instance is at fault. Captain Clark, I have never heard of waterways that flow continuously from one ocean to another. There is no direct waterway from the Atlantic to the Pacific Ocean."

Captain Clark rubbed his chin, "President Jefferson, says there is a water route. The Federalists are in an uproar over 'the folly' of the purchase of this territory. The President is under great pressure to find the waterways that will allow travel across the country. Therefore, I am asking you, where are the best and safest routes to get to the Rockies? Where is the river that flows to the Pacific? How do we communicate with the Indians? We need to know every possible thing you can tell us to make this trip a success."

From this statement, James knew, President Jefferson would not be content to acquire just the Louisiana Territory, but his goal was to acquire the whole continent and with the men and material available to the Americans, there was no way the Spanish or French could stop them, just as the English had not.

James started by looking over their list of goods. The Sioux, James told Captain Clark, would be their most formidable challenge, and would require a considerable amount of trade goods if they were to be allowed passage up the river. They were strong in the numbers of braves they commanded and they were not particularly friendly with the white man. Many of the traders had corrupted the Indians with liquor and free goods. They would find, he thought, it very expensive to get past the Sioux. James told Mr. Clark of his own problems with the Sioux and John Evans brush with death at their hands and his long run to get away from them, saved only by the fall of night.

He told Captain Clark of their lack of enough trade goods to get them past the Mandan Village and of the aborted trip, not only due to the illness of Evans, but they had no trade goods left for the Blackfoot tribes east and west of the Rockies.

Although James told Captain Clark he had explored north and east of the Rockies from Canada and down the Missouri and Yellowstone Rivers, he had found no direct connections of rivers through the Rockies. Captain Clark assured him again that President Jefferson had intelligence that confirmed the entire route could be taken by water. It was not prudent for James to point out that the waterway was not there. He suspected that Captain Clark knew it as well. James had not in all his years of trading the area found a water route directly through the Rockies. His fur trading relationship with the Indians had been a good one, if there were a waterway that flowed from the Missouri into the "great waters," they would have told him so. He had asked them many times where the rivers were located and if they flowed into great bodies of water where white men had come with great boats. None of the Indians he had met knew of any continuous flow of rivers that flowed from the Rockies to the Pacific Ocean. There was always a necessity to take horses or walk long distances from one river to the next before finding a river course that flowed west in the direction of the great water.

Captain Clark did not appear to have copies of the maps of the Missouri River past the Mandan Village. Captain Clark had a copy of the map drawn by Antoine Soulard partly taken from James' notes of his trip down the Saskatchewan River from Canada. Captain Clark also had the pages of instructions and directions he had written for John Evans. Completely missing were the maps he had given to Ambassador Gardoqui in New York of the areas of Canada he had explored and the Missouri River from the Rockies to the Mandan Village. Twenty years had passed since he had made the trip, he could only assure Captain Clark that the Missouri River did in fact reach almost to the Rockies from the Mandan Village and it was at this point he most likely would have problems with the Blackfoot Indians. "When you have reached the source of the Missouri River where it takes its turn south some two hundred miles past the village of the Mandans, you must keep as close as possible within the bounds of the 40th degree north latitude until you have reached the latitude between 111th to 112th degrees west of the meridian of London. Then you will proceed in a northerly direction until about 42nd degree of latitude. You will find my directions in the papers you have, that belonged to John Evans. It is here you will meet with the Blackfoot Indian Nation. If possible, it would be best to avoid the Blackfoot altogether, as they can be unpredictable. My trip to their village in 1787 from Canada was very interesting, and we traded a considerable amount of furs with the Indians and smoked their pipe of peace. Contained in the

Indian Notes you have, you will find an interesting interlude we had with the shaman of the Piegan Blackfoot Indians."

"The tribe," he said, "is very much influenced by their shaman and it will be to him you will need to show your esteem."

James told Captain Clark, that he believed a route along the Platte River, with a long overland trip, might be the best route to take, bypassing the Sioux and the Mandan Village at the great western curve of the Missouri River. James told Captain Clark, he had made a long hunting trip with the Indians during his trip up the river with John Evans and had been well within sight of the Rockies before he had joined John Evans at the Mandan Village and returned to San Luis. There are Indians at the river's end where you can trade for horses to continue your way. When you have reached the divide you can trade your horses for canoes when you have found the river on the other side of the divide that goes to the Pacific. There will be Indians who will show you the river.

Another route, James told Captain Clark about, and more direct than going to the source of the Missouri River was approximately 100 miles past the Mandan village. They would come upon a very good river for navigation; he referred to Rochejaune or the Yellowstone River. The river flowed into the Missouri River from a source in the Rocky Mountains. He had traveled along the river and found it abundant with game and had not encountered any hostilities with the Indians on that side of the Rockies. Going up the river where it flows from the Rockies, the water would have to be abandoned and the group would have to continue overland, by horse, north to northwest for about two or three days of travel. From that point there should be a break in the mountains, with mountains showing to the east. It was there they would have to cross through the mountains to find the river that flowed to the Pacific.

He told Captain Clark he had not personally left the Missouri and Yellowstone Rivers to explore through the divide. There were no connecting waterways. They would find, James told them a long and difficult portage overland before they would reach

a waterway flowing west. However, there was a river that could be found several days across land that would take them into a larger river which ran to the Pacific. It was only hearsay from the Indians that he had his information, but had found them to be correct in all of their directions he followed.

"No question at all Sir, the Indians will know you are there and will come to you. But whether they will be friendly, is something I can not say. I have not personally found them to be vicious toward me, but you must never show fear or treat them in any fashion, but that of respect."

James provided more caution about the women of the tribes who would be willing to take the men to their beds. This causes jealousy and violence between them and the tribe's young braves. Many have become infected with venereal diseases. The small pox, when it is carried into the tribes, caused a great number of deaths among them and many of the tribes will avoid you completely. You will pass their villages without interference and many have already moved away from the banks of the rivers where they had their villages. If they do not meet with you at the water, pass along without stopping.

James related his trip to the Mandans to Captain Clark. "When I made my trip in 1797 to the Mandan Village, I found it much reduced from the numbers I encountered in the years before when I took my trips from Canada. The small pox has reduced the Indians of the Missouri and the plains to about one third of their original numbers. They are naturally wary of the white man when he comes among them. They unfortunately, seem to have no tolerance for the white man's diseases."

"Take with you a number of medicinal herbs, as they will be needed for the chills and fever that will attack many of the men. For this you will need a large quantity of quinine or Peruvian bark or for lack of that, use the sage that grows on the plains. The tea is bitter to drink, but will keep the men well," James told Captain Clark.

"Captain Clark," James said, "you will need more trade goods, especially the blue beads. The tribes are jealous of each other and each will command a large part of your goods. Never let them see what you are taking to the other tribes. They will beg of you that their needs are greater than the next tribe you will encounter."

"I would prefer you called me William, and I will discuss these things you have discussed with me, with Captain Lewis. It has been a relief. Some issues we discussed were fearsome to my mind. Please do not worry yourself on any adverse consequences of our visit. You will be remembered and appreciated by the American Government for your help and cooperation."

When the meeting was concluded, they shared a small shot of whiskey in black coffee.

After leaving Captain Clark's camp, James returned to his cached coracle to cross the river before dark had descended upon him. The return trip from Camp Dubois had been most difficult. He retrieved his coracle from its hiding place and paddled across the Mississippi which was heavy with ice along the edges. It was necessary to break the surface with his paddle to make a passage for his boat. It took a long time to cross the river. James was forced to camp in the cold, near the farmstead of the Lloyds. He knew the Lloyds would welcome him and find him a bed, but he had much on his mind to think about. Camping alone, he could leave at first light to make his way home. James was most anxious to return home to his family. He turned over the coracle to form his tent, and built his fire outside and, in fact, he passed a fairly comfortable night. Leaving the following morning, he retrieved his horses at the Lloyds' farm, long before the family was about their chores. When he left on his trip back to San Carlos, a wet and very cold snow had begun to fall. The whiskey and food he had carried were completely gone by the middle of the afternoon. Arriving home, James was sorely in need of drink and nourishment.

As James and Isabella snuggled together for warmth and he had exhausted his tale of the trip to the Wood River camp, he said, "Bella, I don't know what kind of political things are going on, but it appears to me that President Jefferson has purchased the Louisiana Territory without the consent of the Congress. I hear they will have to make an amendment to the Constitution to accommodate this purchase. I would hate to see things in such a muddle for a democracy just begun."

The morning following James' trip to Wood River we continued our life as usual. James left late in the morning for the Customs House to do his work, and I returned to my household chores. Looking out over the deep drifts of snow that covered our world, I was again reminded of my good fortune that my husband had returned safe and the animals were beneath the house and it would not be necessary to work in the cold. James and I did not speak of his visit with Captain Clark again.

Daily we waited for the confirmations to come that James would turn over the command of his post, at San Carlos, to the American Officials. Secretly we were thrilled that we had become Americans. However, there was a continuing fear that all would not go as anticipated.

It was on the evening of Saturday March 8th that we received notice of confirmation of the sale of the Louisiana Territory to the United States of America. James immediately sent out riders to command all the people of the district to meet in front of the Customs House following Sunday's morning mass.

Attendance to Church Services on Sunday was mandatory in the San Carlos district. All business, following mass, was conducted relative to new laws and ordinances passed down from the Governor or Lieutenant Governor of the territory in front of the church door. All matters of a judicial nature were read out by the post commander.

James and I, along with our children and all the people of the community, attended mass.

Beginning early in the morning, the people began to gather in the town in front of the church and outside the Custom House, headquarters of the Commandant of San Carlos. They came by canoes and flatboats on the river, by cart, on horseback, by carriage and on foot. The place was crowded with every type of people who lived in the area. There were Indians, dressed in their finest skins and feathers and well decorated with beads. Several of our friends from the Osage tribes were in attendance. Col. Boone had brought his family and many of the people of the Femme Osage settlement. Some of the people were dressed in the finest silks that could be purchased from France, others britches and shirts of skins with moccasins on their feet. There were the Indians, Germans, Spanish, French, Creoles and Negroes, both slaves and freemen, and every description of newly arrived Americans.

Taking advantage of the crowd who would be assembled at the Customs House many of the people had brought goods and animals to barter.

At 12:00 Noon James took his place on the stoop of the Customs House and announced that the final confirmation had been received that the territory now belonged to the United States of America. There were shouts of happiness, for many of the groups were not of the Catholic Religion, even though they had pledged to be so when they came into the Spanish territory. In the past few years the numbers of newly arrived Americans already outnumbered the numbers of Spanish and French.

When the crowd had quieted, James began to read the Articles of Purchase that had been agreed upon and signed by all the officials of France and the United States.

Of the most interest to the people who had made their homes for years and even generations in the territories of the Louisiana and the Illinois was Article No. II and James Read:

"Article II

In the cession made by the preceding article are included the adjacent Islands belonging to Louisiana all public lots and Squares, vacant lands and all public buildings, fortifications, barracks and other edifices which are not private property. The Archives, papers & documents relative to the domain and Sovereignty of Louisiana and its dependences will be left in the possession of the Commissaries of the United States, and copies will be afterwards given in due form to the Magistrates and Municipal officers of such of the said papers and documents as may be necessary to them."

From this article, people of the area were assured that the private property granted to them by the Spanish would be honored and the homes and lands they had spent years building would still belong to them. Sadly, this was not to prove true.

There began a great celebration of the people, with shouts of joy and dancing in the streets, even though it was Sunday. The name of San Carlos was immediately anglicized to Saint Charles. San Luis would now be St. Louis. The Spanish coins cut in pieces and referred to as *bits* could now be exchanged for the American dollar.

As soon as order was restored, the ceremony of the Three Flags was commenced. Amongst the many cheers of the people attending the ceremony, the Spanish flag was raised upon the flag pole in front of the Customs House and then lowered. The French flag was raised and lowered. To thunderous applause, cheers and dancing the American flag with its white stars upon a blue background and its red and white stripes was raised to the top of the flag pole where it began to wave in awesome splendor.

Monday, the following morning, James moved all his private papers and equipment back to our home and the American officials took over the Customs House.

Our life returned to normal, and on May 14th, the Corps of Discovery led by Captain William Clark took a five day stop in our little village while he waited for Captain Meriwether Lewis to catch up with the expedition. James was not in town as he had resumed his duties as a surveyor. James had many properties he had accepted for services rendered the Spanish instead of money, which had not been surveyed. All properties would have to be properly surveyed and registered for confirmation to legal title.

CHAPTER TWENTY-SEVEN

The Hanging

BY THE TIME GRAM had completed the last segment of grandfather's life, John had sharpened her knives to a razor's edge. Aunt Catherine Guion put away her needles as well as the needles Gram had been using on the quilt until the next time she would come to visit. John thought he hated to see Aunt Catherine leave, as it was a little bit of sunshine that she took with her. However, it was late in the afternoon and she had her husband Louis as well as many other duties to care for. It was possible that he would not see Aunt Catherine again before he was forced to end his visit with Gram and return to work on the farm for his father, whom he thought resented the influence Gram had with him. Gram was the only link he had with the memory of his mother and he would not let it go, no matter the consequence.

Gram fixed a light supper of farm cheese and greens from the garden and some left over cornbread lightly toasted over the open hearth. It was a fine supper and John was anxious for her to continue her story.

Tonight Gram had decided to work on a set of pillow cases, on which she was putting in the last beautiful stitches of embroidery. I believe they were to be a gift for Gertrude Darling. She had knitted each of us boys a scarf to be taken with me upon my return home.

After stretching the work into an embroidery frame she continued her story.

After a few weeks, the excitement of the Lewis and Clark expedition having died down, our lives settled down into a comfortable routine. Without the demands on James' time with the Dragoons and the Customs House he had time to begin the tedious job of surveying the areas of land he had accumulated for his ten years of service to the Spanish Government.

On May 27th of 1805, James and I welcomed our third child whom we named Catherine Mary. James said she reminded him so very much of his sister Kitty, that there was no other thing he could do but name her Catherine. She had the pale gold and blond hair that was so prevalent in the family of his mother Elizabeth MacDonald who, like James, carried a strong resemblance to their Norse ancestors.

At 4:00 P.M. on the evening of Sunday, September 21, 1806 our good explorers, Captains Lewis and Clark reached St. Charles on their successful return from the Pacific Ocean. Most all of the people of St. Charles turned out to welcome the returning heroes. Families all over town took members of the group into their homes to feed them and make them welcome. We were happy to take into our home Mr. Peter Cruzatte, who had accompanied James on his trip up the Missouri and who had played the fiddle many times with James in the past. We were happy to see he had safely returned home. He was not at all amused when we laughed over the incident of his mistaking Captain Lewis for a moose. When the party departed two days later, our lives quickly returned to a normal routine.

President Jefferson appointed a special Commission to oversee the confirmation of the Land Grants and Concessions made to residents before the time of the Louisiana Territories purchase. He appointed an American born Frenchman named John B.C. Lucas to head up a Commission of three of his own appointees. We all thought he would be a good choice, as he was essentially French himself, he would understand the laws and grants that were made under French and Spanish rule. Our thinking could not have been further from the truth.

The first Concessions brought before him were all denied on the most frivolous reasons. Judge Lucas' attitude towards the residents French, Spanish or otherwise was one of ill respect. He considered the Upper Louisiana peoples of the area to be unready for republican government. He soon became a despised figure of a man to us all. James was spending a lot of time in St. Louis before the Commissioner's Court. Regardless of the documents of proof of his Concessions of land, the Commissioner's Court headed by Judge Lucas found some obscure reason to reject our claims.

James conducted his survey business and the continuation of his court battles kept him from our home. I missed his presence more than I can say. He was always happy to be home when he came, and there was never an ill word between us. I felt the strain of our legal problems, when he was home, should be put aside so he could his enjoy his wife and family and home without trauma.

On February 13, 1808, I birthed our fourth child, Julia Jeanne, named for my best and dearest friend Julia Soulard and James' sister Jean. He said naming Julia for his sister Jean would, in some small way, make up for the teasing and tormenting he had enjoyed at her expense as a small boy in Scotland. He had dearly loved his sister, but she was so very much fun to tease.

Due to the many demands on his time in St. Louis, we decided to move to the plantation on Gravois near where my father had moved the previous year. It was only a few miles from St. Louis, and he could be into the court in a short time. It had already become abundantly clear we were in for a number of lengthy court battles as were most of our friends. At the time, I could not imagine just how time consuming and expensive for us these legal battles would become.

Our plantation house on the Gravois River was made in the traditional French architecture of hewn and squared logs, filled with mud plaster. The house consisted of two large stories with fire places at each end. Downstairs was an office for James as well as the sitting area, a bedroom for James and me and a dining area. Detached from the house was a kitchen in the back where Gloria, the Negro woman James had bought, did the cooking. She was a good cook and made a very good gumbo, but she did not have the refined skills of the Creole cook your Aunt Catherine now enjoys. She was willing to learn and together we spent much of our time out in the little kitchen, teaching each other, while the children played outside or under our feet.

We delighted in the occasion of the marriage of my brother, William Lindsey Long, to the very beautiful Elizabeth Sappington, the daughter of longtime residents John and Jemima Sappington. The wedding, a very lavish and wonderful affair, took place on July 14, 1808. All the Sappington girls were great beauties and William was very lucky to have won the love of Elizabeth. William was a fine man, but being my brother, I didn't consider that he was so very handsome. I remembered him best as a little boy who made a nuisance of himself. I also remembered the times James had to bribe him when we were courting, and now he had a wonderful bride of his own. The farm where he built their house was on part of the land concessions James had received from the Spanish and was near our plantation as well as the plantation now owned by my father, John Long. We were so well placed together that our families spent a lot of time with each other as well as sharing the farm work. When it came time to build a house we had "house raisings" and all got together. A house could be put up in a single day. Sometimes with family, neighbors and friends there were fifty to a hundred people present at these gatherings. The women all brought food and the children played. It was usual for the house raisings to take place in the summer when the weather was good. We had all met in the month of June for a "house raising" for William and Elizabeth. The house was ready for William and his bride to move in when they married in July.

Christmas of 1808 was made even more wonderful with the addition of the Sappington family. We spent many wonderful days in their company.

In March of 1809, we received news from James' sister, Kitty, that James' father George had died on January 19th and that he had been interred with his father and mother in the family vault in the churchyard of the Church of Scotland in Wick. James was particularly distraught that he had not yet had another son to name for his father. To add to our sorrow Uncle Lawrence Long, Papa's brother, also passed away. My cousin John took his death particularly hard. His mother married a Mr. George Gordon in an indecently short time, I thought, after the death of his father, Uncle Lawrence. Mr. Gordon was not too long from the shores of Scotland, and it did not help matters in the least that the Gordons and the Mackays of Scotland were, as clans, not friendly with each other. The Gordons had constantly poached upon the lands of the Mackays. The Mackays of course, did their own poaching which caused many furious battles. Clan battles had been ongoing for centuries. Apparently, they were to be carried to the new world as well.

Uncle Lawrence did not leave a sufficient will to protect his children from the greed and manipulations of a step-father such as George Gordon. John was distraught to see the lands and property acquired by his father being frittered away.

One evening while John was working in the barn, he heard shouts of anger coming from the house. It sounded as if his new step-father George was once again far into his cups with the evening not even drawn. He hurriedly finished the chore of mucking out the stalls and went to the house where he found George had struck his mother and indeed had taken out his gun and was trying to force her into signing some paper that he had set before her. With out any thought, John grabbed his arm to retrieve the pistol before John's mother suffered further damage. They grappled over the gun with the result that the gun, already cocked, discharged, the bullet striking George in the upper part of his chest. John tried to staunch the bleeding, to no avail. George died a short time later, on the floor, where he had fallen.

When the case came before the judge, old cronies of George's testified that John had hated his step-father from the first days of his marriage to John's mother. John of course, could not deny that well known fact, as almost from the first, George had been abusive towards his mother.

The courts, filled with newcomers to the territory were ready to find fault with anything or anyone who had lived in the area long enough to acquire properties they coveted. To our disbelief, John was found guilty of murder instead of an accidental shooting. We believed the judge and jurors were influenced by the now infamous Judge Lucas, who despised all of us, and did what he could through the courts to make our lives a misery. The sentence was handed down that my dear cousin, John was to be hanged and he would be allowed less than a month before the sentence was to be carried out.

Our family was devastated, and we all visited with him as much as we were allowed to do. They allowed us to bring food to the jail where he was incarcerated, so at least he was not subjected to the swill that so many were forced to eat. John's mother was inconsolable with the grief of losing her son as well as her husband. She blamed herself for her unfortunate marriage and was never the person she had been during her lifetime.

The days of John's life sped away like water through a sieve and before we could accept there was to be no reprieve the day had come for his execution.

On the morning of September 16, 1809, I knew I would not be able to stand aside and watch the terrible spectacle of John's death. James and all the men of the family went to be beside him in their support. John, in fact, had not wanted the females of the family in attendance.

All morning long, in my tortured mind I heard the wheels of the wagon that would take him to the hanging tree. I felt every jar and bump that he would have to steady himself against. I felt

the hood they would put upon his head and the tightness of the ropes with which they would bind him. I lay upon my bed in a catatonic state, and Gloria had to mind the children who, thankfully, did not understand the happenings of the morning. Zeno knew, as his friends had made sure to tell him. We tried to explain the injustice that we believed John had received, but it did not change the outcome and that God would surely receive him into heaven.

Even though I did not attend the hanging, even I could not keep myself from reading about it in the paper, and the words will be forever burned into my memory. I tell you Johnny, because I remember the article to this day as clear as if I had read it yesterday.

Missouri Gazette, St. Louis
Wednesday, September 20, 1809

John Long, the younger was executed here last Saturday, pursuant to his sentence, for the murder of George Gordon. The unfortunate criminal was attended by clergymen of several dominations, he appeared much interested in his eternal welfare, his supplication to the throne of grace was earnest and sincere; his fortitude and intrepidity was deserving a better fate; on the way to the gallows he sang several psalms with his spiritual attendants; he mounted the cart and examined the rope very unconcerned, and asked the sheriff if he did not think it necessary to tie his hands, and requested him to give him a cap, having put it on, he placed his hands behind to be tied, exclaiming, "well I hope Jesus Christ will have mercy on me," A chair was placed on the cart to raise him to the rope, he asked the executioner to adjust it, and without waiting for the carts being drawn off he kicked the chair from him and launched into eternity.

The support of our friends was complete and so many of the people of St. Louis thought he had received an unjust sentence, that there was silence among the crowd in reverence for the goodness of the young man who had so unjustly lost his life. The death of my cousin brought us to the attention of the Priest. We had not been regular in our attendance of the Church.

In my marriage to James, I had promised to take the children to the nearest church, which we had done. I did not really understand that it meant we had to take them to the closest Catholic Church. At the time, concerns of the church were not uppermost in my mind. With all the attention of my unfortunate cousin, the Priest was demanding that we bring our four children to the church to be baptized.

We went to mass at the Basilica of St. Louis Cathedral where, following the service, on the 14th of August 1810, they received their baptism. It is necessary to have appointed guardians for each child, if James and I were unable to fulfill our duties as parents. For our son Zenon John Mackay our friends Antoine Soulard, Victoire LaLaddie and Charles Gratiot stood with us as his appointed guardians. For Eliza Lucie Mackay my mother Elizabeth Long and Emilie Gratiot stood with us. For Catherine Maria Mackay, Antoine Soulard and Eulalie Choteau stood with us and for Julia Jeanne Mackay, James Gustave Soulard and Cerre` Soulard stood as their guardians should James and I not perform the duties of parents.

James continued it seemed on a daily basis, in his battles with Judge Lucas. All our family and friends were also having their battles with him and his commissioners, and each was trying to support the other by attending as many of the court sessions as was possible.

On July the 18th of 1811, I birthed another son for James who we named George Antoine Mackay, for his father George and our good friend Antoine Soulard. We dutifully took him to the Cathedral to be baptized and for him stood our friends, Rosalie Saugrain and Antoine Soulard. James, to honor his father, also signed his name to the baptismal record. George was a good baby and as quite and sweet as could be. We now had five children for Gloria and me to care for. James purchased another young Negro woman named Patsy and a young Negro man named Walter. They had lived on different plantations but had wanted to marry and James purchased them because James preferred to have working for us, a married couple. A house had to be constructed for them to live in. Gloria already had her own house behind the cookhouse. The size of our little Gravois farm was growing with houses, barns, smoke house, potato house, tobacco barns, etc. We were becoming a large farm and the needs were many.

Sometimes it seemed as if life were dragging us along, instead of just merely letting us live and enjoy it. Not to say that I was in anyway dissatisfied, I could not have, in any way, been happier, except if I could I would have taken some of the pressures brought on by the lands we were trying to confirm, which kept James busier and under more strain than I would have liked for him to endure.

In the early morning hours of December 16th, with James just coming to bed, after many hours he had spent studying, by the light of a candle, the legal matters he had to face. The earth began to shake and tremble and things began to fall from shelves and the house felt like it was coming apart at its joints. The children upstairs, awakened by the terrible noise and movement, began to scream from their beds. We both leapt from bed and could hardly stand. James pulled on his clothes and ran outside while I made my way upstairs to see to the children. The Negroes were all at the door wanting to come in, as they were very frightened, as was I. We didn't know what was happening; James thought we must be experiencing an earthquake, but he had not heard of such in the area, but it certainly was a large one.

When he returned to the house he told us, as we were all huddled together in our terror, the waters of the Gravois were running in the wrong direction and large chunks of the river banks were falling into the water. The waters had spouted over the banks leaving all manner of fish out of the water. To lighten the matter and soothe ourselves, we determined that when it was light, we would take advantage of this bounty and bring in some fish for eating. We were up the rest of the night with continuous tremors shaking the earth, it seemed, every few minutes.

The next day we heard reports that the worst of the earthquake had taken place on the Mississippi in the area of New Madrid. The waters of the Mississippi were still running in the wrong direction, and boats had been tossed out of the water onto the banks and were smashed and ruined. Some houses had been swept away in the torrents. We learned that a great many people had been killed by falling debris. It was not the last of the earth quakes, and they continued for several years. The people of the area of New Madrid had to find other places to live, the devastations were so great. Special laws were passed to allow people to seek other places to live and they were given special grants of land to replace the lands that were lost to them during the earthquakes.

In the year 1812, we found ourselves in another war with England. My brothers William and John, Jr. were taken to be soldiers for battles to come. William soon became a Lieutenant with Nathan Boone's group. Joining the same group were my brother, John Long Jr., Thomas and Zephaniah Sappington and a number of others from the area who all reported to Fort Mason at Cap au Gris for duty. They were not long in getting into the action. While on patrol, the group which contained both my bothers William and John, Jr. were attacked by a party of Winnebago Indians who had been plundering one of the settlements in the St. Charles District. The group met up with them near Fort Madison. A number of the soldiers were wounded during the attack including my brother John, Jr.

John's wounds did not seem to be so severe that he would have to resign from the service. However, while crossing a swollen river a few weeks later, not having the strength to keep his seat

upon his horse in the swollen stream, fell into the water and drowned.

When we received the news both Papa and Mama could not be consoled they were so devastated. Papa, I believe never again had the zest for life that he had before this tragedy. James took over the running of their farm in addition to our own. The Sappington's were doing their part to keep things in order at the farm of William and Elizabeth. We waded through our days wondering when things would right themselves again.

We added another boy to our growing family on June 24, 1813. We named him William Robert Mackay. The Priest insisted on baptizing him Guillaume Robert in the language used by the French. For the church was not quick to change their ways and still used the French language even though we had now been Americans for some time and all of us used the English language. William was named for James' brother William, who had died in Virginia, and his younger brother Robert in Scotland. He thought the continuation of family names to be very important. I was always happy to do anything that pleased my good husband. Standing for our new son were our good friends Gustave Soulard and Louise Chouteau. It became a custom after each baptism of our children and the children of our friends to gather at the home of one or the other to celebrate the occasion with a hearty dinner and give thanks for our children.

CHAPTER TWENTY-EIGHT

Letter to: "My dear Son"

GRAM SAT FOR A FEW MOMENTS contemplating all the things she had been telling me. She set a few more stitches of embroidery in the pillow cases she was finishing. It was now near the hour of 9:00 P.M., and John suggested perhaps Gram was tired and would like to retire to her bed.

"No, Johnny," she said, "Old people, such as I, need very little sleep. The purpose of my life now is to enjoy my waking hours with my grandchildren or other pursuits that please me, and it pleases me to continue with my story, so you must stay awake and listen."

In the early fall of 1814 we receive a letter from James' dear sister, Kitty. The terrible fate of people of the Scottish Highlands had finally also become the fate of the Mackays. The farm lease that had been held by James' family for seventy-four years had not been renewed by the Sutherland factor. Captain Robert Mackay, James' brother, had written the factor, asking that he be allowed to take over the lease, but was denied. Kitty and her husband George and their family were forced to leave the longhouse-croft at Loch Arichlinie and move to Inverness. Kitty's two older sons were to go into the grocery business with their uncle Robert as their partner.

James had heard many horrifying tales coming from Scotland about the treatment of the crofters. He had hoped that the lands we hoped to confirm would be a place of refuge for some of

our family. However, we still did not have clear titles, as the confirmations of the land concessions were still pending.

On the 24th of August 1815, your uncle James Bennet Mackay was born and James was so very happy to add another son to our family. Mama had long since made peace with her father, Judge James Oliver Bennett of Wales. You may remember the story I told you about Mama's elopement with Papa. It was a long time before grandfather forgave her and welcomed her back into the family. James named our son after him and his grandfather James Mackay.

It was certainly a lot to put upon a child to be named for persons who have been so loved and important in one's life. However, we carried on the family tradition of naming our children for our ancestors, which is the highest compliment one can pay to the memory of loved ones now passed to another world.

It seems, sometimes, that happiness is a very capricious part of life. We lost our little son William Robert, to one of those child hood tragedies that happen so often and quickly in life. It was during this same sad time that we received a letter from the widow of Judge Paul Micheau in New York telling us that James' brother, John and his wife Elizabeth had died during a Cholera outbreak and their three children were now orphans to be raised by their grandmother.

James held a number of offices for the new American Government. The Territorial Governor, William Henry Harrison, appointed James to serve as Judge of Court of Common Pleas and Quarter Sessions. The moneys he earned for these positions, in addition to the moneys we received for lumber and salt from the Saline, helped to make our lives considerably more comfortable. Perhaps James' appointment was due to the anger Judge Lucas had provoked in Governor Harrison. Everyone in the territory knew of Lucas' vigorous denials of our land claims along with the claims of most of the people who had lived in the territory at the time of its purchase. The continued denials of the lands granted by the

Spanish, and denied by Lucas, had become a constant source of embarrassment to Governor Harrison and had caused a terrible backlog in the court system. Judge Lucas was an appointee of the President of the United States, and thus, would be upon his board until he quit or died. With the power he wielded over all of us, he was not likely to quit.

The voters of the county of St. Louis, in 1816, voted James to be their representative as a member of Missouri's territorial legislature. It was a very important position for James to hold and we felt, to have the people of the counties confidence could only help in our battles with Judge Lucas and his board of land commissioners.

It was after his election to the legislature that James decided we would be better served to build a house in town, where we would live during the legislative sessions.

We had loved the wonderful house in St. Charles, where so much of our happiness began. James decided to again build us a two story French style house made of red brick. It would be the first brick house to be built in St. Louis. It was very near the Mississippi River and would allow easy access for travel by boat. For myself, I loved the plantation on the Gravois, but I wanted to be with my husband as much of the time as was at all possible. James had purchased a very nice spot in St. Louis overlooking the Mississippi River. It is at this location that he began the building of our house. Now that the streets have been laid off, it is the house at Fifth and Hickory Streets where the Sacred Heart Academy now stands.

Our many legal battles continued in the Commissioner's Court of Judge Lucas. I would not for anything wish another person misfortune, but I could not weep for Judge Lucas' misfortunes. Charles, the son of the man, who plagued our life with his refusals to confirm our properties, was killed in a duel. In all accounts, of persons present at the duel fought on *Bloody Island* between Charles Lucas and Thomas Hart Benton, it was declared a fair duel. Both young men were attorneys and promising young

politicians. They found themselves on opposite sides in a land claims dispute which began the deadly argument. The tragedy was, that the letting of blood and the injury of Charles Lucas in the first duel, did not end the affair. Insults continued and Benton, who claimed Lucas had defamed him, demanded another duel. The result was that Charles lost his life.

The Lucas-Benton duel was not the only tragedy to fall upon the shoulders of Judge Lucas, he lost a son in the war and another was drowned as well as others who died young. Our claims were not the only claims he found obscure reasons to deny. He was constantly in disagreements with many of the people of St. Louis. He could not stand the thought that the affair was one of honor and that the death of his son was not criminal. He devoted himself thereafter to defend the honor of his son and slander the good name of Thomas Benton.

Judge Lucas became a very wealthy man, buying up the lands of people who could not continue their fight for the confirmation of their lands. There were many of us who considered it a matter of principal to continue with our battles to the District Court of Missouri and, when necessary, to the Supreme Court of the United States. The final insult to Judge Lucas over the affair of the *Lucas-Benton duel* was his loss to Benton, in a race for the United States Senate.

With the tragic deaths of so many of his children, I can only wonder if Judge Lucas found any comfort in his wealth. I wondered if he ever thought about the hanging of my cousin John and his influence in that affair.

On March 13, 1818 we welcomed our Eighth child into the family, a girl, whom we named Emilia Anne Mackay for our good friend Emilie Gratiot. As with all the other children, on the day of her baptism, the Priest wrote our child's name, in the French manner, in the Church Registry. He wrote her name as *Emillienne* leaving her with only one name.

The building of our house continued, and by the end of the summer, the house was finished. James sent to Philadelphia for new furniture. We had a beautiful new bed and a room all to ourselves with a nursery close by for the little ones. It was the first time since the birth of our first child, Zeno, that we did not have a cradle along side our bed. For Emilia Anne and the smaller children we had servants to help us. Seven children is a healthy amount of children for anyone to have living under one roof. James could not be happier with our good fortune in our children, all healthy. However, at the age of thirty-six, it would have suited me if God had not blessed me with another child. I bite my tongue at this, because if I had not had another child, I would not have had the special blessing of my sweet Isabella Louisa and you, Johnny my grandson.

James had such fun and enjoyment buying the furniture for our new home. He wanted to surround me with all the luxuries that life had to offer. In addition to the new bed for our bedroom, he purchased a bureau, to keep our clothes. For the downstairs parlor he purchased a new desk for himself, complete with a book case for his growing collection of books. The first books to go onto his bookcase were the six volumes of *Laws of the United States.* He then added Hume's twelve volumes of the *History of England*, five volumes of *Boyer's Dictionary*, thirteen volumes of the *Classics* and four volumes of *Bibles and Sermons.*

For the dining room James ordered a wonderful new dining table complete with twelve Windsor chairs. We had many visitors to our home, and James was at his happiest when we entertained and he played his fiddle. I must tell you though, that poor violin, through all its travels, had been fiddled to the degree that the chin area was almost completely worn through.

As is human nature, when things are at their very best, then one begins to wonder what is going to happen to take it all away. I knew that the death of my cousin John and the circumstances surrounding it had for many years been a heavy weight upon

James' mind. He told me one morning that he felt he had to make provisions for me and the children just in case something should happen to shorten his life.

It was certainly no secret to us and our friends that many of the newcomers to the area wished ill fortune to fall upon the heads of the French and Spanish or anyone else who had amassed large acres of land in the territories. For every acre we owned, meant they would have to go that much further into the wilderness to claim the lands that were offered to them. There was a lot of resentment from these new arrivals, who had been misled to think the land lay open to anyone, anywhere they wished to build. Many families squatted on our lands and cut the timbers without our permission. To add to the debacle, people were being sold land by unscrupulous persons who did not own the land in the first place. There had been threats upon James' life, which of course, he could not ignore.

On one of those rare winter mornings, when it was so cold, it was far better to stay inside, James sat down at his new desk and began to write a letter to our son Zeno, telling him the things he wanted him to know, in case he was not there to advise him. This was when he started the letter of which you now have a copy. I would like to read it to you because I feel it better to hear the advice directly from me and from your grandfather, than to read it when you are alone. Gram began to read the letter.

"My dear Son:

As it is the natural desire of all persons to know their pedigree, and such knowledge being always pleasing and sometimes useful, I will endeavor to give you (for your satisfaction and that of all my family) as much information on that subject as my recollection can furnish, that you may know from what race you are descended and not remain in that ignorance which is the lot of the generality of those living on this side of the Atlantic, who not only know nothing of their European Ancestors, but have even lost their own real name. You, my dear son, are a descendant of the ancient race of O'Connor, one of the Kings of Ireland, which appears by the genealogy existing in our family these six hundred years. Prince Alexander, son of O'Connor, about the year 1200 came from Ireland with his followers and landed in the north part of Scotland, where he conquered a considerable tract of country, the most of which is still inhabited by his descendants (the Mackays). Alexander's son's name was Ay or I. About this time the great families began to use surnames to distinguish their families, consequently the sons of I were surnamed Mac I or Mackay, which name was ever after retained by their offspring. The word "Mac", or "Mack", in the old language of Scotland signified "son". I was born in Arrichiliney, Parish of Kildonan, County of Sutherland, North part of Scotland. My father, George Mackay, who was a Judge, and my mother, Elizabeth McDonald, both of exemplary virtue and goodness, now deceased, resided at said Arrichiliney, which was also the residence of my grandfather, James Mackay, whose father's name was John, and John's father's name was William, who was the son of Murdoch Mackay, who was called the Great Murdoch, being not only a man of power, in the dark age he lived, but also possessed prodigious personal strength. My memory is not sufficient to trace out the line of our ancestors beyond this great man last mentioned, being the seventh generation back from you. I believe that sometime before this day our family became the youngest branch and consequently was excluded from the paternal inheritance which according to the laws of that country became the right of the oldest son and is now the property of his lineal descendant, George Mackay...Lord Rae. From every information I ever could collect it appears that our ancestors were eminent for personal courage and for their integrity in every situation, public or private, which was their lot to occupy and that their conduct on all occasions was worthy of the noble race from whom they descended. I do not give you this relation respecting your ancestors, that you may think yourself superior to other good men, but for the purpose that you may

emulate their example and thereby render yourself worthy of the esteem and confidence of all good men, and honour and a blessing to your people, your country and yourself. And this maybe the last advice that I may ever be able to give you, I charge you, my dear son, not to neglect it. Remember it is the advice of a tender father who loves thee as his own life and whose advice is founded on a long experience, acquired in a life checkered with various scenes of good and evil inseparable from the rugged path of human life, through which you must also pass and perhaps commence its troubles without a father to guide thee. I am grieved at the thought of leaving you, your worthy mother and the rest of the family, in a corner of the earth removed from society and good examples, almost ruined by the injustice of government and now chiefly inhabited by a new population, the most of whom (considering property their chief good) stick at nothing to acquire it, and with few exceptions, those of them who amassed property since their arrival here, got it by fraud and injustice; therefore watch them as you would a wolf in the desert, for they will try to prey on you also. I do not mean to say that all the American race are of this description, for the Atlantic States (where people are civilized) morality reigns as in other civilized countries. But in all countries there are a certain description of persons, whose conduct is incompatible with the rules of a well regulated society, and of such are the generality of our new population. Men without honour or religion, disregarding even that natural duty which all mankind owes to their parents and other relations; the child prosecutes his parents and reduces them to poverty if he can; brothers and sisters are not ashamed to have their names called in court, against each other. Such is the present depraved state of society in this country, though I hope you will live to see an alteration for the better...and I have noticed it here merely to the end that you may arm yourself against the danger of being tainted by the present infamous state of things. In whatever situation you happen to be, public or private, let the rules of rectitude and your conscience be your guide, let not even pity make you deviate from this rule...leave the events to God who can bring good out of seeming evil. Use civility to all persons and of every description; make as few enemies as possible for the meanest being may find means to injure. Have but few friends, for you will find few in this world worthy of that name. Therefore be circumspect in your choice of them and careful to preserve their confidence after you prove them to be deserving of yours. Honour thy mother, she is worthy of all good and of more than you can do for her; protect her and your sisters and all the family as long as you live. Never place your confidence in a man void of religion, for what the fine and empty men of the world call honour (if not supported by religion) is as frail and false as a shadow and will deceive, soon or late, all who will depend on it. I do not mean the external forms of religion, though that is also necessary. True religion consists of loving merely, acting justly and never forgetting that the Almighty Lord of the Universe is a witness, to all our actions. Preserve to the outmost the confidence and friendship of my excellent and constant friend, Colonel Anthony Soulard, and his family; above all others follow his advise and you will do right. I need not mention your grandfather, Captain John Long, for it is natural for him to be your friend and he will always be so. I have two brothers alive, Robert, who is a Captain in the British Army, where he served twenty years and is lately retired on full pay to a small estate which he owns near the City of Inverness, in Scotland. He has but one child, Margarete, who is lately married to a Major Mackay of the same army. His name is William. My other brother, George, the youngest of our family, is in Nova Scotia, has been overseer of the public works, and is, I believe, removed to the Island of Cape Breton. He has a large family. My oldest brother, John, and his excellent consort are both buried on Long Island, near New York. Their three children, Eliza, Mary and Matilda, live with their grandmother, widow of Judge Paul Micheau, on Statten Island. I recommend them to your friendship for they are deserving. My brother William, younger than me, died many years ago at Petersburg, in Virginia, where he had been to establish a commercial house. My oldest sister, Jean, and her husband are dead and left a large family, some of them in the army and some in Scotland. My other and youngest sister, Catherine, married to George Mackay and lives in Doverary, in the County of Caithness, Scotland. They have a numerous family. Two of her sons, George and John, are merchants in Inverness. I have some relatives in Boston, New England, possessing much property. My Uncle, William Mackay, came to North Carolina with his wife, Isabella and Eleven children, in the year 1774. Before I left Europe, I was told by my father that they lived in Rowan County, before the Revolution, but I never heard anything from them since. I remember that they had several sons; the name of the oldest was James."

It is my hope Johnny, that you will always keep a copy of this letter and pass it down to your children and grandchildren that they may know, honor, and remember the man who left his home in the far away country of Scotland to build a better life for them.

CHAPTER TWENTY-NINE

Boeuf avec Champignons

JOHN INSISTED THAT IT WAS TIME for Gram to take to her bed, his fear was constant, that she would make herself ill. She reluctantly agreed and put away her needlework and went to bed.

John however, couldn't go to bed until he had again read Uncle Zeno's letter. Now that he was to study for the law, he thought the advice, when he needed it the most, could not have come at a better time. While he read, it was if grandfather had written the letter just for him. He made a solemn promise, to himself, to honor the memory of his grandfather and to try in every way to live the kind of life that would make him proud. John then snuffed the oil lamp and sought out his own bed, with thoughts of the letter wafting around in his mind, as sleep overtook him.

In the morning, when the first rays of sunshine hit the horizon, Gram was up puttering around the hearth to fix John a hearty breakfast. Her stamina was truly amazing. She was passed her seventy-fifth birthday and here she was waiting on him and preparing his breakfast, as if he were a helpless child. John promised himself, in the afternoon when Gram took her nap, he would go weed the garden.

John and Gram decided to spend the morning under Gram's arbor of beautifully blooming Eglantines with their fragrance perfuming the air around them.

Gram brought her needlework, and John found a couple of hoes that needed to be sharpened. He remembered the garden

chore for this afternoon. John knew she would tell him this morning about the birth of his mother *Louise*. Gram continued with her story where she had left off the night before.

"Gram," John asked, "why is it that you never remarried after the death of grandfather."

"Johnny, I loved your grandfather very much, and to have another husband was something I never thought to do. For so very long, I was involved with the settlement of his estates, and then there was the incident of Cousin John's death, surely caused by his stepfather. All together, I think, no one could have replaced your grandfather in my affection, and to take another husband would have made me the most miserable of women. I had our children, and that was enough for me."

James continued with his concerns for me and the children. In fact, he seemed to become obsessed with the possible harm that might come to me should his life be shortened. He could not completely ignore the threats upon his life or the many troubles he had with the undesirables who squatted on his land. It was also during this time, that I believe the circumstances of the tragic ending of the life of my cousin, John, that James felt compelled to write a new will and put all things in order. It was uppermost in his mind that he needed to protect me and his daughters against the corruption of future husbands.

Our lives were good lives with the exception of those awful law suits that never ended. James sat down to rewrite his will for my protection and that of our children. It was a very worrisome task, one that he would work on for several months. We now had daughters approaching marriage age. The marriage of your aunts was of great concern to James; as he wished to do all possible to protect them from the attentions of men who would marry them for reasons other than love.

James continuous writing of his Will was during the time I became pregnant with your mother. Since we did not know at the time if the child would be a boy or girl, James could not name the child in his will. He did however, to accommodate my pregnancy make a special provision for unborn children.

This pregnancy did not go as well as the eight previous pregnancies had gone. James put aside his will and did not think about it again for a long time. He was more worried about me than he was about setting things in order for his own demise. We were, of course, extremely happy to be expecting another child.

I believe the pregnancy happened during the time that God chooses for women to cease the production of babies and that is why I had such a hard time of it. Many women continued to have children after my age of 38. Your mother arrived early to us on January 8th, 1820 and was quite small and delicate. James feared constantly for her life as did I. My good friend Julia was also expecting and had a little girl to be a playmate to Louise the next month on February the 27th.

We had our little girls, Isabella Louisa Mackay and Antoine and Julia's little daughter, Julie Antoinnetta le Soulard, baptized on April the 21st. Standing for guardian of Louise was her sister, Eliza Mackay and our good friend, Charles de Hault Delassus. We all retired to the Gravois plantation, home of my brother William Lindsey Long, for a lovely celebration. With all their children, our combined friends, my parents and family and all our children, it was a very large celebration.

Despite Louise's small size and supposed frailty, she thrived and grew, and by the time she was eight months old, could crawl onto her Da's lap.

On the evening of the seventh of November, we were having a dinner party, when James recalled that he had not signed the now finished will. It was not difficult to have three of our friends to witness his signature and to sign their names as witnesses. Having done so, we continued with our dinner party. The men retired to enjoy their brandy and the ladies to enjoy the gossip of the moment

and a little cherry cordial, which I had made from fresh cherries the year before.

I would ask, Johnny, that you now read this copy of your grandfather's will. I know you have never understood just how that James could have forgotten to include his youngest child. He did not forget; it was simply that the task of rewriting the will to include her was very time consuming. The provisions had been made to take care of children not yet born. There was every possibility that he would have to rewrite his will any number of times. He had made every provision possible to care for me and the family. But, so that you will understand, I would like for you to read the will yourself, and then you can ask me any questions you would like.

John began to read his grandfather's will, knowing that in the reading he would understand many things, including the conditions of ownership of the farm, where he now lived. The farm had been part of grandfather's land grant, and his mother's inheritance. He had heard his father tell his step-mother Camelia, on more than one occasion, that sale of the farm was restricted by grandfather's Will.

John had never understood why his father did not own the farm.

Will of James Mackay:

I James Mackay second son of George Mackay, Esq. of Arichliney and Elizabeth McDonald - Parish of Kildonan and County of Sutherland - North East part of the Kingdom of Scotland late - Commandant of St. Andrew, Upper Louisiana. Do declare to all whom it may concern, That though I am now in perfect health, yet not knowing how soon it may please the Almighty Lord of the Universe to call me to Eternity and it being our duty to put our affairs in order before that awful period and leave as little as possible to trouble our last moments. I will and do request by these presents, that after my death, all and every my property real and personal shall be disposed of in the following manner – To wit-

Section 1st...I leave and bequeath to my dear mother, Elizabeth McDonald, mentioned in the above preamble, Fifty pounds Sterling money as a mark of my filial duty and affection towards my Excellent and surviving parent and in case of her death the said money to go to my sister Catherine.

Section 2nd... I leave bequeath to my three nieces, Elvira, Mary and Matilda (all three children of my eldest brother John Mackay and of Elizabeth Micheau his wife, late of Statten Island New York, and now deceased) seven hundred fifty dollars money of the United States that is to say two hundred and fifty dollars each of them my said nieces-

Section 3rd... I leave and bequeath to Mr. John Long of Gravois and Elizabeth of Gravois and Elizabeth Bennet his wife (my father and mother in law) Fifty dollars each as a mark of my friendship for their kindness to my children whom I hope they will not forget when Fatherless and unprotected. And I leave and bequeath to my faithful friend Anthony Soulard Esq. of St. Louis (late Surveyor General of the Upper Louisiana) Fifty dollars to buy him a jewel in memory of our long and sincere friendship.

Section 4th... It is my special request that all the above mentioned legacies amounting in all to the sum of Eleven Hundred and Twenty three dollars money of the United States as also the money necessary for defraying the expense of raising and remitting the same, shall be made and raised out of any part of my personal or Real Estate which may be the least detrimental or injurious to the interest of the rest of my property, and that the whole of said legacies be remitted and paid to the several legates as here above mentioned within one year after my decease or as soon after as possible.

Section 5th... I leave and bequeath to my three sons, John Zeno, George Anthony and James Bennet all my fire arms, my watch, and all my musical and mathematical instruments, all my Books, Charts, Journals, official and familiar letters and papers of every description and my spy glass, my desk and bookcase, all of which I hope my dear Boys will make good use of in due time with that regard to Justice, Friendship and Harmony which ought ever to exist between Brothers; and in the event of the death of any of them, every article mentioned in this section shall go to the Survivors or Survivor.

Section 6th... I give leave and bequeath to my Beloved wife Isabella L. Mackay, to her heirs or assigns in absolute right forever, whether she remains a widow or marries again, one negro man and a negro or mulatto woman or girl, to be chosen by her from among my slaves. Two horses or mares, Two cows and calves all to be chosen by her out of my stock, our Carriages and Harness our best Bed and Bedstead with all its clothing and furniture compleat, all our silver plate all her own clothing and jewels, our Clothes press and the largest Cupboard, a Table of her choice and Twelve chairs, and all the Kitchen Utensils, also Two Hundred Dollars in cash, Her looking glass and Four Hundred arpens of land French superficial measure with all its appurtenances, provided the said land shall be chosen by her or by any other at her request and in one or two pieces at most, to be taken in such a shape as will not injure materially the rest of the tracts of land out of which the said pieces or piece are taken, My said wife to chose the said Four Hundred arpens out of any land I own excepting the lands including my Salines, my two plantations on Gravois, my Town lots in St. Louis and Carondelet and my plantation land South of St. Louis on which my mansion dwelling house stands, But the whole of the said property bequeathed to my said wife as specified and contained in this section is left and bequeathed to her by me on the express and irrevocable condition that the said

Four Hundred arpens or any part thereof or any thing else bequeathed to her my said wife by me, and mentioned in this section, Shall never be sold mortgaged, executed, alienated or disposed of, in any manner or on any pretense or for any debt or debts dues or demands or any cause whatever, or taken or possessed by any person or persons whomsoever, without first obtaining and having the free will and consent of my said wife to the sale disposed or alienation of said property, or any part thereof, thus bequeathed by this Section, provided that if such sale or disposal of said property, shall be made in the presence of my son John Zeno or one of my executors hereafter named, in this my will, such sale to be written and passed and acknowledged before a magistrate and signed sealed and delivered freely and voluntarily by my said wife, whose deed or conveyance made as here before specified and with the advice and consent of (at least) one of my said Executors, who may act at that time, It shall be a legal deed to convey whatever property she my said wife may and will as aforesaid sell, to the purchaser and provided also that my said wife shall have free liberty to bequeath by will or testament whatever part of the property bequeathed to her by me as aforesaid, which may remain at her death, to any person or persons to whom she may chose to leave and bequeath the same according to her free will and pleasure and it is my will that my said wife shall remain in full possession of my mansion house and plantation belonging thereto, situated near St. Louis Bridge, during her natural and single life but no longer, and that all my children while single, shall enjoy, in common with her, the benefit of said house and farm.

Section 7th... It is my special will and request that all the residue and remainder of my estate real and personal goods and chattels of whatever nature quality or quantity they maybe, shall be and remain to and with my said beloved wife, Isabella L. Mackay while she remains a widow, and my seven children, John Zeno, George Anthony, James Bennet, Eliza Lucy, Catherine Mary, Jean Julia

and Emilia Anne, and that my said wife and all my said children do and shall have and hold the same said property and Estate in common between them for their common use and benefit during the minority of my said children and my said Beloved wife is hereby directed and authorized by and with the advise of my Executors hereafter named to provide and take and use out of my said property real and personal whatever may be necessary and sufficient to support and maintain herself and said children in a plentiful decent and becoming manner and nowise inferior to the manner they lived with me, and to give good education to my said daughters and a Classical Education to my said sons, and to dispose of as much of said property and Estate Real and Personal as will be sufficient to pay and defray all costs and expenses due or accruing on account of each and everything done or performed by virtue of this section and when any of my said children becomes of age or gets married with the consent of my said wife and desires and requires to get a share of said property, then (and not till then) an inventory shall be taken and appraisement made under the direction and management of my Executors hereafter named of the whole of my said property and Estate already mentioned in this section and which may be remaining at that time and (after deducting there-from and saving the necessary expenses and sum to finish the education of my said children as above specified) shall be divided into Eight equal shares of which seven shares shall go to my said seven children i.e. an equal share to each of them, and the remaining eighth share shall go to my said wife Isabella who shall have and hold the same during her natural and single life, for her better support and maintenance, which share she shall take in such things as may suit her. And my said Executors shall sell such parts of said estate as may be for the interest of the Heirs and such things as cannot be divided between them, And from and after the day that this division is made those of my said children who shall remain still with their mother, my said wife, or under her care, shall make to her a reasonable compensation, each of them, out of his or her own share, for all

*expense she my said wife shall be at on their account. But it is my
will and request, that if my said wife do marry again, She shall
immediately remove from my said mansion house and plantation
and from and after the day of so marrying shall have no right to
the possessions or benefit of said mansion house or plantation or
any part thereof unless my said children should be disposed to
allow her to remain with them in said house or on said plantation
during their pleasure, and immediately after the day that my said
wife shall marry as aforesaid I will, that my Executors shall take
all my Estate real and personal from her and out of her possession
(except the property and land which I bequeathed to her in
absolute right as specified in the foregoing section the Sixth) and if
not appraised before, to take an inventory of the whole and keep it
safe or dispose of what parts of it that are perishable to the best
advantage for the benefit of my said children, leaving the Real
Estate to be divided and apportioned Equitably and in Equal
Shares among my said seven children, as they get married or come
of age, and to be drawn by lot or otherwise as may seem best and
just, and all the Personal Estate also which remains at the time, of
taking said inventory, and not included in foregoing section the
sixth, shall be equally divided among my said Seven Children
provided nevertheless that my Executors hereafter named and who
may act at the time shall have power to dispose of as much of the
said personal or Real Estate at any time as may be necessary for
the good and decent maintenance and Education (as mentioned
already in this section) of my said children, and in case my said
wife did marry again as aforesaid, I will, that my said children
shall be taken from her by my said Executors and placed at school
or some other good place, except such as they may think proper to
leave with their mother to whom they shall pay a reasonable
compensation for their maintenance - and I fondly hope that my
said Executors will always remember that the charges I leave to
them are helpless orphans and the offspring of a Friend; and a
Father who has not one relation on this side of the ocean to take
their part, to guide them in the way they ought to go, to relieve*

them in their distress and guard them against a crafty and corrupt world. Consequently will act as Fathers to my Dear Children after I have mouldered in the tomb, see that they are treated with justice and humanity, brought up with decency and in the principles of virtue of religion and morality.

Section 8th...It is my will and request that after my said wife has received the property I bequeathed to her in absolute right and all the foregoing legacies being paid to the legatees and prior to any division being made of the remainder of my Estate among my said children: My Executors hereafter named, and who may act at the time, shall take out of the said remainder of my Estate One thousand dollars lawful money, or the value thereof in Real Estate to be safely kept by my said Executors and their Successors for the express purpose of affording relief and support to my said wife in case of her being reduced to poverty or want, in consequence of the misconduct of her future Husband, or other accidents or circumstances so as to need such relief, and to furnish her from time to time with such small sums as she may need while that said One Thousand Dollars or any part thereof remains, and it is my most Earnest request and desire that my said Executors shall never suffer or allow my said Dear and Beloved wife to want or be without a comfortable maintenance while there is any of the said Thousand Dollars left or remaining, and if the said Thousand Dollars be left and kept in Real Estate my said Executors shall dispose of the same to the best advantage and for the benefit of my said wife in the manner aforesaid and whatever is left of the said Thousand Dollars at the death of my said wife I do authorize and empower her by these presents to will and bequeath it as she (my said wife) may think proper and to any person or persons, whom she may think deserving and who, may have acted the most dutiful towards her of which she shall be the sole judge.

And it is my will and desire that my said Dear Wife shall be and remain guardian to my said children while she remains a widow, but no longer and if she marries again my eldest children

*to be guardians to the youngest of them provided they act as such
with the advice of my excellent Friend Madame Julia Cerre`
Soulard who I know will be the faithful friend of my dear orphans.*

*And I charge my Dear and Beloved wife and children by
the regard they owe to my memory, that in whatever situation they
happen to be, To continue during their lives in that duty and
attachment which by nature they owe to each other and which is so
essential to their welfare and never to forget that God will reward
them according to their deeds.*

*Section 9th... It is my will and request that in case any child or
children shall be Born to me by my said Dear Wife Isabella after
the date hereof, such Child or Children shall inherit his or her or
their share and portion of my said Real Estate equally with my
children heretofore named and in the same manner and on the
same conditions as expressed in this my Will and in as ample a
manner as if he, she or they, had been mentioned by name herein.*

*Section 10th...It is my will and request that while my before said
wife remains a widow none of my Daughters before mentioned
shall marry without her consent, and that any of them who acts to
the contrary shall receive no part or share of my aforesaid Estate
or property real personal or mixed, except One Dollar, and that
all the remainder of the equal share mentioned in the foregoing
section 7th and intended for her Such daughters shall be equally
divided among the rest of my said children.*

*I leave and bequeath to my youngest brother George now
in the Island of Cape Breton, near Nova Scotia, Four hundred
dollars to be taken and remitted to him or his heirs in the same
manner as the other legacies, mentioned in the foregoing part of
this my will.*

*And I do by these presents nominate constitute and appoint
my good and trusty friend, Mr. John Long, my Father in Law, of
Gravois, and Col. Anthony Soulard of St. Louis and my said Dear
Wife, while she remains a widow, no longer to be Joint Executors*

of this my last Will and Testament and my older son John Zeno as soon as he is Twenty One years of age to be Joint Executor of this my Will and Testament and on the demise of any of my said Executors, I will that the survivors of them, my said Executors, shall choose another to replace such deceased Executor taking care to choose a friend to my family –

And it is my special will and request, that, no court or law whatever which do exist or may or shall exist, shall ever meddle or interfere with anything concerning this my will and testament or my property or estate specified therein, and that all difficulties which may or shall occur respecting the same or any part thereof shall be settled by the arbitration of friends and honest men chosen, by those concerned, for that purpose.

And I do declare this to be my last will and testament hereby revoking all former wills and testaments by me made. In testimony whereof I have hereunto sit my hand and seal at St. Louis, State of Missouri, the Seventh day of November, year of our Lord One Thousand Eight Hundred and Twenty One - mine words underlined before signed and the word "made" in the margin -

James Mackay

(seal)

Codicil - Will of James Mackay

In explanation of and to remove all doubt that might hereafter arise upon my intention as expressed in the tenth section of my will as above written hereby declare it to be my will that if any of my daughters shall marry or shall have married without my consent or without the consent of my said wife that in such she or they shall be entitled only to an Estate for and during the term of their and each of their lives respectively in that portion of my property hereby bequeathed and devised to each and any of them and each of their children shall be entitled to the absolute property and title to said portion and portions after the death of each of them respectively and it is my will that in case said daughters do marry without consent as aforesaid should or any should die without lawful issue then and in that case her or their respective shares and portions should and shall become distributable in equal shares to my surviving children and their legal survivors.

In testimony whereof I have hereunto set my hand this sixteenth day of March one thousand eight hundred and twenty two hereby republishing my said will as well as the clause or codicil aforesaid subjected thereto...

James Mackay

*Signed and published in
the presence of the witness herein...
Signed and attested said will in presence
of said testator and of each other*

L.E. Lawless   Cerre`   P. Proveuchere

"Gram, that is the most incredible document, I am so very glad I have decided to be an attorney. I will remember always this moment. Grandfather certainly made sure there would be no incidents like that of your cousin John to destroy your life and the lives of my aunts. I believe, since my mother died so very young, father would have sold the farm and returned to Kentucky had it been possible. I then would not have known and loved you as well as I have. I owe my good fortune to the care grandfather took to protect his family."

"Yes, Johnny, some people might look at this document and feel that James was being harsh spirited or dictatorial in some of his stipulations. I understood, the anguish he felt when he wrote

the will. He would not have condemned me to a life without a husband even though he could not bear the thought that I might be someone else's wife. All he stated was for my protection and the protection of our daughters. I feel even today, that his love is still with me, and I have never felt a necessity or even an interest to remarry."

"Gram, do you think you could possibly tell me about grandfather's death. Some of my cousins have said that grandfather was poisoned by some of his enemies. I know there are many evil people who can easily take the life of another. However, I do not believe it could ever be in me, to take the life of another, unless my own life was threatened."

"I am glad to hear you say this, for it tells me that you have a gentle and loving mind, and you will be able to handle the things that life will throw your way. The lessons you learn will be many and hard. The hardest, I think, is to lose one's child. I hope you will never have to experience that event. Speaking of the death of your grandfather is always hard, even now, so many years later, but I will try."

A few days before James died, our friends Antoine and Julia Soulard joined us at the hotel in town for luncheon. There was something special going on, but I have forgotten the occasion that brought so many people into the city. Anyway, the dining room was extremely crowded. As you can imagine we saw many of our friends who came by our table to say Hello. In the room of distinguished people of town was Nathan Boone the son of James' good friend Col. Daniel Boone, there was Louisa's godfather, Charles de Hault Delassus and several members of the Chouteau family. The room was full of people we knew and cared about. There were a few there we had rather not seen. However, we were very happy that we did not see the parsimonious face of Judge Lucas or his equally dour commissioners.

We ordered our food, James and I both ordering veal. It is amazing that one remembers such simple things as what you ate.

My veal was put before me, but James received *Boeuf avec Champignons*. The waiters were so busy James didn't feel he could take the time to have them fix him another meal. James said, "Well then, I guess it is to be steak and mushrooms for me." We all laughed because, steak or veal with morel mushrooms was one of his favorite dishes. Since someone had thought to preserve mushrooms in a vinegar spice, they could be enjoyed the year around. The taste of the vinegar added a special flavor to the sauce served with the steak and mushrooms.

Julia and I left in our carriage to spend the afternoon together while Antoine would come with James after the court sessions were finished. They were staying with us for dinner that evening. It was a rare occasion that Julia and I spent an entire afternoon together. We were both very happy to spend the afternoon catching up on the activities of the children and the local gossip.

When James and Antoine arrived at our home late in the evening, James had a headache and stomach cramps and could not eat his dinner. Because James was not feeling well, Antoine and Julia departed soon after dinner.

The next day James was still not feeling well and we decided to leave the noise and smell of the city and retire to the plantation on the Gravois, which was a much more peaceful place to rest.

By the following morning, we knew James was ill enough to send for the doctor. He was suffering from severe headache, stomach distress and vomiting. We could not possibly understand what was wrong. He was acutely distressed. There was no fever but the terrible stomach pain would not go away.

The doctor did not know the cause of the problems, as anything internal was not at that time understood. He only shook his head and left a large bottle of laudanum for James to ease his pain.

By late afternoon with the help of doses of laudanum the doctor had given him, the pain was eased. I sent Zeno to bring

Antoine and Julia to us. They came and stayed for the night, each of us staying by James' side. James refused to take more laudanum and insisted he needed to make an addition to his will. I went into his office and retrieved his Will and sat down to write as he directed upon the paper. It was his fear for our safety that he added a codicil to his will. He signed his name to the document with great difficulty, as the lack of laudanum had allowed the pain to return. Our good friends Antoine and Julia refused to go home but sent one of the servants to their home saying they would not return and leave us alone.

I sent another servant to bring my parents, for I surely needed their love and support. We sent for the parish Priest.

Our children, my parents and our good friends were with me in the room where James lay dying upon our bed. The Priest came into our room, nodded to me, and put on the vestments of the church. Taking out his holy oil, he began to anoint James for the last rites of the church. James, in another world, talked softly with his brother John who had long since passed to the other side. He failed to recognize the administrations of the Priest but lay in a world of his own. Finishing the rites, the Priest stepped aside and folded away his vestments and put away his oils making ready to depart the room. I had laid my head upon James chest as a last gesture of love and devotion. Talking to his brother, James said, "John, I have kept the faith, and the oaths we made at the chapel in Rosslyn, I come to join you in the arms of Christ."

After a time, James roused and came back to us. He turned his head and looked at me, his lovely silver eyes shining with love. He had a beautiful and serene smile upon his face and then, looking to heaven, he raised his arms, shaking with weakness, and said, "Lord, by the sacred oaths I have taken to the keepers of the secrets of Christ, and by my sign, I give now, my soul into your keeping," and he made a sign.

I heard a strangled exclamation from the Priest in the room and turned my head to see the cause of the horrible sound in this room of death and sorrow. The Priest had become flushed with anger his face was red and molted as if his clerical collar was choking the life from him. He gasped out, and pointing his finger at James, and with a hard and hateful voice he said, "He has blasphemed the Holy Father in Rome, and there will be no burial for him in the sacred grounds of the Church."

"I was truly shocked and didn't understand." The Priest with a swirl of his robes turned and hurriedly left the room. Looking at James' face there was nothing but peace to be seen there, even a small smile upon his lips. I leaned down, kissed him and returned my head to his chest. I couldn't help but want the last connection that was possible. He very weakly laid his arm upon my shoulder and closed his eyes. There was wonderful warmth and love between us as he breathed in those too small shallow breaths.

My parents and our friends left us together and put our children to bed, leaving us alone for these last moments we would be together.

We stayed thus, all night with his arm around me each of us dozing now and then, until the first streaks of the morning light began to steal into the room.

"Bella, my love, tell M`athair" he whispered. My arms tightened upon him, and I listened and waited for just a few more words. I could hear the beat of his heart, so very loud it seemed in that quiet room, and then there was only silence.................

CHAPTER THIRTY

A Man to Cherish

Tears rolled unchecked down Gram's sweet face as she dipped her tiny foot to the ground and set the white wicker swing where she sat into motion. She handed John a copy of his grandfather's obituary.

John took the obituary and began to read.....

The St. Louis Inquirer – March 23, 1822

Died – On the 16th inst, at his residence near the town of St. Louis, after a painful illness of a few days, JAMES MACKAY,   Esq.

We trust that in offering a small tribute to the memory of this worthy citizen, we shall escape the charge of being impertinent or ridiculous – importations that have well attached on divers "obituary notices" of late years. Mr. Mackay's life was one of considerable enterprise – about 40 years ago he emigrated from Scotland, the country of his birth, to Canada; he there became engaged in the Indian fur trade, and had occasion to explore the region of the upper lakes and the country as far west as the Rocky Mountains – after some years past in the perilous occupation, he transferred his domicile to upper Louisiana and availed himself the protection which the Spanish government extended to foreign settlers. By that government he was employed to explore the country watered by the Missouri and its tributary rivers, a region almost without a civilized man. On his return from that expedition he made a report to the Spanish government, which met its fullest approbation. In remunerations of his services he received a grant of a large tract of land on the waters of the Missouri, when this grant was made the land was scarcely worth the expense of sovereign gain from that moment to the present, the concession, in consequence of the delay of confirmation, has not only been unproductive but has been a positive annual loss to Mr. Mackay. It is to be hoped that the justice which has been so long withheld from the father will not be denied to the mother and the orphans. The Spanish government testified its sense of Mr. Mackay's merits, not only by this grant, but by investing him with different offices of importance, in all of which he was distinguished for his activity, intelligence, and disinterestedness. As military commandant of one of the subdivisions of Upper Louisiana, the duty devolved on him of providing for settlement of a multitude of American emigrants, who were induced by the advantages which the government and country presented to establish themselves in Louisiana. There are many of them yet alive to bear witness to the kind and honorable manner in which Mr. Mackay conducted himself towards them. On the cession of Louisiana to the United States, he continued to co-operate with the constituted authorities until the second grade of government was organized and Upper Louisiana divided into districts – since that time he has served in the various capacities of Major Militia, Judge of District Court, and Representative in the Legislature, with credit to himself and advantage to his fellow citizens. It is a consolatory fact that the last moments of his life were worthy of its whole blameless tenor the perfect calmness with which he viewed his approaching dissolution was the best comment on the character of the man. Neither the illusions of superstition, nor the abstractions of philosophy, could create the bright serenity which marked his latter end – this could only have been the result of a quite conscience – the best proof of his innocence in this world and his title to happiness hereafter.

When John had finished reading, he thought, I don't know where grandfather is buried. He looked at Gram, who had dried her eyes and now had a bright and happy smile upon her face. As if she had read John's thoughts she said, "Johnny, you see the cemetery the other side of that fence. I do not plan to be buried there, but here beneath this arbor where I now sit, next to my beloved James."

EPILOGUE

After the death of James Mackay on March 16, 1822, all his personal property, the beautiful furniture purchased for his Hickory and Fifth Street Mansion House and all the Real Estate property which had been confirmed was placed in a Sheriff's sale to pay the debts which had accrued due to the status of the unconfirmed lands he owned. All the items mentioned were listed as assets in his estate inventory.

Isabella continued to fight the court battles until 1835 when the last of the of the lower court decisions to deny their claims was overturned and the lands were confirmed by the Supreme Court of the United States of America. Records can be found in the pages of the American State Papers. The Papers include many claims of well know Americans, including Col. Daniel Boone who fought in court for six years before his Spanish Land Grants were confirmed.

Missouri Republican 3 March, 1861 – Obituary

MACKAY, Isabella wife of James at the home of Louis Guion in Carondelet 25 February age 77 years.

Elizabeth Louise Long, better known as Isabella Mackay was born September 2, 1783, the daughter of John Long and his wife Elizabeth Bennett, and died on February 25, 1861. She did not get her wish that she would not experience the death of another child. Her beloved daughter Catherine Mary Mackay Guion who was married to Louis Guion died on the 22nd day of February age 56 years, three days before her mother. Their obituaries are in the March 3, 1861 Missouri Republican Newspaper.

John "Johnny" Milton Barker, son of Simeon Lumpkin Barker and Isabella Louisa Mackay Barker, became a lawyer and for a time was the prosecuting attorney in Wellsville, Missouri. He lived his life in a way that would have made his grandfather proud. He served as a Captain in the Union Army during the American

Civil War. He added to his grandfather's legacy by writing a letter to his children and leaving behind his families' genealogy, kept by his daughter Margaret Barker Turner who died in 1969. The papers were found at the home of Flora Mackay Borom now 103 years old, when she was recently moved to an assisted living apartment.

In 2002 records concerning the Library of Congress "Indian Map" was found by Thomas C. Danisi and Dr. W. Raymond Wood. The records provided documentation that the most complete map used by the Lewis and Clark's *Corps of Discovery* was a map drawn by James Mackay. In the spring of 2003 the missing "Original Will" of James Mackay was found in the Civil Court Records of the City of St. Louis, Missouri by employee Mike Everman. The six page document left by John Barker was found in a packet of old letters, pictures and poems, in November of 2002. To honor the life of James Mackay, on May 1, 2003 the bagpipes were played in Scotland at the ruined home site of his birth, of the same day of May 1st, 242 years ago. Andrew Innes played *The White Banner of Mackay* and *Donald Mackay's Lament*. The recent discoveries became the catalyst for writing this book.

The following is the six page legacy of John Barker; grandson of James Mackay and Elizabeth Long or Isabella Mackay, better known in these pages as: *"Gram."*

I John M Barker am an American and would not exchange its form of Government for all the glories of Kingly rule of all the ages past or future and I do not recommend the fostering of family pride further than to [line torn through.....] with the hope that if any of them become distinguished in any way for goodness or greatness, it may serve succeeding generations to follow in their honorable footsteps.

I do not know much of my father's ancestry. His name was Simeon L. Barker born in Harrisburg, Ky. on the 13th July 1815, 4 miles East of Middleton, Mo. at Barker's Ford, where his body now sleeps. He was one of the sons of Stephen Barker born of English American parents at Poughkeepsie, Dutchess Co. N.Y. August 25 in the year 1769 [looks like he originally wrote 1759], and he ran away from College at 16 and joined Washington's Army participating in long battles commanded by that Great Soldier. He was in the Indian Wars afterward and in the battle where Tecumseh was killed, he died in 1844 in Grant Co. Ky. and was buried with marked military honors. His wife, my grandmother (paternal) was Elizabeth Lloyd daughter of Col. Thomas Lloyd of Virginia. My good wife Maggie (Pace) Barker was the oldest daughter of Wm. H. Pace Esq. and Mary Elizabeth (Davis) Pace his wife, The Paces formerly were distinguished among the [line torn through....] related to the Irvines, Wycliffs and Davises of Ky. and other good families in that state and Missouri. Her father Wm H. Pace Esq. was born in Madison Co. Ky. and died on the 12th March 1891 at his home in Woodson Co. Kansas and now sleeps in the Wellsville, Mo. Cemetery, her mother is yet living in Kansas.

My father Simeon L. Barker and my mother Louise Isabella Mackay were married to each other on the 21st day of August 1839 in the town of Crittenden Ky. and from there returned to St. Charles Co., Mo. and made their home on the Mackay Survey, my mother's land.

My darling little mother was born in a brick residence of grandfathers afterward converted into the academy of the Sacred Heart by the Catholics on Hickory and 5th streets of St. Louis (before the streets were laid off she was born on the 8th of Jany. 1820 and died of cholera at Flint Hill, St. Charles Co. Mo. on the 8th of June 1851 at six o'clock in the morning on Sunday without an enemy on earth aged 30 years and 5 months.

The last words she spoke was to myself, my little bother Mackay, Zeno, LeGrand and little sister Gertrude. It was "Be Good Children."

John M Barker is the 2nd son of Simeon L. Barker & Louise (Mackay)[this Mackay is crossed out] Isabella (Mackay) Barker born Dec 20th 1841.

Louisa Isabella (Mackay) Barker was the youngest child of Captain James Mackay born in Arichliney, Scotland on May 1st 1761 and died in St. Louis, Mo. on the 16 March 1822. He was the 2nd son of Judge George Mackay of Arichliney, Scotland. He was the son of James Mackay who was the son of John Mackay who was the son of William Mackay who was the son of Murdock Mackay who was called in Scotland the Great Murdock, being a man of giant strength and great influence in the dark ages in which he lived.

The first known of this Mackay, The ancient race of O'Conner, Kings of Ireland, are the Parent Stock:

In the year about 1200 Prince Alexander son of King O'Connor went over to Scotland from Ireland with his followers and captured a large tract of Country. Alexander's sons name was Ay or I and he was named Mac (meaning the son) or Mack in the old language of Scotland - so it was they took the name MacKay - The country they took embraces the Parish of Kildonan County of Sutherland North Scotland as it appears from history and a large part of the Ancestral Estate was held in 1822 by George MacKay Lord Rae he being in line of succession.

We sometimes get interesting letters from our kinsmen across the sea, and many of them accompany places of importance and honor.

This statement is written by me on Sunday the 19th day of July 1896. At this writing my wife and daughter Leona are at the house of our dear son Justin, who has been near death for weeks at Atkins, Ark. but thank God is better.

John M. Barker

Genealogy

*Children of George Mackay of Arichliney Scotland who died
Jan. 19, 1809
Jean was born Feb 1, 1756 died Oct 4, 1784
John was born 10th Nov 1758
James was born May 1, 1761. Died March 16, 1822
William was born March 15, 1763
Kitty was born Dec 31, 1767
Robt was born March 15, 1770
George was born August 15, 1774*

*John Long was born March 1752 died March 8[?], 182[6] age of
74 years and his wife Elizabeth Long died in St. Louis Co. aged 77
years on Apr. 5 1832.
And their daughter Elizabeth Long (Elizabeth Mackay) was the
wife of said Captain James Mackay who were the parents of
Louise Isabella (Mackay) Barker.*

*Elizabeth Mackay died in 1860 [25th February age 77 years at the
home of Louis Guion - Missouri Republican 3 March 1861] and
sleeps on the hill side about 1/4 of a mile south of the old Mackay
house on the Gravois - 4 miles West of South St. Louis. Capt James
Mackay's last resting place was lost in the field, although long
searched for and is built over by the city of St. Louis. She was born
Sept. 2nd 1783 in Philadelphia. Pa.*

*Children of Simeon L and Louise Mackay Barker
Stephen Mackay Barker was born near Flint Hill, St. Charles Co.,
Mo on the 28th July 1843 Monday 10 AM and died on the ___ 18th
at Wellsville, Mo. [no year of death is given]
John Milton Barker was born near Flint Hill at 8 AM on Monday
the 20th Dec. 1841 [written in by different hand writing - died Jan
1913].*

Zeno Trudeau Barker was born on Monday 10 O'clock P.M. Oct 2nd 1843 at the same place died. [Flint Hill]
James LeGrand Barker was born on Monday 27 [torn] 1845
Twin boys - born on June 5, 1849 not named one died June 11, 1849 the other died on June the 25th 1849.
Gertrude (Darling) Barker was born on June 7, 1850.

John Barker died the 19th day of January 1913 in Bartlesville, Oklahoma age 71 years.

Copies of the letters to Mackay's son Zeno, Mackay's Will, The Obituary and the six page document written by John Barker have been passed down through his descendants and are contained in these pages just as they were written, including misspellings and errors.

James Mackay's obituary as it appeared in The St. Louis Inquirer of March 23, 1822 was placed in the St. Louis Post-Dispatch on March 16, 2004 as a memoriam to him and the legacy he left his descendants.

Learn more about the life of James Mackay, his family and his explorations and contributions to society at:

http://www.jamesmackay.us

REMEMBRANCE

I would not that no burial mound,
Should mark my last resting ground
No friend, no simple tribute ever bring
But oh, remember while I'm living

Nor would I escape the common lot
To have my faults in the grave forgot
And brightest Angel, let thy mantle fall
Above around my brier only once for all

I would not that death's Lethean Streams
Nor that lonely land of the silent dreams
Should leave on earth no record of me
Should one dark night of sleeping be.

I would not, that no lofty pines
Surround my grave of Eglantine Vines
When wildwood trees would lock thin arms
And kindly guard and watch me from the storms

Nor that no humble stone, with curving lines
By friendly hand to tell the times
When once I was, and then am not
A sign to passers by, I'm not forgot

But while I'm living, Oh let me know
By clasping hand and friendship glowing
That on your heart my name is showing
And give on earth to me, a proof of knowing

John Milton Barker

Maps:

Map Plate No. 1....Outline of Modern day Scotland with location of Helmsdale and Loch Arichlinie, home of James Mackay in the Far North of Scotland.

Map Plate No. 2....Far North of Scotland - Outline of Modern day counties of Sutherland and Caithness. Location of Mackay Croft Loch Arichlinie and Strath Halladale.

Map Plate No. 3....Partial overlay of Eastern Canada Fur Trade Route taken from the old maps of Voyages and Travels of Daniel Harmon published in 1905 from his Journals written in early 1800.

Map Plate No. 4....Partial overlay of Western Canada Fur Trade Route taken from the old maps of Voyages and Travel of Daniel Harmon published in 1905 from his Journals written in early 1800.

Map Plate No. 5....Modern map of the Eastern United States with the locations Missouri, Ohio and Mississippi Rivers.

Map Plate No. 6....Modern map of the Mid-Western United States with locations of rivers flowing into the Missouri which were explored by James Mackay from Canada and the United States.

Map Plate No. 7....Location of Ohio River, a main travel route for early emigrants from the East United States to the Spanish Territory. Location of some early emigration routes and old Indian trails.

Map Plate No. 8....Confluence of Rivers near St. Louis, Missouri. Mackay's Salt Lick Road from St. Charles to Boonville, Missouri. Local location of places mention in *James Mackay a man to cherish.*

Map Plate No. 9....Library of Congress "Indian Map" or "The Mackay-Evans Map."

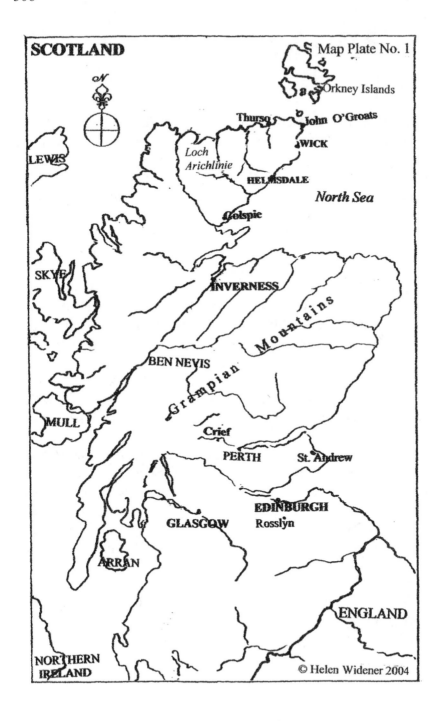

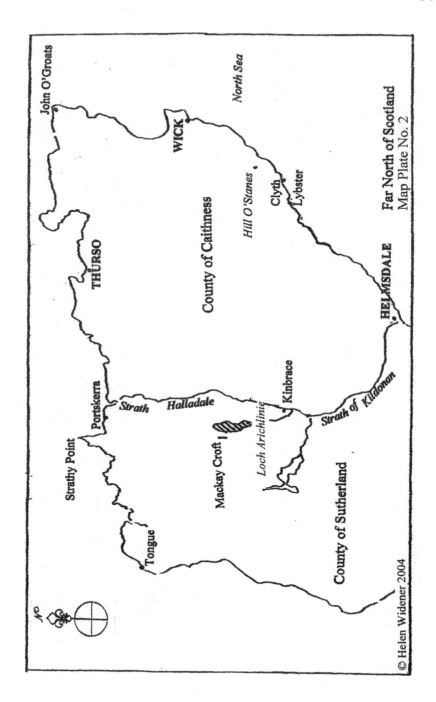

John O'Groats

North Sea

WICK

Hill O'Stanes

Clyth

Lybster

County of Caithness

THURSO

HELMSDALE

Portskerra

Kinbrace

Strath   Halladale

Loch Arichlinie

Strath of Kildonan

Strathy Point

Mackay Croft

Tongue

County of Sutherland

Far North of Scotland
Map Plate No. 2

© Helen Widener 2004

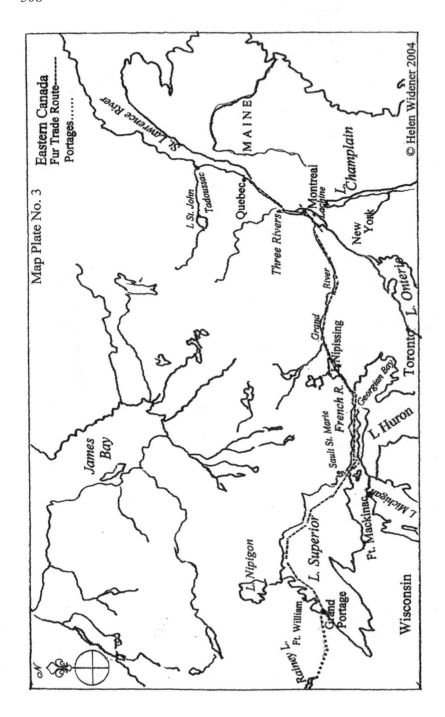

Map Plate No. 3   Eastern Canada
Fur Trade Route ------
Portages ......

© Helen Widener 2004

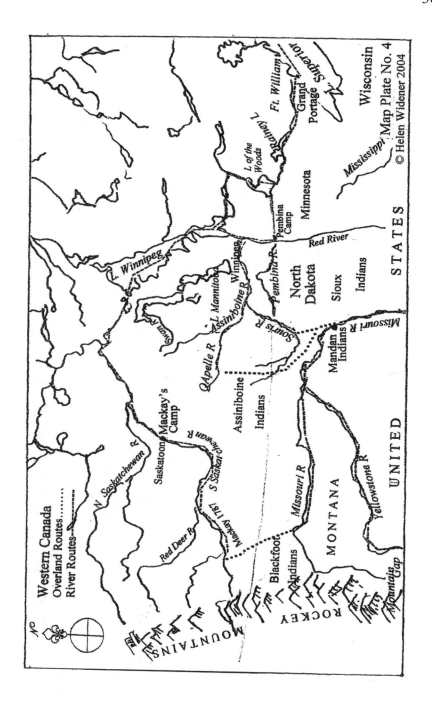

Map Plate No. 4
© Helen Widener 2004

310

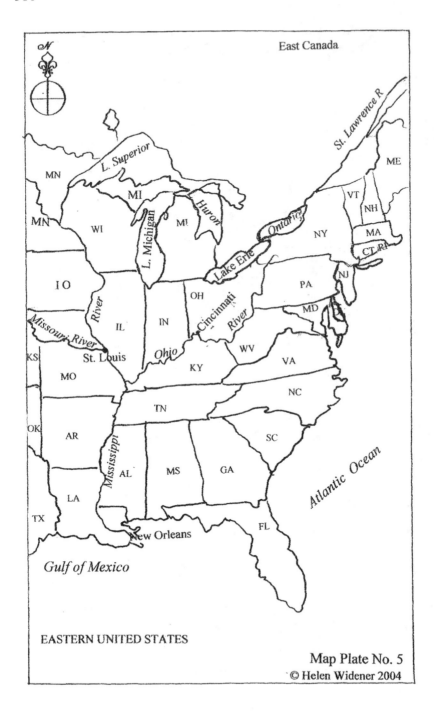

EASTERN UNITED STATES

Map Plate No. 5
© Helen Widener 2004

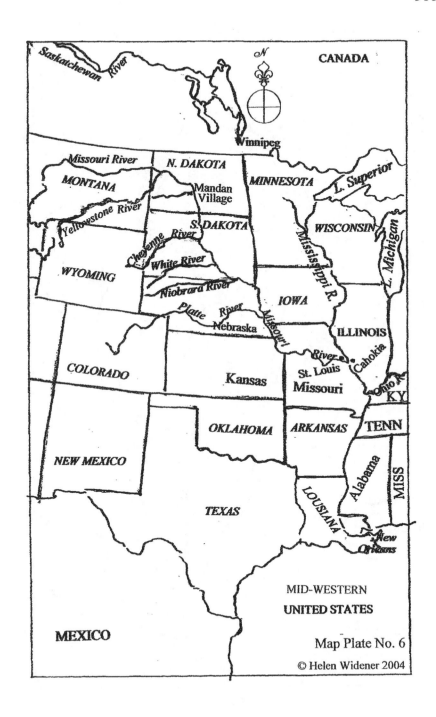

MID-WESTERN
UNITED STATES

Map Plate No. 6

© Helen Widener 2004

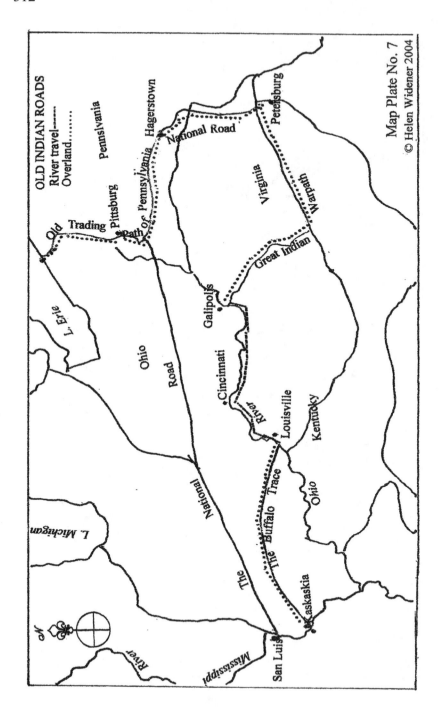

OLD INDIAN ROADS
River travel——
Overland........

Map Plate No. 7
© Helen Widener 2004

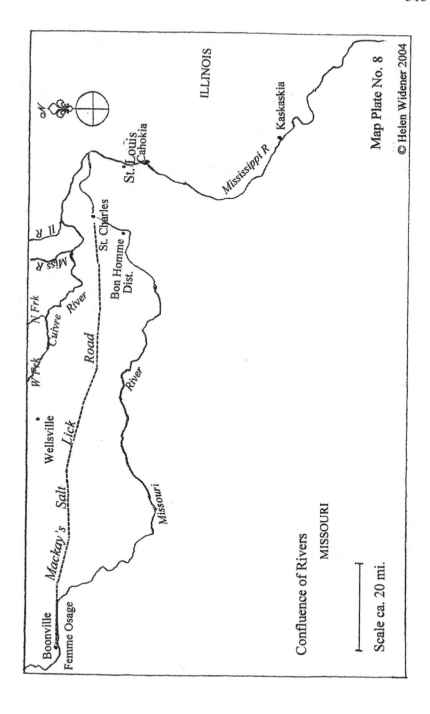

Confluence of Rivers

MISSOURI

Scale ca. 20 mi.

Map Plate No. 8

© Helen Widener 2004

314

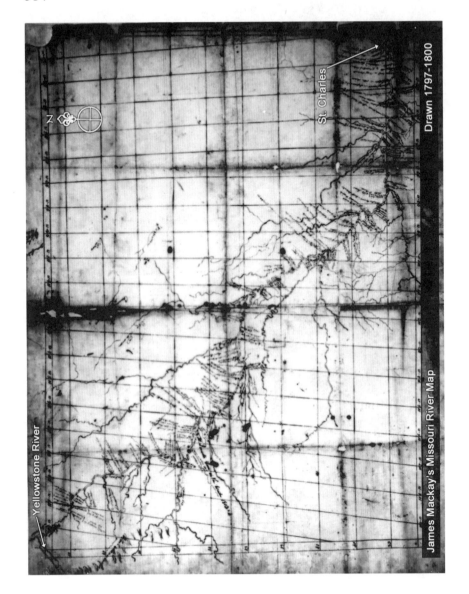

Yellowstone River

St. Charles

James Mackay's Missouri River Map

Drawn 1797-1800

Library of Congress "Indian Map"
or
"The Mackay-Evans Map"

After a harrowing journey during the years of 1795 to 1797, an expedition led by James Mackay and his Lieutenant John Evans returned to San Luis. The job of mapping the great Missouri River had just begun. Notes from the journals of both men would now have to be consulted in order to prepare a map drawn from their field notes - a map beginning at St. Charles, Missouri and extending to the Yellowstone River and up toward the Rockies.

The expedition had a two-fold purpose. One was to make peace with the Indians and establish trade with them for the new Missouri Fur Company. The second purpose of the expedition was to map the areas owned by His Majesty the King of Spain.

James Mackay had previously, as a Canadian Fur Trader, mapped areas of Canada, made a map to the Mandan Indian Village, discovered the Yellowstone River, and as he said, "made numerous trips into the area."

At the time of the Louisiana Purchase when San Luis became St. Louis, all maps, journals and correspondence of the French and Spanish officials were turned over to American Government officials.

Sometime around 1817 the Map of the Missouri River made by James Mackay and his Lieutenant came into the possession of the Governor of the Missouri Territory, William Henry Harrison. On the back of the map he wrote, "Map used by Lewis and Clark."

In 2003 Historians Thomas Danisi and Raymond Wood researched the paper trail that proved what Mackay's numerous descendants had always known: The Library of Congress "Indian Map" was indeed the work of their ancestor James Mackay.

There are only fragments of Mackay's Journals and Indian Notes surviving. On one of those pages he writes he had established peace with the Indians and paved the way for those who would come after him.

The Mackay-Evans Map, with his instructions and Indian Notes would, almost a decade later, prove to be of the greatest benefit to the new American Territories and its Explorers.

SOURCES OF INFORMATION

List of Source Documents and Books:

1. James Mackay's Letter, *"My Dear Son"* written to his son, John Zeno Mackay, before his death in 1822. A family document, typed copies handed down through Barker Family descendants.
2. *Obituary Editorial in the St. Louis Inquirer* - dated March 23, 1822, a family document. Type written document handed down Barker Family descendants.
3. *List of marriage questions* on 24 day of February, 1800 by Brother Leadre Lusson, Priest Recolet, and Parish of St. Charles of the Missouri. Barker Family Documents, Type written.
4. *Genealogy Worksheet,* as written by Leta Barker Gr. Grand daughter of James Mackay. Handwritten Barker Family Document.
5. *Notes on Mackay* - Long family of Mrs. E.D.C. Leek, hand written Barker Family Documents.
6. *Missouri Historical Papers* - The Boon's Lick County Letter to Miss Dalton from John Barker Jan. 27, 1904, relative to James Mackay and the destruction of family papers by fire. Barker Family Documents.
7. *Indian Tribes Note #1- 8* Mackay's Notes which were attributed to John Evans, but the contents clearly makes them Mackay's Indian Notes. Missouri Historical Society Archives.
8. *Mackay's Journal of a Voyage up the Missouri toward the South Sea, 1794 - 1796.* Missouri Historical Society
9. *Maps and Journal of John Evans,* Beinecke Rare book and Manuscript Library, Yale University.
10. *Notes on James Mackay' Table of Distance.* American State Papers Vol. 6 p. 718-20.
11. *Letter to Frederick Bates from James Mackay* Sept. 17, 1818. (Regarding the destruction of Mackay's timber.)

12. *Notes on Lewis and Clark regarding Mackay's Map.* (Thwaites includes in the atlas "copies of contemporary French and Spanish Maps". (Original Journals of Lewis and Clark Expedition, 1804-1806, edited by Reuben Gold Thwaites, New York, 1904-5 8 volumes. Copies from American Historical Association.

13. *Letter James Mackay to Carlos Dehault De Lassus* Recommendation for land grants for settlers Dec.1799.

14. *Claim of James Mackay for 1800 arpens of land* in district of St. Louis. - St. Charles Papers - English - hand written.

15. *Archives General de Indian - Sevilla Mackay's Journal* - No. 78 (Houck – Spanish Regime in Missouri Vol. II. p. 181 # 42.) 34 hand written pages in Spanish.

16. *Soulard Papers,* Missouri Historical Society - 3 pages hand written.

17. *Proving Last Will and Testament of James Mackay* recorded by Silas Bent, Clerk of County of St. Louis. Recorded April 29, 1822.

18. *Record of Legal Proceedings relating to James Mackay Claim* handwritten - 12 pages

12. *Survey made by James Mackay* in 1806 for Mordecai Bell

13. *Copy of "Original hand written Will"* written by James Mackay found in the Civil Court Records 2003.

14. *Hand written Will of James Mackay with Inventory,* (Will Book Copy) Missouri Historical Society.

15. *Yale University Collection of Western Americana.* Beinecke Rare Book and Manuscript Library (Extracts from Capt. McKay's Journal and others) The State Historical Society of Wisconsin, Separate No.171. Proceedings of the Society for 1915.

16. *John Milton Barker - Document - Genealogy of Mackay Family of Scotland and America.* Barker Family Documents.

17. *Birth and Baptism Records* of the Basilica of St. Louis, Old Cathedral records of Baptism; written in French of the nine children of James Mackay and Isabella Long Mackay.

318

18. *Death Records from Missouri Newspapers*. The Civil War Years – compiled by Lois Stanley, George F. Wilson, and Maryhelen Wilson March 1893.
19. Sage, Rev. Donald - *Memorabilia Domestica; or Parish Life in the North of Scotland*. Second Edition published at Wick: by William Rae, Edinburgh: John Menzies & Co. 1899. Reproduction CD by Scotdisc.
20. Dods, Mistress Margaret, *Cleikum Inn, St Ronan's – Scotland. The Cook and Housewife's Manuel: A practical system of modern domestic cookery and family management.* Published by Oliver and Boyd, Edinburgh; Simpkin & Marshall, London 1833 - Fifth Edition.
21. Ramsay, Dean - *Reminiscences of Scottish Life and Character* Published 1872 by Messrs. Gall & Inglis Author's Copyright Edition.
22. Mackay, Angus M.A. - *Book of Mackay* - Reprint by Tuttle Antiquarian Books.
23. Moncreiffe, Sir Iain - *The Highland Clans* Albany Herald Revised Edition, Clarkson N. Potter, Inc. Publisher New York
24. Grimble, Ian - *Clans & Chiefs* Published in 2000 by Birlinn Limited.
25. Grimble, Ian - *Chief of Mackay* Published by the Saltire Society 1993.
26. Haldane, A.R.B. - *The Drove Roads of Scotland* Published by Birlinn 1997.
27. McCulloch, J.H.-*The Men of Kildonan* McClelland and Stewart Publishers – Toronto.
28. Mackay, Donald - *Scotland Farewell: The People of the Hector*
Published by McGraw-Hill Ryerson Limited/Toronto
Paul Harris Publishing/Edinburgh – 1980.
28. Ross, David & Smith, Gavin D. *Scots-English Dictionary compiled by:* Hippocrene paperback edition, 1999.
29. Renton, R.W. and MacDonald, J.A. *Scottish Gaelic/English Dictionary*, seventh printing 2002.

30. Webster, *English-French Dictionary.*
31. Haywood, John – *Atlas of the Celtic World* Published by Thames & Hudson Ltd. London 2001.
32. Mackenzie, Alexander - *The History of the Highland Clearances,* 1883, Reprint Published by Mercat Press Edinburgh 1999.
33. Wallace-Murphy, Tim & Hopkins, Marilyn – *Rosslyn Guardian of the Secrets of the Holy Grail* Published by Thorsons, an Imprint of HarperCollins Publishers.
34. Sinclair, Andrew - *The Secret Scroll* Published 2002 by Birlinn Limited.
35. Long, J. - *Voyages and Travels of an Indian Interpreter and Trader Describing the Manners and Customs of the North American Indian 1791.* Microfilm Western Americana Collection. Southern Methodist University – Fonden Library - DeGolyer Rare Books and Manuscripts Collection.
36. Maclennan, Hugh - *Seven Rivers of Canada* Published 1961 by MacMillian of Canada – Toronto.
37. Duckworth, Harry W. - *The English River Book* of 1786 Edited by McGill-Queen's University Press 1990.
38. Harmon, Daniel Williams - *Voyages and Travels* – First Edition a Partner in the Northwest Company. Published by Allerton Book Co., New York. Copyright 1903 by Williams-Barker Co. Book complete with early Canadian Fur Map.
39. Davidson, Gordon Charles, Ph.D - *The North West Company* Publisher New York/Russell & Russell. Reprint of 1916 Edition.
40. Newman, Peter C. - *Empire of the Bay-*The Company of Adventurers that Seized a Continent; The Story of the Hudson's Bay Company - Published by Penguin Putman, Inc. 1998.
41. Duckworth, Harry W. - *The Madness of Donald Mackay An Iron Man of the Fur Trade Made His Own Claim to Immortality* The Beaver Magazine June/July 1988 Pages 25 - 42
42. Catlin, George - *Letters and Notes on the North American Indians 1844.* Reproduction CD by Guild Press of Indiana, Inc.

43. Moerman, Daniel E., *Native American Ethnobotany* Timber Press, Portland, Oregon 1998.
44. Nute, Grace Lee - *The Voyageur* -Minnesota Historical Society Press, St. Paul. First published in 1931.
45. Russell, Carl P. - *Firearms, Traps, & Tools of the Mountain Men* University of New Mexico Press, Albuquerque 1992.
46. Peters, Virginia Bergman - *Women of the Earth Lodges Tribal Life on the Plains.* Archon Books, 1995.
47. Christenson, Lawrence O.; Foley, William E.; Kremer, Gary R. and Winn, Kenneth H.: Editors of *Dictionary of Missouri Biography.* Articles by Danisi, Thomas on *James Mackay* page 511, *John Evans* pages 286 and 287 and by Kuntson, Kaia A. *Antoine Pierre Soulard* page 712.
48. Wood, W. Raymond - *Prologue to Lewis and Clark -The Mackay and Evans Expedition.* University of Oklahoma Press.
49. *American State Papers – Vols. 1 thru 10* Southern Historical Press-Reprint 1994.
50. Getsinger, Kathy B. - *Exploration in Ethnography Highlights in the Recording of Mandan and Hidatsa Culture-* unpublished document.
51. Smith, Thomas E.V. - *The City of New York In the Year of Washington's Inauguration 1789.* The Chatham Press, Inc. Riverside, Connecticut 1972. First Edition printed for the Author in 1889 by Trow's Printing and Bookbinding Company, New York. The 1972 version was produced in cooperation with the United States Department of the Interior, National Park Service, Federal Hall National Memorial, New York City.
52. McClellan, Elizabeth - *Historic Dress in America 1607- 1870* Arno Press, New York, 1977.
53. Cassin-Scott, Jack – *The Illustrated Encyclopaedia of Costume and Fashion.* Published by Studio Vista.
54. Olsen, Edna McElhiney – *Historical Saint Charles, Missouri* Published 1967.

55. Nasatir, A.P. - *Before Lewis and Clark* Documents illustrating the History of the Missouri, 1785-1804 Red River Books, Published by University of Oklahoma Press 2003. Vol. 79 in the American Exploration and Travel Series.

56. Wood, W. Raymond and Thiessen, Thomas D. *Early Fur Trade on the Northern Plains Canadian Traders Among the Mandan and Hidatsa Indians, 1738-1818.* Published by University of Oklahoma Press, Norman, Oklahoma.

57. DeVoto, Benard – *The Journals of Lewis and Clark* Houghton Mifflin Company – Boston 1953

58. Nebenzahl, Kenneth, Kenneth Nebenzahl Rand McNally, *Atlas of the American Revolution.* Text by Don Higginbotham. Copyright Rand McNally and Company.

ABOUT THE AUTHOR

Helen Ogden Widener was born in Conway, Arkansas and has an interest in all things historical. She loves old books, antiques, and the cultural and social history of people who came to America during its early years. She enjoys converting old recipes into good modern foods and is interested in the ancient use of herbal remedies. Helen is the author of *Irving Centennial Cookbook and family histories* and *Hutchins of Pine Mountain, three hundred years of migration.*

Visit the James Mackay Website at
http://www.jamesmackay.us